Assessment and Evaluation Masters

Mathematics

Applications and Connections

Course 1

Glencoe
McGraw-Hill

New York, New York   Columbus, Ohio   Woodland Hills, California   Peoria, Illinois

Glencoe/McGraw-Hill

A Division of The McGraw·Hill Companies

Send all inquiries to:
Glencoe/McGraw-Hill
936 Eastwind Drive
Westerville, Ohio 43081-3374

ISBN: 0-02-833068-4   *Assessment and Evaluation Masters,* Course 1

2 3 4 5 6 7 8 9 10 066 05 04 03 02 01 00 99

Contents

Chapter 1 Test, Form 1A

1. Find the next three numbers in the pattern 17, 26, 35, _?_, _?_, _?_.
   A. 44, 53, 62   **B.** 54, 63, 72   **C.** 42, 55, 68   **D.** 52, 78, 87

   1. _____

2. Find the next three numbers in the pattern 972, 324, 108, _?_, _?_, _?_.
   A. 54, 22, 11   **B.** 108, 324, 972   **C.** 36, 12, 4   **D.** 50, 38, 24

   2. _____

3. Round 283 to the nearest ten.
   A. 280   **B.** 290   **C.** 300   **D.** 200

   3. _____

4. Round 2,350 to the nearest hundred.
   A. 2,000   **B.** 3,000   **C.** 2,300   **D.** 2,400

   4. _____

5. Round 1,499 to the nearest thousand.
   A. 1,300   **B.** 1,400   **C.** 1,000   **D.** 2,000

   5. _____

6. Estimate 3,321 + 1,504 using rounding.
   A. 3,000   **B.** 4,000   **C.** 5,000   **D.** 6,000

   6. _____

7. Estimate 6,138 ÷ 2,604 using rounding.
   A. 3   **B.** 2   **C.** 1   **D.** 4

   7. _____

8. Find the value of $18 + 2 \times 3$.
   A. 39   **B.** 60   **C.** 23   **D.** 24

   8. _____

9. Find the value of $16 - 3 + 2 \times 5$.
   A. 130   **B.** 23   **C.** 55   **D.** 75

   9. _____

10. Find the value of $11 \times 12 + 24 \div 3$.
    A. 140   **B.** 52   **C.** 220   **D.** 139

    10. _____

11. Find the value of $28 - 13 \times 2 + 1$.
    A. 11   **B.** 31   **C.** 45   **D.** 3

    11. _____

12. Evaluate ab if $a = 91$ and $b = 8$.
    A. 918   **B.** 99   **C.** 728   **D.** 891

    12. _____

13. Evaluate $42 - 5r$ if $r = 4$.
    A. 148   **B.** 41   **C.** 33   **D.** 22

    13. _____

14. Evaluate $x \div y - z$ if $x = 32$, $y = 4$, and $z = 2$.
  A. 6 **B.** 16 **C.** 10 **D.** 34

14. _____

15. Write $3 \cdot 3 \cdot 3 \cdot 3 \cdot 5 \cdot 5$ using exponents.
  A. $3^3 \cdot 5$ **B.** $3^4 \cdot 5^2$ **C.** $4^3 \cdot 2^5$ **D.** $3 \cdot 4 \cdot 5 \cdot 2$

15. _____

16. Evaluate 5 cubed.
  A. 15 **B.** 125 **C.** 243 **D.** 25

16. _____

17. Write 8^5 as a product.
  A. $8 \cdot 8 \cdot 8 \cdot 8 \cdot 8$ **B.** $8 \cdot 5$
  C. $8 \cdot 8 \cdot 8 \cdot 8 \cdot 8 \cdot 8$ **D.** $5 \cdot 8$

17. _____

18. Evaluate $4 \cdot 2^3 - 5$.
  A. 24 **B.** 3 **C.** 19 **D.** 27

18. _____

19. The sum of a number and eight is twice the number. Use the guess-and-check strategy to find the number.
  A. 4 **B.** 5 **C.** 6 **D.** 8

19. _____

20. Which number is the solution of $x + 6 = 24$?
  A. 4 **B.** 18 **C.** 20 **D.** 30

20. _____

21. Which number is the solution of $3 = 18 \div n$?
  A. 6 **B.** 15 **C.** 21 **D.** 54

21. _____

22. Solve $n - 8 = 16$ mentally.
  A. 8 **B.** 24 **C.** 2 **D.** 128

22. _____

23. Solve $28 \div x = 4$ mentally.
  A. 32 **B.** 7 **C.** 24 **D.** 112

23. _____

24. A train is traveling at an average speed of 55 miles per hour. Use the four-step plan to find how far it will travel in 5 hours.
  A. 275 miles **B.** 60 miles **C.** 11 miles **D.** 50 miles

24. _____

25. Amad went to the fair four days in a row. The first day he spent $2. The second day he spent $4. The third day he spent $8. If this pattern continues, how much did Amad spend on his fourth day?
  A. $16 **B.** $10 **C.** $12 **D.** $14

25. _____

Mathematics: Applications
and Connections, Course 1

Chapter 1 Test, Form 1B

1. Find the next three numbers in the pattern 1, 5, 9, 13, _?_, _?_, _?_.   1. _____
   A. 3, 7, 9   **B.** 15, 17, 19   **C.** 17, 21, 25   **D.** 19, 25, 31

2. Find the next three numbers in the pattern 3, 9, 27, _?_, _?_, _?_.   2. _____
   A. 54, 108, 216   **B.** 81, 243, 729
   C. 36, 45, 54   **D.** 30, 90, 270

3. Round 158 to the nearest ten.   3. _____
   A. 100   **B.** 200   **C.** 150   **D.** 160

4. Round 785 to the nearest hundred.   4. _____
   A. 700   **B.** 780   **C.** 790   **D.** 800

5. Round 3,450 to the nearest thousand.   5. _____
   A. 3,000   **B.** 3,200   **C.** 4,000   **D.** 3,300

6. Estimate $3,912 - 1,122$ using rounding.   6. _____
   A. 3,000   **B.** 2,000   **C.** 1,000   **D.** 3,800

7. Estimate 17×391 using rounding.   7. _____
   A. 4,000   **B.** 5,000   **C.** 6,000   **D.** 8,000

8. Find the value of $20 - 8 \div 4$.   8. _____
   A. 18   **B.** 3   **C.** 22   **D.** 48

9. Find the value of $28 + 6 \times 4 - 2$.   9. _____
   A. 134   **B.** 50   **C.** 68   **D.** 40

10. Find the value of $51 - 2 \times 13 + 14$.   10. _____
    A. 1,323   **B.** 3   **C.** 39   **D.** 651

11. Find the value of $42 \times 3 - 10 \div 5$.   11. _____
    A. 23   **B.** 7   **C.** 124   **D.** 84

12. Evaluate mn if $m = 23$ and $n = 5$.   12. _____
    A. 115   **B.** 235   **C.** 28   **D.** 523

13. Evaluate $3 + 2m$ if $m = 6$.   13. _____
    A. 30   **B.** 29   **C.** 15   **D.** 11

Chapter 1 Test, Form 1B (continued)

14. Evaluate $a + b - c$ if $a = 20$, $b = 10$, and $c = 5$.
    A. 5   **B.** 35   **C.** 25   **D.** 22

14. _____

15. Write $7 \cdot 7 \cdot 7 \cdot 7 \cdot 7 \cdot 7$ using exponents.
    A. 6×7 **B.** 7^6 **C.** 6^7 **D.** 7×6

15. _____

16. Evaluate 10^5.
    A. 10,000   **B.** 50   **C.** 100,000   **D.** 1,000,000

16. _____

17. Write 4^3 as a product.
    A. $4 \cdot 3$ **B.** $3 \cdot 3 \cdot 3 \cdot 3$ **C.** $4 \cdot 4 \cdot 4$ **D.** $4 \cdot 4 \cdot 4 \cdot 4$

17. _____

18. Evaluate $5^2 \cdot 3 - 2$.
    A. 73   **B.** 28   **C.** 25   **D.** 60

18. _____

19. The sum of a number and its double is 30. Use the guess-and-check strategy to find the number.
    A. 15   **B.** 10   **C.** 20   **D.** 5

19. _____

20. Which number is the solution of $x - 7 = 42$?
    A. 29   **B.** 35   **C.** 49   **D.** 52

20. _____

21. Which number is the solution of $42 = 7x$?
    A. 6   **B.** 35   **C.** 49   **D.** 294

21. _____

22. Solve $5 + n = 14$ mentally.
    A. 10   **B.** 19   **C.** 8   **D.** 9

22. _____

23. Solve $36 \div r = 9$ mentally.
    A. 5   **B.** 45   **C.** 27   **D.** 4

23. _____

24. A television sells for $495 plus tax. The tax is $24. Use the four-step plan to find the total cost of the television.
    A. $471   **B.** $419   **C.** $529   **D.** $519

24. _____

25. Wendie decided to start training for track. The first day, she jogged 6 laps. The second day, she jogged 12 laps. The third day, she jogged 18 laps. If this pattern continues, how many laps did she jog on the fourth day?
    A. 22   **B.** 24   **C.** 36   **D.** 30

25. _____

Chapter 1 Test, Form 1C

1. Find the next three numbers in the pattern 25, 4, 25, 4, _?_, _?_, _?_.
   A. 3, 20, 3   **B.** 21, 29, 21   **C.** 25, 4, 25   **D.** 29, 21, 29

   1. _____

2. Find the next three numbers in the pattern 10, 20, 40, _?_, _?_, _?_.
   A. 50, 60, 70   **B.** 60, 80, 100   **C.** 30, 60, 90   **D.** 80, 160, 320

   2. _____

3. Round 248 to the nearest ten.
   A. 240   **B.** 250   **C.** 200   **D.** 300

   3. _____

4. Round 3,542 to the nearest hundred.
   A. 3,500   **B.** 3,600   **C.** 3,000   **D.** 4,000

   4. _____

5. Round 2,221 to the nearest thousand.
   A. 2,200   **B.** 2,300   **C.** 2,000   **D.** 3,000

   5. _____

6. Estimate 123 + 496 using rounding.
   A. 800   **B.** 500   **C.** 700   **D.** 600

   6. _____

7. Estimate 324 × 19 using rounding.
   A. 6,000   **B.** 7,000   **C.** 5,000   **D.** 600

   7. _____

8. Find the value of 5 + 7 × 4.
   A. 48   **B.** 33   **C.** 574   **D.** 39

   8. _____

9. Find the value of 21 + 4 − 5 × 2.
   A. 81   **B.** 40   **C.** 74   **D.** 15

   9. _____

10. Find the value of 58 − 2 × 3 + 1.
    A. 50   **B.** 53   **C.** 169   **D.** 224

    10. _____

11. Find the value of 4 × 3 + 9 × 8.
    A. 84   **B.** 168   **C.** 384   **D.** 59

    11. _____

12. Evaluate cd if $c = 9$ and $d = 8$.
    A. 98   **B.** 72   **C.** 17   **D.** 89

    12. _____

13. Evaluate $2 + 3n$ if $n = 5$.
    A. 37   **B.** 25   **C.** 10   **D.** 17

    13. _____

14. Evaluate $s + t - u$ if $s = 12$, $t = 8$, and $u = 20$.
   A. 10   **B.** 0   **C.** 15   **D.** 18

14. _____

15. Write $5 \cdot 5 \cdot 5 \cdot 5$ using exponents.
   A. 5×4 **B.** 5^6 **C.** 5^4 **D.** 4^5

15. _____

16. Evaluate 3^4.
   A. 12   **B.** 34   **C.** 7   **D.** 81

16. _____

17. Write 9^4 as a product.
   A. $9 \cdot 9 \cdot 9 \cdot 9$ **B.** 9×4
   C. 4×9 **D.** $9 \cdot 9 \cdot 9 \cdot 9 \cdot 9$

17. _____

18. Evaluate $2 \cdot 4^2 + 3^2$.
   A. 50   **B.** 25   **C.** 11   **D.** 41

18. _____

19. The sum of a number and twelve is twice the number. Use the guess-and-check strategy to find the number.
   A. 8   **B.** 10   **C.** 12   **D.** 14

19. _____

20. Which number is the solution of $x - 4 = 3$?
   A. 1   **B.** 7   **C.** 9   **D.** 12

20. _____

21. Which number is the solution of $39 = 3n$?
   A. 10   **B.** 13   **C.** 15   **D.** 36

21. _____

22. Solve $x + 27 = 29$ mentally.
   A. 2   **B.** 56   **C.** 12   **D.** 40

22. _____

23. Solve $27 = 9n$ mentally.
   A. 18   **B.** 36   **C.** 3   **D.** 243

23. _____

24. Juyong saves $5 of her allowance each week. Use the four-step plan to determine how many weeks she must save to buy a $40 radio.
   A. 45 weeks   **B.** 8 weeks   **C.** 6 weeks   **D.** 10 weeks

24. _____

25. Luis mows lawns. The first week of spring he mowed 2 lawns. The second week he mowed 4 lawns. The third week he mowed 6 lawns. If this pattern continues, how many lawns did Luis mow the fourth week?
   A. 8   **B.** 12   **C.** 5   **D.** 10

25. _____

Chapter 1 Test, Form 2A

Find the next three numbers in each pattern.

1. 5, 8, 11, _?_, _?_, _?_

2. 51, 46, 41, _?_, _?_, _?_

3. 224, 112, 56, _?_, _?_, _?_

4. 6, 18, 54, _?_, _?_, _?_

1. _____

2. _____

3. _____

4. _____

Round each number to the underlined place-value position.

5. $\underline{8}$,500

6. 1,$\underline{3}$64

7. $\underline{2}$,526

8. 7,$\underline{1}$27

5. _____

6. _____

7. _____

8. _____

Estimate using rounding.

9. 7,234 + 1,988

10. 523 × 18

11. 8,721 − 5,142

12. 923 ÷ 27

9. _____

10. _____

11. _____

12. _____

Find the value of each expression.

13. 14 + 3 × 8

14. 9 − 3 × 2 + 6

15. 99 ÷ 9 + 2 × 5

16. 8 × 7 − 6 × 5

13. _____

14. _____

15. _____

16. _____

Evaluate each expression if r = 6, s = 10, and t = 8.

17. rt

18. $r + s - 2t$

19. $3t \div r$

20. $rs + t \div 4$

17. _____

18. _____

19. _____

20. _____

Mathematics: Applications and Connections, Course 1

Evaluate.

21. 9^4 21. _____

22. x^5 if $x = 3$ 22. _____

23. 8 cubed   23. _____

24. $3^2 \times 4^2 - 2^2$ 24. _____

Identify the solution to each equation from the list given.

25. $a - 6 = 20$; 14, 26, 120   25. _____

26. $18 \div x = 3$; 6, 21, 54   26. _____

27. $8b = 72$; 9, 10, 11   27. _____

28. $62 + c = 81$; 18, 19, 20   28. _____

Solve each equation mentally.

29. $8m = 40$ 29. _____

30. $17 - x = 8$ 30. _____

31. $q \div 32 = 3$ 31. _____

32. The product of two numbers is 40. One number is 3 more than the other. Use the guess-and-check strategy to find the numbers.   32. _____

33. A pizza parlor sold 78 pizzas on Monday, 54 pizzas on Tuesday, and 89 pizzas on Wednesday. How many more pizzas were sold on Wednesday than on Tuesday?   33. _____

Chapter 1 Test, Form 2B

Find the next three numbers in each pattern.

1. 8, 14, 20, _?_, _?_, _?_

2. 27, 23, 19, _?_, _?_, _?_

3. 7, 14, 28, _?_, _?_, _?_

4. 2, 6, 18, _?_, _?_, _?_

1. _____

2. _____

3. _____

4. _____

Round each number to the underlined place-value position.

5. $\underline{6},244$

6. $\underline{4}35$

7. $1,\underline{3}24$

8. $\underline{8}79$

5. _____

6. _____

7. _____

8. _____

Estimate using rounding.

9. $743 + 578$

10. 52×9

11. $267 - 113$

12. $67 \div 8$

9. _____

10. _____

11. _____

12. _____

Find the value of each expression.

13. $24 - 8 \times 2$

14. $7 \times 5 + 6 \times 2$

15. $3 + 4 \times 5 - 1$

16. $15 - 5 \times 3 + 8$

13. _____

14. _____

15. _____

16. _____

Evaluate each expression if $a = 7$, $b = 5$, and $c = 9$.

17. $8 + b + c$

18. $a + b \times c$

19. $a - b + ab$

20. $ac - ab$

17. _____

18. _____

19. _____

20. _____

Mathematics: Applications and Connections, Course 1

Evaluate.

21. 5^3

21. _____

22. x^3 if $x = 12$

22. _____

23. eight squared

23. _____

24. $2^4 + 3^2$

24. _____

Identify the solution to each equation from the list given.

25. $x + 10 = 30$; 20, 30, 40

25. _____

26. $50 \div x = 25$; 2, 75, 25

26. _____

27. $3a = 21$; 6, 7, 8

27. _____

28. $85 - b = 70$; 5, 15, 25

28. _____

Solve each equation mentally.

29. $8m = 56$

29. _____

30. $x - 12 = 4$

30. _____

31. $p \div 4 = 8$

31. _____

32. The sum of a number and its double is 24. Use the guess-and-check strategy to find the number.

32. _____

33. At the library, 2,312 books were checked out on Friday, and 3,234 books were checked out on Saturday. Late charges of $74 and $87 were collected on Friday and Saturday, respectively. Find the total amount of late charges collected.

33. _____

Chapter 1 Test, Form 2C

Find the next three numbers in each pattern.

1. 51, 21, 51, _?_, _?_, _?_

2. 29, 27, 25, _?_, _?_, _?_

3. 15, 30, 60, _?_, _?_, _?_

4. 6, 10, 14, _?_, _?_, _?_

1. _____

2. _____

3. _____

4. _____

Round each number to the underlined place-value position.

5. $\underline{8}3$

6. $\underline{6}6$

7. $1\underline{7}8$

8. $\underline{7}67$

5. _____

6. _____

7. _____

8. _____

Estimate using rounding.

9. $375 + 422$

10. $4,267 - 1,976$

11. 37×6

12. $61 \div 9$

9. _____

10. _____

11. _____

12. _____

Find the value of each expression.

13. $37 - 6 \times 2$

14. $40 + 6 \div 2$

15. $3 \times 4 - 2 \times 2$

16. $9 \times 6 + 6$

13. _____

14. _____

15. _____

16. _____

Evaluate each expression if $a = 5$, $b = 8$, and $c = 6$.

17. $a + b$

18. ac

19. $2a + 4$

20. $2b - a$

17. _____

18. _____

19. _____

20. _____

Evaluate.

21. 9^2

21. _____

22. a^3 if $a = 4$

22. _____

23. seven squared

23. _____

24. $2^2 + 5$

24. _____

Identify the solution to each equation from the list given.

25. $x - 5 = 15$; 10, 20, 30

25. _____

26. $24 \div x = 3$; 6, 8, 10

26. _____

27. $p - 7 = 15$; 20, 21, 22

27. _____

28. $48 \div s = 6$; 6, 7, 8

28. _____

Solve each equation mentally.

29. $7t = 63$

29. _____

30. $r + 5 = 31$

30. _____

31. $a - 9 = 10$

31. _____

32. The sum of a number and its double is 21. Use the guess-and-check strategy to find the number.

32. _____

33. On Saturday 221 adults were at the swim club. On Sunday there were 198 adults. How many more adults were at the swim club on Saturday than on Sunday?

33. _____

Chapter 1 Performance Assessment

Instructions: Demonstrate your knowledge by giving a clear, concise solution to each problem. Be sure to include all relevant drawings and justify your answers. You may show your solution in more than one way or investigate beyond the requirements of the problem.

1. The number of Calories per serving of certain food items is given in the table below.

Food	Serving	Calories
Apple	1 large	117
Banana	1 large	176
Carrots	1 cup	42
Fried Chicken	$\frac{1}{2}$ breast	232
Egg	1 medium	77

   a. Ayani had an apple, banana, and half chicken breast for lunch. Estimate the number of Calories he ate for lunch. Explain each step.
   b. If Ayani had an apple and a banana on alternating days, how would you write that as a pattern?
   c. Estimate the number of Calories in four eggs. Explain each step. Find the number of Calories in four eggs. How close was your estimate to the exact answer?
   d. Kristin ate three eggs, a whole chicken breast, and a banana. How many Calories did she eat?

2. Write the order of operations, in your own words.
3. Explain one situation where you could use exponents in real life.

4. Let a bag, ⬛, represent the phrase "some number" and a piece of popcorn, 🍿, represent 1 for the following exercises.
   a. Draw a picture to represent each phrase.
      (1) some number and five more
      (2) the sum of five and three times some number
   b. Write a phrase representing the diagram below.

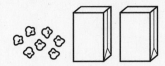

Chapter 1 Mid-Chapter Test

(Lessons 1-1 through 1-4)

Use the four-step plan to solve each problem. Use a calculator if necessary.

1. Rayna studied 315 vocabulary words in three weeks for her French class. If Rayna studied the same number of words each day, how many vocabulary words did she study a day?

2. A computer diskette holds 1,440K of memory. If four programs are on the diskette and they use 32K, 54K, 68K, and 72K of memory, how much memory is left on the diskette?

3. The Hartmans want to buy a 31-inch television that costs $750. They plan to make a down payment of $275 and pay the rest in five equal payments. What will be the amount of each payment?

Find the next three numbers in each pattern.

4. 6, 7, 9, 12, _?_, _?_, _?_

5. 7, 8, 7, 8, _?_, _?_, _?_

6. 8, 16, 32, _?_, _?_, _?_

7. 35, 28, 21, _?_, _?_, _?_

Estimate.

8. $721 - 53$

9. $905 + 273$

10. 27×9

11. 95×24

12. $520 \div 5$

13. $776 \div 42$

14. $1,729 + 5,681$

15. $4,921 - 2,602$

Find the value of each expression.

16. $24 - 5 + 2 \times 8$

17. $81 \div 9 + 2 \times 4$

18. $15 \div 5 - 3$

19. $6 \times 5 + 8 \times 7$

20. $37 - 14 \div 2 - 3 \times 7$

1. _____
2. _____
3. _____
4. _____
5. _____
6. _____
7. _____
8. _____
9. _____
10. _____
11. _____
12. _____
13. _____
14. _____
15. _____
16. _____
17. _____
18. _____
19. _____
20. _____

Chapter 1 Quiz A

Use the four-step plan to solve each problem. Use a calculator if necessary.

1. On a trip to Florida, the Juarez family bought 4 adult plane tickets costing a total of $920. What was the cost of each ticket?

   1. _____

2. Jill saved $12 per week for 50 weeks. How much did she save in all?

   2. _____

Find the next three numbers in each pattern.

3. 222, 202, 182, _?_, _?_, _?_   4. 3, 12, 48, _?_, _?_, _?_

   3. _____

   4. _____

5. At the class play, 135 adult tickets were sold for $4 each, and 236 student tickets were sold for $2 each. How many more student tickets were sold than adult tickets?

   5. _____

Chapter 1 Quiz B

Round each number to the underlined place-value position.

1. <u>7</u>,499   2. 4<u>9</u>5

   1. _____

   2. _____

Estimate using rounding.

3. $865 + 276$ 4. $78 - 56$

   3. _____

   4. _____

5. 994×27 6. $4,106 \div 1,824$

   5. _____

   6. _____

Find the value of each expression.

7. $5 + 7 \times 9$ 8. $36 - 27 \div 3 + 1$

   7. _____

   8. _____

9. $6 \times 7 - 7 \times 3$ 10. $10 \div 2 + 15 \div 3$

   9. _____

   10. _____

Mathematics: Applications and Connections, Course 1

Chapter 1 Quiz C

(Lessons 1-5 and 1-6)

Evaluate each expression if s = 4 and t = 6.

1. $st - 2s$ 2. $s + 3t$

1. _____

2. _____

Evaluate each expression if a = 6, b = 9, and c = 11.

3. $5 + a + bc$ 4. $ab - c$

3. _____

4. _____

5. Write $8 \times 8 \times 8 \times 3 \times 3$ using exponents.

5. _____

Evaluate.

6. 9 cubed   7. n^4 if $n = 10$

6. _____

7. _____

8. $3^2 + 4$ 9. $8^2 + 5^2$

8. _____

9. _____

10. The area of a circle can be found by multiplying the number 3.14 times the square of the radius. If the radius of the circle is r, write an expression that represents the area of the circle.

10. _____

- -

Chapter 1 Quiz D

(Lesson 1-7)

Identify the solution to each equation from the list given.

1. $x \div 3 = 13$; 33, 36, 39   2. $92 = 4a$; 22, 23, 24

1. _____

2. _____

Solve each equation mentally.

3. $17 = n + 9$ 4. $5m = 35$

3. _____

4. _____

5. The product of a number and 22 is 154. Use the guess-and-check strategy to find the number.

5. _____

Mathematics: Applications and Connections, Course 1

Chapter 1 Standardized Test Practice

Choose the best answer. Write A, B, C, or D.

1. On a map of Illinois, each inch represents approximately 21 miles. Helena is planning to travel from Springfield to Chicago. If the distance on the map from Springfield to Chicago is about 10 inches, how far will she travel?
   A. 21 miles **B.** 10 miles **C.** 210 miles **D.** 21 inches

   1. _____

2. Find the next three numbers in the pattern 250, 275, 300, _?_, _?_, _?_.
   A. 325, 350, 375 **B.** 275, 250, 225
   C. 350, 400, 450 **D.** 305, 310, 315

   2. _____

3. Find the next three numbers in the pattern 52, 46, 40, _?_, _?_, _?_.
   A. 38, 36, 32 **B.** 34, 28, 22 **C.** 46, 52, 58 **D.** 50, 60, 70

   3. _____

4. Round 57 to the nearest ten.
   A. 55 **B.** 70 **C.** 50 **D.** 60

   4. _____

5. Round 3,521 to the nearest thousand.
   A. 4,000 **B.** 3,000 **C.** 3,500 **D.** 3,525

   5. _____

6. If each of the nine members of Bexley Middle School's tennis team brings a dozen bagels to the sports banquet, estimate how many total bagels they will have.
   A. 20 **B.** 160 **C.** 100 **D.** 180

   6. _____

7. Evaluate $29 - 3 + 2$.
   A. 24 **B.** 28 **C.** 30 **D.** 27

   7. _____

8. Evaluate $3 \times 1 + 7 \times 9$.
   A. 192 **B.** 216 **C.** 90 **D.** 66

   8. _____

9. Evaluate $2 + 24 \div 4 \times 2 - 7$.
   A. 7 **B.** 5 **C.** 3 **D.** 26

   9. _____

10. Evaluate $a + bc$ if $a = 2$, $b = 1$, and $c = 4$.
    A. 8 **B.** 10 **C.** 6 **D.** 12

    10. _____

11. Evaluate $2r$ if $r = 37$.

    A. 39   **B.** 74   **C.** 18.5   **D.** 35

11. _____

12. The area of a rectangle is found by multiplying length times width. Find the area of a rectangle 12 inches wide and 13 inches long.

    A. 25 sq. in.   **B.** 1 sq. in.   **C.** 144 sq. in.   **D.** 156 sq. in.

12. _____

13. Write $3 \cdot 5 \cdot 5 \cdot 7$ using exponents.

    A. 525   **B.** $3 \cdot 5^2 \cdot 7$ **C.** $3 \cdot 25 \cdot 7$ **D.** $21 \cdot 25$

13. _____

14. Write 3^4 as a product.

    A. 81   **B.** $3 \cdot 3 \cdot 3$

    C. $3 \cdot 3 \cdot 3 \cdot 3$ **D.** $3 \cdot 3 \cdot 3 \cdot 3 \cdot 3$

14. _____

15. Evaluate $4 \cdot 3^3 - 7^2$.

    A. 59   **B.** 5   **C.** 88   **D.** 0

15. _____

16. Write $b \cdot b \cdot b \cdot b \cdot b \cdot b \cdot b$ using exponents.

    A. b^6 **B.** $7b$ **C.** $6b$ **D.** b^7

16. _____

17. Which number is the solution of $x + 12 = 19$?

    A. 6   **B.** 7   **C.** 8   **D.** 9

17. _____

18. Solve $3x = 27$ using mental math.

    A. 24   **B.** 7   **C.** 8   **D.** 9

18. _____

19. Solve $242 - c = 204$ using mental math.

    A. 36   **B.** 40   **C.** 38   **D.** 446

19. _____

20. Cole purchased a new tennis racquet and tennis glove. The cost of the racquet was $120 and he spent $132 total. If g represents the cost of the glove, the equation $120 + g = 132$ results. Find the cost of the glove.

    A. $12   **B.** $15   **C.** $10   **D.** $22

20. _____

Cumulative Review, Chapter 1

1. Mr. Chin earned a bonus of $1,000 this year. If tax deductions of $274 were made from the bonus check, how much did he actually receive? Solve using the four-step plan. (Lesson 1-1)

Round to the nearest ten. (Lesson 1-3)
2. 48   3. 111

Round to the nearest hundred. (Lesson 1-3)
4. 438   5. 2,387

Round to the nearest thousand. (Lesson 1-3)
6. 1,756   7. 7,106

Estimate using rounding. (Lesson 1-3)
8. $725 + 199$ 9. $348 - 129$

10. Find the next three numbers in the pattern 21, 23, 25, 27, ... (Lesson 1-2)

11. Write $11 \cdot 11 \cdot 11 \cdot 11 \cdot 11$ using exponents. (Lesson 1-6)

12. Evaluate $2 \cdot 5^2 - 3^2$. (Lesson 1-6)

Find the value of each expression. (Lesson 1-4)
13. $8 - 2 \times 3$

14. $18 - 3 \times 5 + 2$

Evaluate each expression if x = 12, y = 6, and z = 3. (Lesson 1-5)
15. $x + y \div z$

16. $yz + 5$

Identify the solution to each equation from the list given. (Lesson 1-7)
17. $m - 8 = 24$; 3, 16, 32

18. $7m = 28$; 4, 21, 35

Solve each equation mentally. (Lesson 1-7)
19. $x \div 5 = 8$

20. $m + 8 = 15$

1. _____
2. _____
3. _____
4. _____
5. _____
6. _____
7. _____
8. _____
9. _____
10. _____
11. _____
12. _____
13. _____
14. _____
15. _____
16. _____
17. _____
18. _____
19. _____
20. _____

Chapter 1 Answer Key

Page 1		Page 2	
1. A		14. A	
2. C		15. B	
3. A		16. B	
4. D		17. A	
5. C		18. D	
6. C		19. D	
7. B		20. B	
8. D		21. A	
9. B		22. B	
10. A		23. B	
11. D		24. A	
12. C		25. A	
13. D			

Page 3		Page 4	
1. C		14. C	
2. B		15. B	
3. D		16. C	
4. D		17. C	
5. A		18. A	
6. A		19. B	
7. D		20. C	
8. A		21. A	
9. B		22. D	
10. C		23. D	
11. C		24. D	
12. A		25. B	
13. C			

Mathematics: Applications and Connections, Course 1

Chapter 1 Answer Key

Page 5

1. ___C___

2. ___D___

3. ___B___

4. ___A___

5. ___C___

6. ___D___

7. ___A___

8. ___B___

9. ___D___

10. ___B___

11. ___A___

12. ___B___

13. ___D___

Page 6

14. ___B___

15. ___C___

16. ___D___

17. ___A___

18. ___D___

19. ___C___

20. ___B___

21. ___B___

22. ___A___

23. ___C___

24. ___B___

25. ___A___

Chapter 1 Answer Key

Page 7

1. 14, 17, 20
2. 36, 31, 26
3. 28, 14, 7
4. 162, 486, 1,458

5. 9,000
6. 1,400
7. 3,000
8. 7,100

9. 7,000 + 2,000 = 9,000
10. 500 × 20 = 10,000
11. 9,000 − 5,000 = 4,000
12. 900 ÷ 30 = 30

13. 38
14. 9
15. 21
16. 26

17. 48
18. 0
19. 4
20. 62

Page 8

21. 6,561
22. 243
23. 512
24. 140

25. 26
26. 6
27. 9
28. 19

29. 5
30. 9
31. 96
32. 5, 8

33. 35

Mathematics: Applications and Connections, Course 1

Chapter 1 Answer Key

Page 9		Page 10	
1.	26, 32, 38	21.	125
2.	15, 11, 7		
3.	56, 112, 224	22.	1,728
4.	54, 162, 486		
		23.	64
		24.	25
5.	6,000		
6.	400		
7.	1,300	25.	20
8.	900		
		26.	2
9.	700 + 600 = 1,300	27.	7
10.	50 × 10 = 500		
11.	300 − 100 = 200	28.	15
12.	70 ÷ 10 = 7		
		29.	7
13.	8		
14.	47	30.	16
15.	22		
16.	8	31.	32
		32.	8
17.	22		
18.	52	33.	$161
19.	37		
20.	28		

Mathematics: Applications and Connections, Course 1

Chapter 1 Answer Key

Page 11   Page 12

1. 21, 51, 21
2. 23, 21, 19
3. 120, 240, 480
4. 18, 22, 26

5. 80
6. 70
7. 180
8. 800

9. 400 + 400 = 800
10. 4,000 − 2,000 = 2,000
11. 40 × 6 = 240
12. 60 ÷ 10 = 6

13. 25
14. 43
15. 8
16. 60

17. 13
18. 30
19. 14
20. 11

21. 81
22. 64
23. 49
24. 9

25. 20
26. 8
27. 22
28. 8

29. 9
30. 26
31. 19
32. 7
33. 23

Chapter 1 Scoring Guide

Level	Specific Criteria
3 Superior	• Shows thorough understanding of the concepts *estimation of sums, differences, and products, order of operations, use of exponents,* and *modeling and evaluating expressions.* • Uses appropriate strategies to solve problems and to evaluate and model expressions. • Computations are correct. • Written explanations are exemplary. • Diagrams are accurate and appropriate. • Goes beyond requirements of some or all problems.
2 Satisfactory, with Minor Flaws	• Shows understanding of the concepts *estimation of sums, differences, and products, order of operations, use of exponents,* and *modeling and evaluating expressions.* • Uses appropriate strategies to solve problems and to evaluate and model expressions. • Computations are mostly correct. • Written are explanations are effective. • Diagrams are accurate and appropriate. • Satisfies all requirements of problems.
1 Nearly Satisfactory, with Serious Flaws	• Shows understanding of most of the concepts *estimation of sums, differences, and products, order of operations, use of exponents,* and *modeling and evaluating expressions.* • May not use appropriate strategies to solve problems and to evaluate and model expressions. • Computations are mostly correct. • Written explanations are satisfactory. • Diagrams are mostly accurate or appropriate. • Satisfies most requirements of problems.
0 Unsatisfactory	• Shows little or no understanding of the concepts *estimation of sums, differences, and products, order of operations, use of exponents,* and *modeling and evaluating expressions.* • May not use appropriate strategies to solve problems and to evaluate and model expressions. • Computations are incorrect. • Written explanations are not satisfactory. • Diagrams are not accurate or appropriate. • Does not satisfy requirements of problems.

Chapter 1 Answer Key

Performance Assessment Sample Answers
Page 13

1. **a.** Round each number to the nearest hundred and add.
   100 + 200 + 200 = 500
   He ate about 500 Calories.

   b. a, b, a, b, a, . . .

   c. Round 77 to 80. 4 × 80 = 320; 4 × 77 = 308 Calories in 4 eggs. Estimate is 12 more than the exact answer.

   d. 3(77) + 2(232) + 176 = 871 Calories

2. Multiply and divide in order from left to right. Then add and subtract in order from left to right.

3. writing metrics, measurements in science, populations

4. **a.** (1)

   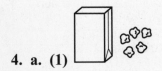

   (2)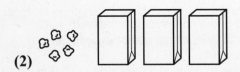

   b. seven plus 2 times some number

Mid-Chapter Test
Page 14

1. _____ 15
2. _____ 1,214K
3. _____ $95
4. _____ 16, 21, 27
5. _____ 7, 8, 7
6. _____ 64, 128, 256
7. _____ 14, 7, 0
8. _____ 700 − 50 = 650
9. _____ 900 + 300 = 1,200
10. _____ 30 × 10 = 300
11. _____ 100 × 20 = 2000
12. _____ 500 ÷ 5 = 100
13. _____ 800 ÷ 40 = 20
14. _____ 2,000 + 6,000 = 8,000
15. _____ 5,000 − 3,000 = 2,000
16. _____ 35
17. _____ 17
18. _____ 0
19. _____ 86
20. _____ 9

Chapter 1 Answer Key

Quiz A, Page 15

1. $230
2. $600
3. 162, 142, 122
4. 192, 768, 3,072
5. 101

Quiz B, Page 15

1. 7,000
2. 500
3. $900 + 300 = 1,200$
4. $80 - 60 = 20$
5. $1,000 \times 30 = 30,000$
6. $4,000 \div 2,000 = 2$
7. 68
8. 28
9. 21
10. 10

Quiz C, Page 16

1. 16
2. 22
3. 110
4. 43
5. $8^3 \cdot 3^2$
6. 729
7. 10,000
8. 13
9. 89
10. $3.14r^2$

Quiz D, Page 16

1. 39
2. 23
3. 8
4. 7
5. 7

Mathematics: Applications and Connections, Course 1

Chapter 1 Answer Key

Standardized Test Practice

Page 17
1. C
2. A
3. B
4. D
5. A
6. C
7. B
8. D
9. A
10. C

Page 18
11. B
12. D
13. B
14. C
15. A
16. D
17. B
18. D
19. C
20. A

Cumulative Review

Page 19
1. $726
2. 50
3. 110
4. 400
5. 2,400
6. 2,000
7. 7,000
8. $700 + 200 = 900$
9. $300 - 100 = 200$
10. 29, 31, 33
11. 11^5
12. 41
13. 2
14. 5
15. 14
16. 23
17. 32
18. 4
19. 40
20. 7

Mathematics: Applications and Connections, Course 1

Chapter 2 Test, Form 1A

Refer to the frequency table for Questions 1–2.

1. What is the most common age of music store shoppers?
   A. 17–20   B. 13–16
   C. 9–12   D. 5–8

Music Store Shoppers	
Age	Frequency
5–8	2
9–12	8
13–16	28
17–20	21
20–24	6

2. How many people 13 years or older shopped at the music store?
   A. 21   B. 55
   C. 65   D. 28

3. Determine the stems for this set of data: 41, 16, 12, 12, 2, 29, 34, 33.
   A. 0, 1, 2, 3, 4   B. 1, 2, 3, 4, 6, 9   C. 2, 4, 6, 8, 10   D. 1, 3, 5, 7, 9

4. Choose the best interval for a frequency table for this set of data: 7, 29, 63, 17, 35, 48, 98, 76, 34.
   A. 1   B. 10   C. 100   D. 84

5. Which line graph below correctly shows the following amounts of precipitation: March, 7 inches; April, 9 inches; May, 8 inches; June, 7 inches.

   A.
   Mar. Apr. May June

   B.
   Mar. Apr. May June

   C.
   Mar. Apr. May June

   D.
   Mar. Apr. May June

6. Use the bar graph at the right to determine how many more points were scored in the fourth quarter than in the third.
   A. 4   B. 14
   C. 18   D. 2

   Points Scored Per Quarter
   Number of Points

7. Use the pictograph at the right to determine how many fewer tickets were sold in Week 4 than in Week 5.
   A. 2   B. 6
   C. 4   D. 24

   Tickets Sold Per Week
   □ = 4 tickets

1. _____
2. _____
3. _____
4. _____
5. _____
6. _____
7. _____

Refer to the circle graph.

8. Which language has the largest enrollment?
   A. Spanish   **B.** French
   C. German   **D.** Japanese

8. _____

Foreign Language Enrollment

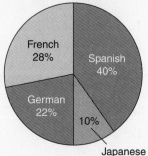

9. The Spanish enrollment is higher than the French enrollment by what percent?
   A. 14%   **B.** 10%
   C. 12%   **D.** 28%

9. _____

Refer to the line graph.

10. Find the expected temperature for Miami in December.
    A. about 80°   **B.** about 70°
    C. about 60°   **D.** about 50°

10. _____

Average Temperature

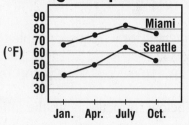

11. Find the difference in April temperatures for Miami and Seattle.
    A. 20°   **B.** 10°   **C.** 25°   **D.** 30°

11. _____

Refer to the table for Questions 12–13.

12. Find the mean of the test scores.
    A. 86   **B.** 81
    C. 82   **D.** 27

12. _____

Test Scores		
73	80	96
69	91	86
76	86	81

13. Find the median of the test scores.
    A. 86   **B.** 81   **C.** 82   **D.** 27

13. _____

14. Which stem-and-leaf plot correctly displays these data: 83, 76, 89, 94, 73?

14. _____

A. Stem	Leaf		**B.** Stem	Leaf		**C.** Stem	Leaf		**D.** Stem	Leaf
7	3		3	7 8		7	3 6		8	9 3
7	6		4	9		8	3 9		7	6 3
8	3		6	7		9	4		9	4
8	9		9	8						
9	4									

15. The range of a set of data for a vertical axis from 1,500 to 2,150 is 650. Which number would not be a misleading starting point for the vertical axis?
    A. 0   **B.** 1,300   **C.** 1,400   **D.** 1,500

15. _____

16. Name the ordered pair for point *M*.
    A. (2, 3)   **B.** (3, 2)
    C. (2, 2)   **D.** (3, 3)

16. _____

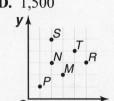

Mathematics: Applications and Connections, Course 1

Name_____ Date_____

Chapter 2 Test, Form 1B

Refer to the frequency table for Questions 1–2.

Hours Watching Sports Per Week	
Interval	Frequency
0–2	6
3–4	9
5–6	4
7–8	1

1. What is the least common interval of hours of sports watched?
   A. 0–2   B. 3–4
   C. 5–6   D. 7–8

1. _____

2. How many people spent 3 hours or more per week watching sports events?
   A. 9   B. 20   C. 14   D. 6

2. _____

3. Determine the stems for this set of data: 15, 23, 18, 7, 2, 16, 12.
   A. 0, 1, 2   B. 1, 2, 3, 4, 5   C. 2, 4, 6, 8, 10   D. 0, 1, 3, 5

3. _____

4. Choose the best interval for a frequency table for this set of data: 178, 165, 189, 173, 205, 188, 202.
   A. 1   B. 10   C. 100   D. 210

4. _____

5. Which bar graph below correctly shows the following frequencies: 18 bears, 5 reptiles, 10 fish, and 8 elephants?

5. _____

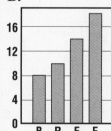

A.   B.   C.   D.

6. Use the bar graph at the right to determine how much more the receipts were for April than for March.
   A. $3,000   B. $7,000
   C. $4,000   D. $11,000

6. _____

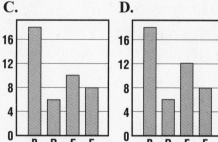

Cafe Receipts

7. Use the pictograph at the right to determine how many more compact discs were sold on Friday than on Thursday.
   A. 5   B. 65
   C. 125   D. 15

7. _____

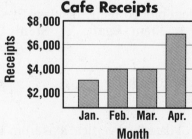

Compact Disc Sales

Mon. ⊙ ⊙ ⊙ ⊙ ◖
Tues. ⊙ ⊙ ⊙ ⊙ ⊙
Wed. ⊙ ⊙ ⊙ ⊙
Thur. ⊙ ⊙ ⊙ ⊙ ⊙
Fri. ⊙ ⊙ ⊙ ⊙ ⊙ ⊙ ◖
Sat. ⊙ ⊙ ⊙ ⊙ ⊙ ⊙ ⊙
⊙ = 10 discs

Mathematics: Applications and Connections, Course 1

Refer to the circle graph.

Favorite Dogs

8. _____

8. Which type of dog is most popular?
   A. collie   B. cocker spaniel
   C. boxer   D. dachshund

9. _____

9. Which two have the same popularity?
   A. cocker spaniel and dachshund
   B. cocker spaniel and collie
   C. collie and boxer
   D. collie and dachshund

Refer to the line graph.

Average Monthly Temp.

10. _____

10. Find the expected temperature for Bean City in November.
    A. about 60°   B. about 30°
    C. about 40°   D. about 25°

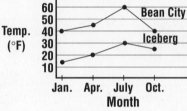

11. Find the difference in January temperatures for Bean City and Iceberg.
    A. 15°   B. 40°   C. 55°   D. 25°

11. _____

Refer to the table for Questions 12–13.

12. _____

12. Find the mean of the golf scores.
    A. 74   B. 81
    C. 79.5   D. 21

Golf Scores			
71	85	74	74
90	92	88	74

13. _____

13. Find the median of the golf scores.
    A. 74   B. 81   C. 79.5   D. 21

14. _____

14. Which stem-and-leaf plot correctly displays these data: 75, 68, 77, 67?

A.
Stem	Leaf
6	7 8
7	5 7

B.
Stem	Leaf
5	7
7	6 7
8	6

C.
Stem	Leaf
6	7
6	8
7	5
7	7

D.
Stem	Leaf
7	7 5
6	8 7

15. _____

15. The range of a set of data for a vertical axis from 1,200 to 1,600 is 400. Which number would not be a misleading starting point for the vertical axis?
    A. 1,200   B. 0   C. 1,100   D. 1,000

16. _____

16. Name the ordered pair for point U.
    A. (1, 4)   B. (4, 1)
    C. (2, 2)   D. (3, 5)

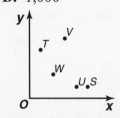

Chapter 2 Test, Form 1C

Refer to the frequency table for Questions 1–2.

Interval	Frequency
0–5	10
6–10	8
11–15	4
16–21	7

1. What is the most common age of cartoon watchers?
   A. 0–5   **B.** 6–10
   C. 11–15   **D.** 16–21

1. _____

2. How many people 11 years or older watched cartoons?
   A. 18   **B.** 19   **C.** 11   **D.** 15

2. _____

3. Determine the stems for this set of data: 5, 2, 7, 14, 3, 18.
   A. 2, 3, 5, 7, 8   **B.** 0, 1   **C.** 1   **D.** 1, 2

3. _____

4. Choose the best interval for a frequency table for this set of data: 9, 7, 4, 6, 7.
   A. 1   **B.** 10   **C.** 100   **D.** 9

4. _____

5. Which bar graph below correctly shows the following frequencies: 5 dogs, 3 cats, and 2 birds?

5. _____

   A.
   Dog Cat Bird

   B.
   Dog Cat Bird

   C.
   Dog Cat Bird

   D.
   Dog Cat Bird

6. Use the bar graph at the right to determine how many pairs of blue jeans were sold on Wednesday.
   A. 70   **B.** 80
   C. 60   **D.** 120

6. _____

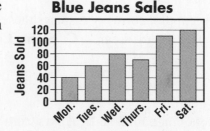

Blue Jeans Sales
Jeans Sold: 120 100 80 60 40 20 0
Mon. Tues. Wed. Thurs. Fri. Sat.

7. Use the pictograph at the right to determine how many more students did 46–60 sit-ups than did 61 or more.
   A. 4   **B.** 25
   C. 100   **D.** 75

7. _____

NUMBER OF SIT-UPS

0–35(poor)	～～～
36–45(satisfactory)	～～～～～
46–60(good)	～～～～～～～
61 or more(excellent)	～～～

～ = 25 students

Chapter 2 Test, Form 1C (continued)

Refer to the circle graph.

Favorite Movies

8. Which movie is the most popular?
   A. *Raiders of the Lost Ark*
   B. *Star Wars*
   C. *Gone with the Wind*
   D. *It's a Wonderful Life*

8. _____

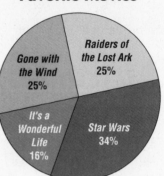

9. Which two movies have the same popularity?
   A. *Raiders of the Lost Ark* and *Star Wars*
   B. *Star Wars* and *Gone with the Wind*
   C. *Gone with the Wind* and *It's a Wonderful Life*
   D. *Raiders of the Lost Ark* and *Gone with the Wind*

9. _____

Refer to the line graph.

Life Expectancy of Women

10. Find the additional number of years a 20-year-old woman can expect to live.
    A. 20 years   B. 80 years
    C. 60 years   D. 53 years

10. _____

11. Find the additional number of years a 45-year-old woman can expect to live.
    A. 35 years   B. 75 years
    C. 40 years   D. 30 years

11. _____

Refer to the table for Questions 12–13.

Test Scores		
78		94
	91	
78		89

12. Find the mean of the test scores.
    A. 78   B. 86
    C. 89   D. 16

12. _____

13. Find the median of the test scores.
    A. 78   B. 86   C. 89   D. 16

13. _____

14. Which stem-and-leaf plot correctly displays these data: 15, 12, 21, 22?

    A.
Stem	Leaf
1	2 5
2	1 2

    B.
Stem	Leaf
1	2
2	1 2
5	1

    C.
Stem	Leaf
1	5 2
2	2 1

    D.
Stem	Leaf
1	2
2	2 1
5	1

14. _____

15. The range of a set of data for a vertical axis from 120 to 160 is 40. Which number would not be a misleading starting point for the vertical axis?
    A. 120   B. 0
    C. 110   D. 100

15. _____

16. Name the ordered pair for point *H*.
    A. (1, 1)   B. (4, 3)
    C. (3, 2)   D. (2, 4)

16. _____

Mathematics: Applications and Connections, Course 1

Chapter 2 Test, Form 2A

Refer to the frequency table.

Books Read Per Year	
Interval	**Frequency**
0–2	6
3–4	7
5–6	8
7–8	5
9 or more	6

1. How many people read 6 books or fewer per year?

   1. _____

2. Can you tell from the table if any person read more than 12 books?

   2. _____

3. Can you tell from the table how many people read 3 or more books per year? If so, how many?

   3. _____

Laps swum by seven swimmers: Mia, 9; Kobla, 16; Akira, 38; Doyle, 22; Bernie, 28; Yoko, 50; Kris, 57

4. Make a stem-and-leaf plot for the data.

   4. _____

5. What is the range of the data?

   5. _____

6. Make a vertical bar graph showing these data.

   6.

Refer to the bar graph.

7. What month showed the greatest increase from the previous month?

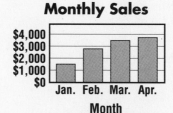

Monthly Sales

8. What were the total sales for March and April?

   7. _____

Refer to the circle graph.

9. What type of music is most popular?

   8. _____

10. Which two types of music together have about the same popularity as rock?

   9. _____

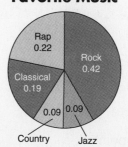

Favorite Music

   10. _____

Chapter 2 Test, Form 2A (continued)

The number of miles Ed has driven his car so far this year is: Jan., 900; Feb., 1,150; Mar., 1,200; Apr., 1,300; May, 1,150; June, 1,450. Use the data to find the following.

11. mean

12. median

13. mode

14. Use the mileage data above to make a line graph.

15. Name three ways to make the line graph misleading.

16. Does the mean, median, or mode best describe the data?
    3, 3, 97, 98, 100, 107.

Refer to the line graph.

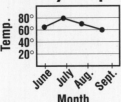

17. Predict the average May temperature.

18. Predict the average October temperature.

Refer to the grid.

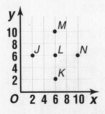

19. Name the point for the ordered pair (2, 6).

20. Name the ordered pair for point *N*.

11. _____

12. _____

13. _____

14.

15. _____

_____

_____

16. _____

17. _____

18. _____

19. _____

20. _____

Mathematics: Applications and Connections, Course 1

Chapter 2 Test, Form 2B

Refer to the frequency table.

Passes Completed	
Interval	**Frequency**
0–4	3
5–8	6
9–12	9
13–16	8
17–20	5

1. How many players completed 9 or more passes?

1. _____

2. Can you tell from the table if any player completed exactly 12 passes?

2. _____

3. Can you tell from the table how many players completed 12 or fewer passes? If so, how many?

3. _____

Points scored by five basketball players in a game: Majko, 26; Ertl, 32; Min, 11; Naylor, 8; Ben, 17

4. Make a stem-and-leaf plot for the data.

4. _____

5. What is the range of the data?

5. _____

6. Make a vertical bar graph showing these data.

6.

Refer to the bar graph.

7. In what month were sales the least?

Camera Sales

8. How many cameras were sold in April?

7. _____

8. _____

Refer to the circle graph.

9. Which type of dessert is most popular?

9. _____

10. Which two types of desserts together are equal to about one half of the desserts?

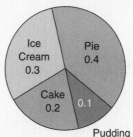

Favorite Desserts

10. _____

_____

Mathematics: Applications and Connections, Course 1

Chapter 2 Test, Form 2B (continued)

When Tessa totaled the tips she had earned while working at Badlands Steak-a-Rama, she found she had earned $89 in July, $110 in Aug., $120 in Sept., $100 in Oct., $120 in Nov., and $97 in Dec. Use the data to find the following.

11. mean

12. median

13. mode

14. Use the tip data above to make a line graph.

15. Name two ways to make your graph misleading.

16. Does the mean, median, or mode best describe the data?
    4, 20, 26, 29, 30?

11. _____

12. _____

13. _____

14.

15. _____

_____

16. _____

Refer to the line graph.

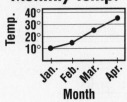

Monthly Temp.

17. Predict the average February temperature.

18. Predict the average May temperature.

17. _____

18. _____

Refer to the grid.

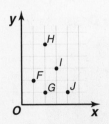

19. Name the point for the ordered pair (1, 2).

20. Name the ordered pair for point *J*.

19. _____

20. _____

Name_____ **Date**_____

Chapter 2 Test, Form 2C

Refer to the frequency table.

Test Scores	
Interval	**Frequency**
0–59	2
60–69	4
70–79	10
80–89	8
90–100	12

1. How many students got 80 or higher on their test?

1._____

2. Can you tell from the table if any students got a 100 on their test?

2._____

3. Can you tell from the table how many students got 69 or lower on their test? If so, how many?

3._____

Money earned by five friends: Terri, $22; Juan, $18; Sonja, $25; Jamaal, $30; Ida, $16

4. Make a stem-and-leaf plot for the data.

4._____

5. What is the range of the data?

5._____

6. Make a vertical bar graph showing these data.

6._____

Refer to the bar graph.

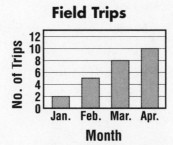

Field Trips

7. In what month were the least field trips?

8. What was the total number of field trips in February?

7._____

8._____

Refer to the circle graph.

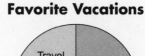
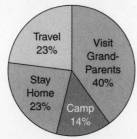

Favorite Vacations

9. Which type of vacation is the most popular?

9._____

10. Which two types of vacation are equal in popularity?

10._____

_____

Mathematics: Applications and Connections, Course 1

Chapter 2 Test, Form 2C (continued)

The gas mileage per gallon for a car is shown for five months: Jan., 17 mpg; Feb., 20 mpg; Mar., 20 mpg; Apr., 22 mpg; May, 21 mpg. Use the data to find the following.

11. mean

11. _____

12. median

12. _____

13. mode

13. _____

14.

14. Use the gas mileage data above to make a line graph.

15. Name one way to make your graph misleading.

16. Does the mean, median, or mode best describe the data?
2, 59, 60, 61?

15. _____

Refer to the line graph.

16. _____

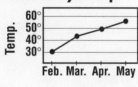

Monthly Temp.

17. Predict the average January temperature.

17. _____

18. Predict the average June temperature.

18. _____

Refer to the grid.

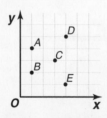

19. Name the point for the ordered pair (1, 4).

19. _____

20. Name the ordered pair for point *C*.

20. _____

Mathematics: Applications and Connections, Course 1

Chapter 2 Performance Assessment

Instructions: Demonstrate your knowledge by giving a clear, concise solution to each problem. Be sure to include all relevant drawings and to justify your answers. You may show your solutions in more than one way or investigate beyond the requirements of the problems.

1. Use the following table to answer each question.

Planet	Average Distance from Sun
Mercury	36,000,000 miles
Earth	93,003,000 miles
Jupiter	483,900,000 miles
Neptune	2,796,700,000 miles

   a. Draw a misleading graph of the average distances from the Sun to the planets listed above.

   b. Did you draw a pictograph, bar graph, or line graph? Why?

   c. Why is the graph misleading?

   d. Tell how to change the graph so that it is not misleading.

   e. Tell why a circle graph would be inappropriate for this data.

   f. Predict the average distance from the Sun to Venus. Venus is between Mercury and Earth. Check your prediction in an encyclopedia.

2. The scores in the Indianapolis Golf Tournament were 71, 73, 66, 75, 71, 82, 69, 72, 74, 64, 77, 71, 73, 70, 78, and 69.

   a. Find the mean, median, and mode for the set of golf scores. Round to the nearest tenth.

   b. These measures are said to be measures of central tendency. Explain in your own words what a measure of central tendency is.

   c. Tell what a stem-and-leaf plot is. Make one for the golf data.

   d. Choose a scale and interval and form a frequency table for the set of golf scores. Label your table.

   e. List the ordered pairs you would use to graph the data.

   f. Construct a line graph for the data in your table. Label your graph.

   g. Tell what the line graph shows.

Chapter 2 Mid-Chapter Test

(Lessons 2-1 through 2-5)

Refer to the table.

TV Times	
Interval	**Frequency**
7:00–8:00	4
8:00–9:00	6
9:00–10:00	15
10:00–11:00	13

1. How many people watched TV from 9:00 to 11:00?

2. Can you tell from the table if anyone watched only from 8:00 to 8:30?

3. What is the scale of the frequency data?

Five friends participated in a library reading program. The number of books each had read at its conclusion is as follows: Chris, 52; Amar, 33; Tara, 47; Wei, 21; Brad, 43.

4. What is the range of the data?

5. Make a vertical bar graph showing these data.

1. _____

2. _____

3. _____

4. _____

5. _____

Refer to the line graph.

6. For what week were sales highest?

7. What four weeks had the same sales?

8. Predict the sales for week 14.

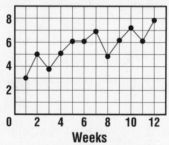

Sales for Third Quarter

6. _____

7. _____

8. _____

Refer to the circle graph.

9. Which type of food is most popular?

10. Which two types of food are equal in popularity?

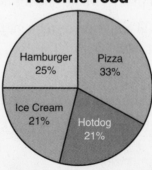

Favorite Food

9. _____

10. _____

_____

Mathematics: Applications and Connections, Course 1

Chapter 2 Quiz A

At the annual flower show, people were asked to vote for their favorite flower. The results are as follows: Rose, 9; Tulip, 7; Lotus, 5; Iris, 6; Lily, 4.

1. Make a frequency table for the data.

1.

2. What was the least popular flower?

2. _____

3. What scale would be used to make a vertical bar graph?

3. _____

4. What interval would be used to make a vertical bar graph?

4. _____

5. Make a vertical bar graph for the data.

5.

Chapter 2 Quiz B

Refer to the circle graph.

1. Which vegetable is the least popular? the most popular?

Favorite Vegetables

Green Beans 30%
Corn 35%
Carrots 15%
12%
8% Broccoli
Lettuce

1. _____

_____

2. Which two vegetables combined received more than half the votes?

2. _____

_____

Refer to the line graph.

3. Predict the population of Sun City in 2004.

Estimated Population for Sun City

Pop.
8,000
6,000
4,000
2,000

1998 2000 2002
Year

3. _____

4. Predict the population of Sun City in 2008.

4. _____

5. In what year will the population reach 8,000?

5. _____

Mathematics: Applications and Connections, Course 1

Chapter 2 Quiz C

Refer to the following data: 80, 77, 91, 77, 81, 90, 92.

1. What is the range of the data?

1. _____

2. Make a stem-and-leaf plot for the data.

2. _____

3. Find the mean.

3. _____

4. Find the median.

4. _____

5. What is the mode?

5. _____

Chapter 2 Quiz D

1. Tell whether the mean, median, or mode would best describe the following data: 3, 97, 98, 99.

1. _____

2. A real estate company shows that their median house listing is $150,000. Is it possible for them to have a house listed for $1 million?

2. _____

Refer to the grid.

3. Name the point for the ordered pair (2, 3).

3. _____

4. Name the ordered pair for point *C*.

4. _____

5. Name the point for the ordered pair (1, 5).

5. _____

Mathematics: Applications and Connections, Course 1

Chapter 2 Standardized Test Practice

1. For the last day of school, sixth graders get to vote for the movie that they will see. The results of the voting are in the frequency table shown. Which movie should they see?

Movie	Frequency
Space Jam	33
Star Wars	81
Jurassic Park	52
Apollo 13	41

   A. *Space Jam*   **B.** *Star Wars*
   C. *Jurassic Park*   **D.** *Apollo 13*

   1. _____

2. To estimate the temperature in degrees Fahrenheit, you can count the number of times a cricket chirps in 15 seconds and then add that number to 40. What is the temperature if the cricket chirps 70 times in 30 seconds?
   A. 70°F   **B.** 40°F   **C.** 110°F   **D.** 75°F

   2. _____

3. The high temperatures in Des Moines over a four day period were 72, 68, 78, and 73. Which line graph represents these data?

   3. _____

   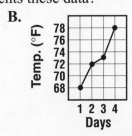

   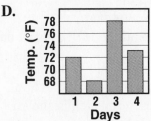

4. Evaluate $9 + ab - 6$ if $a = 3$ and $b = 4$.
   A. 42   **B.** 25   **C.** 15   **D.** 24

   4. _____

5. Ingrid made a circle graph for her science class. When she adds the percentages in all the portions of the graph, what number should she get?
   A. 100%   **B.** not enough information
   C. 75%   **D.** 125%

   5. _____

6. The graph shows average hourly earnings of U.S. production workers. Predict the average hourly earnings in the year 2000.
   A. $11.00   **B.** $16.00
   C. $10.00   **D.** $13.00

   6. _____

   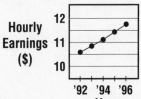

   Earnings of Workers

7. Dion is watching his fat intake. He is allowed 30 grams of fat for dinner and he has a sandwich that contains 22 grams of fat. $22 + x = 30$ represents his fat intake for the meal if x equals the grams of fat in the rest of his dinner. Find x.

   A. 82   **B.** 8   **C.** 18   **D.** 28

7. _____

8. The table below lists six major earthquakes. Samantha needs to describe the data in a report. Which measure of central tendency best represents the number of deaths?

8. _____

Year	Location	Magnitude	Deaths
1995	Russia	7.6	2,000+
1995	Japan	7.2	5,000+
1994	U.S.	6.6	61
1992	Indonesia	7.5	2,500
1990	Iran	7.7	40,000+
1989	U.S.	6.9	62

   A. mean   **B.** median   **C.** mode

9. What is the purpose of a box-and-whisker plot?

   A. Count the number of whiskers on a cat.
   B. Record data from a satellite dish.
   C. Display and summarize a set of data.
   D. Define the mean, median, and mode of a set of data.

9. _____

10. Seniqua made a map for history class. For part of the indexing, she must list ordered pairs of locations. She drew a grid on her map, part of which is shown. What ordered pairs are shown?

   A. $(1, 1)$, $(1, 2)$, $(3, 2)$, $(2, 4)$, $(5, 3)$
   B. $(1, 1)$, $(2, 1)$, $(2, 3)$, $(4, 2)$, $(3, 5)$
   C. $(1, 2)$, $(2, 4)$, $(2, 3)$, $(5, 3)$
   D. $(1, 1)$, $(1, 3)$, $(3, 5)$, $(4, 2)$

10. _____

11. Round 5,377 to the nearest hundred.

   A. 5,380   **B.** 5,400   **C.** 5,300   **D.** 5,000

11. _____

12. Solve $r = 13 \times 2 - 15 \times 1$.

   A. 27   **B.** 169   **C.** 27   **D.** 11

12. _____

13. Find the next three numbers in the pattern: 13, 21, 29, _?_ , _?_ , _?_ .

   A. 34, 41, 48   **B.** 35, 41, 46   **C.** 37, 45, 53   **D.** 33, 41, 49

13. _____

14. Evaluate $3^2 + 5^2$.

   A. 34   **B.** 64   **C.** 16   **D.** 35

14. _____

Name_____ **Date** _____

Cumulative Review, Chapters 1–2

1. Round 789 to the nearest hundred. (Lesson 1-3)

2. Round 3,509 to the nearest thousand. (Lesson 1-3)

Estimate using rounding. (Lesson 1-3)
3. $763 + 124$ 4. $935 - 228$

Find the value of each expression. (Lesson 1-4)
5. $16 + 14 \div 2 - 4$ 6. $32 \div 8 - 1 \times 4$

Evaluate each expression if m = 6 and n = 9. (Lesson 1-5)
7. $6m - 3n$ 8. $6 + mn$

Solve each equation mentally. (Lesson 1-7)
9. $x - 9 = 11$ 10. $x \div 3 = 9$

Refer to the table for Questions 11–13. (Lessons 2-1 and 2-7)

11. How many students scored 80 or above?

12. Can you tell from the table if anyone got a 75?

13. What is the range of the frequency data?

Test Scores	
Interval	Frequency
0–59	4
60–69	8
70–79	17
80–89	12
90–100	10

Use the following set of data for Questions 14–18. 17, 19, 22, 18, 17, 20, 24, 23 (Lessons 2-2 and 2-7)

14. Find the range.

15. Choose the best interval to form a scale for a frequency table for the data.

16. Find the mean.

17. Find the median.

18. Find the mode.

Use the graph for Questions 19–20. (Lesson 2-4)

19. Which sport is most popular?

20. Which two sports add up to half of the sports listed?

Favorite Sport

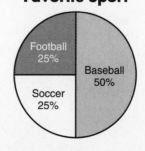

1. _____

2. _____

3. _____

4. _____

5. _____

6. _____

7. _____

8. _____

9. _____

10. _____

11. _____

12. _____

13. _____

14. _____

15. _____

16. _____

17. _____

18. _____

19. _____

20. _____

Mathematics: Applications and Connections, Course 1

Chapter 2 Answer Key

Page 29

1. B

2. B

3. A

4. B

5. C

6. A

7. B

Page 30

8. A

9. C

10. B

11. C

12. C

13. B

14. C

15. A

16. B

Page 31

1. D

2. C

3. A

4. B

5. A

6. A

7. D

Page 32

8. B

9. D

10. C

11. D

12. B

13. C

14. A

15. B

16. B

Chapter 2 Answer Key

Page 33

1. _____A_____

2. _____C_____

3. _____B_____

4. _____A_____

5. _____D_____

6. _____B_____

7. _____C_____

Page 34

8. _____B_____

9. _____D_____

10. _____C_____

11. _____D_____

12. _____B_____

13. _____C_____

14. _____A_____

15. _____B_____

16. _____B_____

*Mathematics: Applications
and Connections, Course 1*

Chapter 2 Answer Key

Page 35

1. _____ 21 _____

2. _____ no _____

3. _____ yes, 26 _____

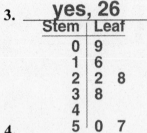

Stem	Leaf
0	9
1	6
2	2 8
3	8
4	
5	0 7

4. _____

5. _____ 48 _____

6. **Laps Swum**

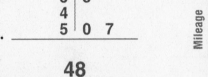

7. _____ February _____

8. _____ about $7,250 _____

9. _____ rock _____

10. _____ rap and classical _____

Page 36

11. _____ 1,192 miles _____

12. _____ 1,175 miles _____

13. _____ 1,150 miles _____

14. **Car Mileage**

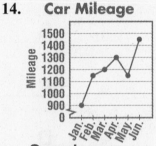

15. _____ Sample answers: Make scale uneven; don't include all data; omit labels. _____

16. _____ median _____

17. _____ around 50° _____

18. _____ around 50° _____

19. _____ J _____

20. _____ (10, 6) _____

Mathematics: Applications and Connections, Course 1

Chapter 2 Answer Key

Form 2B

Page 37		Page 38	
1.	**22**	11.	**$106**
2.	**no**	12.	**$105**
		13.	**$120**
3.	**yes, 18**	14.	**Tips Earned**

Stem	Leaf
0	8
1	1 7
2	6
3	2

4.

5. **24**

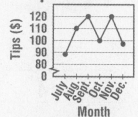

Month

6. **Points scored**

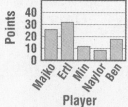

Player

15. Sample answers: **Make scale uneven, omit labels.**

16. **median**

7. **August**

8. **7**

17. **15°**

18. **45°**

9. **pie**

10. **pie and pudding or ice cream and cake**

19. **F**

20. **(4, 1)**

Chapter 2 Answer Key

Page 39

1. _____ 20

2. _____ no

3. _____ yes, 6

4.
Stem	Leaf
1	6 8
2	2 5
3	0

5. _____ 14

6. **Money Earned**

$30
$20
$10
$0

Terri Juan Sonja Jamal Ida

Students

7. _____ January

8. _____ 5

9. _____ visit grandparents

10. _____ travel and stay home

Page 40

11. _____ 20 mpg

12. _____ 20 mpg

13. _____ 20 mpg

14. **Car Gas Mileage**

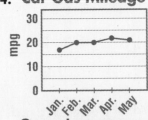

mpg
30
20
10
0

Jan. Feb. Mar. Apr. May

15. _____ Sample answer: Omit labels.

16. _____ median

17. _____ 25°

18. _____ 60°

19. _____ A

20. _____ (3, 3)

Mathematics: Applications and Connections, Course 1

Chapter 2 Scoring Guide

Level	Specific Criteria
3 Superior	• Shows thorough understanding of the concepts *frequency tables; bar, circle, and line graphs; stem-and-leaf plots; mean, median, and mode;* and *organization of data into a table.* • Computations are correct. • Written explanations are exemplary. • Graphs and tables are accurate and appropriate. • Goes beyond requirements of some or all problems.
2 Satisfactory, with Minor Flaws	• Shows understanding of the concepts *frequency tables; bar, circle, and line graphs; stem-and-leaf plots; mean, median, and mode;* and *organization of data into a table.* • Computations are mostly correct. • Written explanations are effective. • Graphs and tables are mostly accurate and appropriate. • Satisfies all requirements of problems.
1 Nearly Satisfactory, with Serious Flaws	• Shows understanding of most of the concepts *frequency tables; bar, circle, and line graphs; stem-and-leaf plots; mean, median, and mode;* and *organization of data into a table.* • Computations are mostly correct. • Written explanations are satisfactory. • Graphs and tables are mostly accurate and appropriate. • Satisfies most requirements of problems.
0 Unsatisfactory	• Shows little or no understanding of the concepts *frequency tables; bar, circle, and line graphs; stem-and-leaf plots; mean, median, and mode;* and *organization of data into a table.* • Computations are incorrect. • Written explanations are not satisfactory. • Graphs and tables are not accurate or appropriate. • Does not satisfy requirements of problems.

Mathematics: Applications and Connections, Course 1

Chapter 2 Answer Key

Performance Assessment Sample Answers
Page 41

1. **a.** Sample graph:

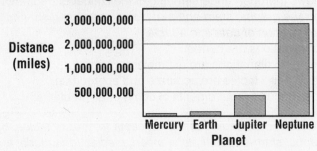

Average Distance from Sun

Distance (miles)

3,000,000,000
2,000,000,000
1,000,000,000
500,000,000

Mercury   Earth   Jupiter   Neptune
Planet

   b. A bar graph is the best type of graph to show and compare distances.
   c. Sample answer: The intervals on the vertical axis of the sample are not uniform.
   d. Sample answer: Represent each 500,000,000 by the same distance.
   e. A circle graph is best to show parts of a whole.
   f. Prediction from the graph = 64,500,000 miles.
   Actual distance = 66,650,000 miles.

2. **a.** mean: 72.2, median: 71.5, mode: 71
   b. A measure of central tendency is an attempt to describe a set of numbers by using a number near the center of the set of numbers.
   c. A stem-and-leaf plot is a table that puts the ones digits (the leaves) to the right of the vertical line and the other digits (the stems) to the left.

Stem	Leaf
6	4 6 9 9
7	0 1 1 1 2 3 3 4 5 7 8
8	2

$7|0 = 70$

   d.

Indianapolis Golf Tournament		
Score	Tally	Frequency
81–85	I	1
76–80	II	2
71–75	ℋℋ III	8
66–70	IIII	4
61–65	I	1

   e. (61-65, 1); (66-70, 4); (71-75, 8); (76-80, 2); (81-85, 1)
   f. See students' graphs.
   g. See students' graphs.

Mid-Chapter Test
Page 42

1. **28**
2. **no**
3. **7:00 to 11:00**
4. **31**
5. **Books Read**

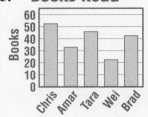

Books

60
50
40
30
20
10
0

Chris   Amar   Tara   Wei   Brad

6. **week 12**
7. **weeks 5, 6, 9, and 11**
8. **about $9,000**
9. **pizza**
10. **ice cream and hot dogs**

Mathematics: Applications and Connections, Course 1

Chapter 2 Answer Key

1.

Flower	Votes
Rose	9
Tulip	7
Lotus	5
Iris	6
Lily	4

2. **lily**

3. **0–10**

4. **2**

5. **Favorite Flowers**

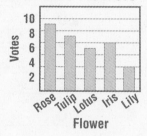

1. **15**

Stem	Leaf
7	7 7
8	0 1
9	0 1 2

2.

3. **84**

4. **81**

5. **77**

1. **broccoli; corn**

2. **green beans and corn**

3. **about 5,000**

4. **about 7,000**

5. **2010**

1. **median**

2. **yes**

3. **A**

4. **(4, 4)**

5. **E**

Mathematics: Applications and Connections, Course 1

Chapter 2 Answer Key

Standardized Test Practice		Cumulative Review
Page 45	Page 46	Page 47

Page 45

1. B

2. D

3. A

4. C

5. A

6. D

Page 46

7. B

8. B

9. C

10. A

11. B

12. D

13. C

14. A

Page 47

1. 800

2. 4,000

3. 800 + 100 = 900

4. 900 − 200 = 700

5. 19

6. 0

7. 9

8. 60

9. 20

10. 27

11. 22

12. no

13. 13

14. 7

15. 2

16. 20

17. 19.5

18. 17

19. baseball

20. football and soccer

Mathematics: Applications and Connections, Course 1

Chapter 3 Test, Form 1A

1. What is the decimal for $\frac{10}{100}$?
   A. 0.10　　　B. 0.01　　　C. 100　　　D. 0.001

   1. _____

2. What is the decimal for one hundred six and four tenths?
   A. 106.4　　B. 10.64　　C. 1064　　D. 106.04

   2. _____

3. What is the decimal for eighty and two hundredths?
   A. 82　　　B. 8.2　　　C. 80.02　　D. 80.2

   3. _____

4. What is the decimal for $\frac{141}{1,000}$?
   A. 0.0141　　B. 0.141　　C. 1.041　　D. 1410

   4. _____

5. What is the decimal for twelve and twenty-one thousandths?
   A. 12.21　　B. 1221　　C. 12.0021　　D. 12.021

   5. _____

6. What is the decimal for $\frac{25,743}{10,000}$?
   A. 0.25743　　B. 2.5743　　C. 25.743　　D. 25.0743

   6. _____

7. What is the length of the segment to the nearest centimeter?

   ━━━━━━━━━━━━━

   A. 80 cm　　B. 75 cm　　C. 7 cm　　D. 8 cm

   7. _____

8. What is the length of the segment to the nearest millimeter?

   ━━━━━━━

   A. 4.8 mm　　B. 45 mm　　C. 48 mm　　D. 50 mm

   8. _____

9. How many millimeters are in a kilometer?
   A. 100　　　B. 1,000　　C. 10,000　　D. 1,000,000

   9. _____

10. Which decimal is greater than 0.099?
    A. 0.098　　B. 0.09　　C. 0.1　　D. 0.01

    10. _____

11. Which decimals are ordered from least to greatest?
    A. 7.2, 7.02, 7.002　　　B. 0.23, 0.21, 0.22
    C. 1.5, 1.005, 1.05　　　D. 7.002, 7.02, 7.2

    11. _____

12. Which decimals are ordered from greatest to least?
    A. 9.2, 9.02, 9.21　　　B. 37.7, 37.07, 3.707
    C. 20.091, 20.8, 20.003　　D. 0.006, 0.06, 0.6

    12. _____

13. Round 721.549 to the nearest tenth.
    A. 722   B. 721.5   C. 721.55   D. 721.6

    13. _____

14. Round 23.8697 to the nearest thousandth.
    A. 23.900   B. 24   C. 23.870   D. 23.861

    14. _____

15. Round 90.005 to the nearest hundredth.
    A. 90.00   B. 90.01   C. 90   D. 90.006

    15. _____

16. Round $989.57 to the nearest dollar.
    A. $990   B. $989   C. $989.60   D. $1,000

    16. _____

17. Estimate $17.23 + $21.62 using rounding.
    A. $45   B. $35   C. $40   D. $39

    17. _____

18. Estimate 24.73 − 5.96 using rounding.
    A. 20   B. 10   C. 19   D. 15

    18. _____

19. Use clustering to estimate 4.03 + 4.21 + 3.78 + 4.43.
    A. 16   B. 16.40   C. 15   D. 20

    19. _____

20. Estimate $1,529.43 − $982.13.
    A. $547.36   B. $500   C. $600   D. $2,500

    20. _____

21. Subtract: 59.37 − 47.219.
    A. 11.169   B. 11.151   C. 12.151   D. 12.169

    21. _____

22. Solve $47.982 − 39.0947 = m$.
    A. 8.8873   B. 8.8887   C. 12.8873   D. 9.8887

    22. _____

23. Evaluate $s + t$ if $s = 4.79$ and $t = 0.341$.
    A. 8.2   B. 5.131   C. 4.131   D. 7.2

    23. _____

24. Karl is shelving books. One has a call number of 204.013. The librarian said it should be 56.98 higher than that. What is the correct call number?
    A. 147.033   B. 261   C. 260.893   D. 260.993

    24. _____

25. Sandrine received $40 for her birthday. She plans to use the money to buy compact discs costing $11.99 each. What is a reasonable number of discs that she can buy?
    A. 2   B. 3   C. 4   D. 5

    25. _____

1. What is the decimal for $\frac{9}{100}$?
   A. 0.9   B. 0.90   C. 0.09   D. 900

   1. _____

2. What is the decimal for twenty-three and seven tenths?
   A. 0.237   B. 237   C. 23.07   D. 23.7

   2. _____

3. What is the decimal for twenty-eight hundredths?
   A. 2.8   B. 0.28   C. 280   D. 0.028

   3. _____

4. What is the decimal for $\frac{93}{1,000}$?
   A. 0.093   B. 0.93   C. 0.930   D. 930

   4. _____

5. What is the decimal for sixteen and six thousandths?
   A. 16.006   B. 16.6000   C. 16.06   D. 16.060

   5. _____

6. What is the decimal for $\frac{9,563}{10,000}$?
   A. 9,563   B. 9.563   C. 956.3   D. 0.9563

   6. _____

7. What is the length of the segment to the nearest centimeter?

   A. 70 cm   B. 72 cm   C. 7 cm   D. 8 cm

   7. _____

8. What is the length of the segment to the nearest millimeter?

   A. 30 mm   B. 38 mm   C. 3.8 mm   D. 40 mm

   8. _____

9. How many millimeters are in 5.21 centimeters?
   A. 52.1 mm   B. 0.521 mm   C. 521 mm   D. 50 mm

   9. _____

10. Which decimal is greater than 0.073?
    A. 0.07   B. 0.008   C. 0.08   D. 0.072

    10. _____

11. Which decimals are ordered from least to greatest?
    A. 0.006, 0.0005, 0.07   B. 0.054, 3.06, 1.013
    C. 1.013, 0.054, 3.06   D. 0.0005, 0.006, 0.07

    11. _____

12. Which decimals are ordered from greatest to least?
    A. 2.138, 2.158, 1.35   B. 5.0101, 5.01, 5.0103
    C. 5.0103, 5.0101, 5.01   D. 1.35, 2.138, 2.158

    12. _____

13. Round 43.628 to the nearest tenth.
  A. 43.6   **B.** 43.7   **C.** 43   **D.** 44

13. _____

14. Round 1.7968 to the nearest thousandth.
  A. 1.796   **B.** 1.8   **C.** 1.80   **D.** 1.797

14. _____

15. Round 0.053 to the nearest hundredth.
  A. 0.06   **B.** 0.05   **C.** 0.53   **D.** 0.5

15. _____

16. Round $72.81 to the nearest dollar.
  A. $73   **B.** $72   **C.** $72.80   **D.** $70

16. _____

17. Estimate $9.15 + $7.89 using rounding.
  A. $16   **B.** $17   **C.** $18   **D.** $20

17. _____

18. Estimate 0.93 − 0.19 using rounding.
  A. 0.8   **B.** 0.7   **C.** 8   **D.** 7

18. _____

19. Use clustering to estimate 3.98 + 4.01 + 4.03 + 4.01.
  A. 16   **B.** 17   **C.** 18   **D.** 20

19. _____

20. Estimate $29.42 − $16.21.
  A. $13.25   **B.** $15   **C.** $13   **D.** $20

20. _____

21. Subtract: 76.9 − 52.84.
  A. 24.14   **B.** 24.16   **C.** 24.06   **D.** 23.06

21. _____

22. Add: 81.1 + 3.04.
  A. 814.40   **B.** 78.06   **C.** 111.5   **D.** 84.14

22. _____

23. Evaluate $a - b$ if $a = 3.542$ and $b = 0.432$.
  A. 3.111   **B.** 3.974   **C.** 3.110   **D.** 7.862

23. _____

24. Neal had $32 and earned $8.60. How much money does he have?
  A. $40.60   **B.** $11.80   **C.** $41.60   **D.** $12.80

24. _____

25. Alice has $10 with which to buy blank video tapes. Each tape costs $2.98.
What is a reasonable number of tapes that she can buy?
  A. 2   **B.** 3   **C.** 4   **D.** 5

25. _____

Chapter 3 Test, Form 1C

1. What is the decimal for $\frac{2}{10}$?

   A. 0.02   **B.** 0.2   **C.** 2.0   **D.** 20

   1._____

2. What is the decimal for one and three tenths?

   A. 1.03   **B.** 1.3   **C.** 0.13   **D.** 13

   2._____

3. What is the decimal for two and seventeen hundredths?

   A. 2.17   **B.** 217   **C.** 21.7   **D.** 0.217

   3._____

4. What is the decimal for $\frac{74}{1,000}$?

   A. 0.740   **B.** 0.74   **C.** 0.074   **D.** 740

   4._____

5. What is the decimal for three and three thousandths?

   A. 3.300   **B.** 3.03   **C.** 0.330   **D.** 3.003

   5._____

6. What is the decimal for $\frac{1,234}{10,000}$?

   A. 0.1234   **B.** 1.234   **C.** 12.34   **D.** 123.4

   6._____

7. What is the length of the segment to the nearest centimeter?

   ▬▬▬▬▬▬▬▬▬▬

   A. 50 cm   **B.** 5 cm   **C.** 6 cm   **D.** 60 cm

   7._____

8. What is the length of the segment to the nearest millimeter?

   ▬▬▬▬▬▬▬▬▬▬

   A. 61 mm   **B.** 6 mm   **C.** 6.1 mm   **D.** 70 mm

   8._____

9. How many millimeters are in 0.37 centimeter?

   A. 40 mm   **B.** 370 mm   **C.** 3.7 mm   **D.** 37 mm

   9._____

10. Which decimal is less than 0.08?

    A. 0.09   **B.** 0.07   **C.** 0.085   **D.** 0.098

    10._____

11. Which decimals are ordered from least to greatest?

    A. 0.03, 0.29, 0.3   **B.** 0.3, 0.03, 0.29

    C. 0.29, 0.03, 0.3   **D.** 0.3, 0.29, 0.03

    11._____

12. Which decimals are ordered from greatest to least?

    A. 1.03, 1.3, 1.0003   **B.** 1.3, 1.0003, 1.03

    C. 1.0003, 1.03, 1.3   **D.** 1.3, 1.03, 1.0003

    12._____

Mathematics: Applications and Connections, Course 1

13. Round 17.319 to the nearest tenth.   13. _____
   A. 17.4   **B.** 17.32   **C.** 17.31   **D.** 17.3

14. Round 3.7839 to the nearest thousandth.   14. _____
   A. 3.783   **B.** 3.79   **C.** 3.784   **D.** 3.8

15. Round 0.767 to the nearest hundredth.   15. _____
   A. 0.77   **B.** 0.76   **C.** 0.770   **D.** 0.700

16. Round $1.29 to the nearest dollar.   16. _____
   A. $2   **B.** $1   **C.** $1.30   **D.** $1.25

17. Estimate $2.68 + $4.13 using rounding.   17. _____
   A. $6   **B.** $6.50   **C.** $6.60   **D.** $7

18. Estimate $7.83 − $4.58 using rounding.   18. _____
   A. $4   **B.** $3.30   **C.** $3   **D.** $11

19. Use clustering to estimate 1.89 + 2.02 + 2.01 + 1.97.   19. _____
   A. 6   **B.** 7   **C.** 8   **D.** 9

20. Estimate 499.50 + 20.45.   20. _____
   A. 521   **B.** 520   **C.** 519   **D.** 518

21. Subtract: 28 − 2.7.   21. _____
   A. 26.7   **B.** 26.3   **C.** 25.7   **D.** 25.3

22. Add: 39.75 + 4.2.   22. _____
   A. 43.95   **B.** 40.17   **C.** 35.55   **D.** 42.95

23. Evaluate $a + b$ if $a = 7.2$ and $b = 2.5$.   23. _____
   A. 7.46   **B.** 9.7   **C.** 4.7   **D.** 8.7

24. Juanita has $204.13 in savings. She deposits $50.50. How much does she   24. _____
   have in savings?
   A. $153.63   **B.** $264.13   **C.** $709.13   **D.** $254.63

25. Scott bought two items costing $7.89 and $5.98. He gave the clerk a $20   25. _____
   bill. Which amount is reasonable for the change he will get back?
   A. $8   **B.** $7   **C.** $6   **D.** $5

Chapter 3 Test, Form 2B

Write each fraction or mixed number as a decimal.

1. $2\frac{5}{10}$

2. $\frac{29}{1,000}$

3. $\frac{38}{100}$

4. $\frac{123}{10,000}$

5. forty-four ten-thousandths

6. nineteen and three thousandths

1. _____

2. _____

3. _____

4. _____

5. _____

6. _____

Measure each line segment to the nearest centimeter.

7. ━━━━━━━━━

8. ━━━━━━

7. _____

8. _____

Measure each line segment to the nearest millimeter.

9. ━━━━━━━

10. ━━━━━━━━

9. _____

10. _____

11. Estimate the height of a minivan using the metric system.

11. _____

State the greatest number in each group.

12. 0.315 or 0.0325

13. 0.799, 0.08, or 0.8

14. 0.290, 0.30, 0.280

15. Order the set of decimals from least to greatest: 0.038, 0.4, 0.35, 0.0005.

16. Order the set of decimals from greatest to least: 0.089, 0.090, 0.009.

12. _____

13. _____

14. _____

15. _____

_____

16. _____

_____

Mathematics: Applications and Connections, Course 1

Round each number to the underlined place-value position.

17. 0.34<u>4</u>4

18. 38.<u>9</u>49

19. 4<u>3</u>.61

20. Round $1.32 to the nearest dollar.

17. _____

18. _____

19. _____

20. _____

Estimate. Use any method.

21. $5.49 + $4.75 + $5.08

22. 75.42 − 12.81

23. 3.05 + 2.99 + 3.47 + 2.72

24. 70.4 − 35.1

25. 98.2 + 25.46

21. _____

22. _____

23. _____

24. _____

25. _____

Add or subtract.

26. 89.4 + 78.56

27. 98.1 − 17.89

28. 50 − 9.3

29. 4.9 + 3.876 + 13.029

30. How much is 48 minus 35.47?

31. Evaluate $r - s$ if $r = 6.792$ and $s = 3.9994$.

26. _____

27. _____

28. _____

29. _____

30. _____

31. _____

Solve.

32. Emily wants to buy notebooks at $2.95 each. She has $10 to spend. About how many notebooks can she buy?

33. Four same-priced items were purchased. Based on rounding, the estimate for the total was $20. What is the maximum price each item could have cost?

32. _____

33. _____

Name_____ **Date** _____

Chapter 3 Test, Form 2C

Write each fraction or mixed number as a decimal.

1. $\frac{29}{100}$

2. $\frac{17}{1,000}$

3. $3\frac{7}{10}$

4. $\frac{19}{10,000}$

5. seventy-four and nineteen thousandths

6. three hundred seven ten-thousandths

1. _____

2. _____

3. _____

4. _____

5. _____

6. _____

Measure each line segment to the nearest centimeter.

7. ■━━━━━━

8. ■━━━━━━━━━━

7. _____

8. _____

Measure each line segment to the nearest millimeter.

9. ■━━━━━━━

10. ■━━━━━━━━━

9. _____

10. _____

11. Estimate the length of a standard light bulb using the metric system.

11. _____

State the greatest number in each group.

12. 0.003 or 0.01

13. 0.3, 0.1, or 0.2

14. 0.65, 0.6, or 0.06

15. Order the set of decimals from least to greatest: 0.0009, 0.08, 0.007, 0.6.

16. Order the set of decimals from greatest to least: 1.9, 1.99, 1.09.

12. _____

13. _____

14. _____

15. _____

_____

16. _____

Mathematics: Applications and Connections, Course 1

Round each number to the underlined place-value position.

17. 71.8<u>9</u>

18. 0.9<u>3</u>39

19. 1<u>9</u>.39

20. Round $1.89 to the nearest dollar.

17. _____

18. _____

19. _____

20. _____

Estimate. Use any method.

21. 4.9 + 5.1

22. $11.98 − $4.07

23. 1.983 + 2.0548 + 1.7891 + 2.003

24. 4.5 − 1.7

25. 12.8 + 3.25

21. _____

22. _____

23. _____

24. _____

25. _____

Add or subtract.

26. 17.9 + 28.06

27. 38.79 − 7.9

28. 86 − 3.7

29. $21.60 + $93.52

30. Find the sum of 3.7 and 4.37.

31. Evaluate $a + b$ if $a = 5.896$ and $b = 2.104$.

26. _____

27. _____

28. _____

29. _____

30. _____

31. _____

Solve.

32. Jorge bought a shirt for $16.95 and paid for it with a $20 bill. Should he expect about $3 or $5 in change?

33. Three same-priced items were purchased. Based on rounding, the estimate for the total was $18. What is the minimum price each item could have cost?

32. _____

33. _____

Name_____ Date _____

Chapter 3 Performance Assessment

Instructions: Demonstrate your knowledge by giving a clear, concise solution to each problem. Be sure to include all relevant drawings and justify your answers. You may show your solutions in more than one way or investigate beyond the requirements of the problems.

1. Use the table to answer each question.

Amounts of Gases in Dry Air	
Gas	Amount
Nitrogen	$\frac{7,802}{10,000}$
Argon	ninety-four ten-thousandths
Oxygen	$\frac{201}{1,000}$
Other	$\frac{94}{10,000}$

   a. Write the amount of argon in dry air as a decimal.

   b. Write each fraction in the table as a decimal.

   c. Order the decimals from least to greatest.

   d. Find the total amount of oxygen and nitrogen in dry air.

   e. How much more oxygen than argon is there in dry air?

   f. Tell how to round a decimal without using a number line.

   g. Round each decimal in parts a and b to the nearest hundredth.

2. Refer to the rectangle. The perimeter of a rectangle is $l + l + w + w$.

   a. Use a centimeter ruler to measure the length and width of the rectangle.

   b. Estimate the perimeter of the rectangle. Explain why you would consider this a reasonable number for the perimeter of the rectangle.

Mathematics: Applications and Connections, Course 1

Chapter 3 Mid-Chapter Test
(Lessons 3-1 through 3-3)

Write each fraction or mixed number as a decimal.

1. $371\frac{5}{10,000}$

2. $\frac{71}{100}$

3. ninety-nine and ninety-nine hundredths

4. twenty-eight and three hundred forty-one ten-thousandths

5. A barrel of cranberries is equivalent to ninety-five and forty-six hundredths liters. Write the number of liters as a decimal.

1. _____

2. _____

3. _____

4. _____

5. _____

Measure each segment to the nearest centimeter.

6. ▬▬▬▬▬▬

7. ▬▬▬

6. _____

7. _____

Measure each segment to the nearest millimeter.

8. ▬▬▬▬

9. ▬▬▬▬▬

10. How many millimeters are in 262.4 centimeters?

8. _____

9. _____

10. _____

Order each set of decimals from least to greatest.

11. 3.277, 2.101, 3.666, 2.121

12. 1.68, 1.55, 2.1, 1.478

11. _____

12. _____

Order each set of decimals from greatest to least.

13. 5.34, 2.637, 4.52, 4.319

14. 1.0003, 1.03, 1.0313, 1.003

15. Which is greatest: 9.599, 9.59, or 9.5999?

16. A librarian needs to shelve books. He wants to arrange the call numbers in order from least to greatest. Put these call numbers in order for him: 159.563, 170.012, 159.873, 170.146, 163.638.

13. _____

14. _____

15. _____

16. _____

_____

Chapter 3 Quiz A

(Lessons 3-1 and 3-2)

Write each fraction as a decimal.

1. $\frac{8}{10}$

2. $\frac{3}{1,000}$

3. six hundredths

4. four ten-thousandths

5. Measure the line segment below to the nearest centimeter.

   ━━━━━━━━━━━

6. Measure the line segment below to the nearest millimeter.

   ━━━━━━━

7. In 1996, Michael Johnson ran the Olympic men's 200-meter run in nineteen and thirty-two hundredths of a second. Write his time as a decimal.

8. Write $\frac{29}{100}$ as a decimal.

9. How many millimeters are in 6.942 centimeters?

10. How many centimeters are in 427 millimeters?

1. _____

2. _____

3. _____

4. _____

5. _____

6. _____

7. _____

8. _____

9. _____

10. _____

Chapter 3 Quiz B

(Lesson 3-3)

Order each set of decimals from greatest to least.
1. 48.679, 48.68, 478.6, 48.06

2. 0.083, 0.8, 0.0095, 8.01

Order each set of decimals from least to greatest.
3. 16.74, 16.07, 16.074, 16.007

4. 50.05, 50.55, 50.5, 50.555

5. Antoine has $10.25, Margarita has $10.15, Camille has $11.25, and Miriam has $10.55. Put the people in order from greatest to least money.

1. _____

2. _____

3. _____

4. _____

5. _____

_____

Mathematics: Applications and Connections, Course 1

Chapter 3 Quiz C

(Lessons 3-4 and 3-5)

Round each number to the underlined place-value position.

1. 3.<u>7</u>06

2. 5.19<u>2</u>5

3. 258.7<u>5</u>38

4. 72.3<u>9</u>9

1. _____

2. _____

3. _____

4. _____

Estimate. Use any method.

5.	2.78	6.	0.876	7.	$47.89
	+ 6.18		+ 0.599		− $29.99

5. _____

6. _____

7. _____

8. Name a number that rounds to 7 when rounded to the nearest whole number and to 6.8 when rounded to the nearest tenth.

8. _____

9. Estimate 3.76 + 6.58 + 8.42.

9. _____

10. In the deli, there are four pieces of cheese with the following weights: 3.52 lb, 0.96 lb, 2.63 lb, and 5.23 lb. Which two pieces would you choose if you wanted about 6 pounds of cheese?

10. _____

Chapter 3 Quiz D

(Lesson 3-6)

Add or subtract.

1.	7.13	2. 89.7 − 1.96	3. 7.54 + 1.006 + 8
	+ 9.86		

1. _____

2. _____

3. _____

4. Geraldo purchased three items costing $1.99, $0.89, and $3.25. He paid for the purchases with a $10 bill. How much should he expect in change?

4. _____

5. Bart places an empty dish on a scale. Its mass is 12.9982 grams. He puts a chemical on the dish. Now the mass is 13.3001 grams. What is the mass of the chemical?

5. _____

Name_____ Date _____

Cumulative Review, Chapters 1–3

Round to the underlined place-value position. (Lesson 1-3)
1. $\underline{4}82$ 2. $\underline{7}8$ 3. $6,891$

Find the value of each expression. (Lesson 1-4)
4. $21 - 4 + 2 \times 3$ 5. $6 \times 3 + 6 \times 5$

Evaluate each expression if b = 5 and c = 7. (Lesson 1-5)
6. $3b$ 7. $4c - 2$ 8. $bc + 1$

Use the graph for Questions 9–11. (Lessons 2-3 and 2-7)
9. For what month were the sales highest?

10. What two months had the same sales?

11. What were the average sales for the four months?

Monthly Sales

Amount ($): 4,000 3,000 2,000 1,000 0

Sept. Oct. Nov. Dec.

Month

For Questions 12–16, use this set of data: 38, 37, 39, 41, 38, 42, 48, 50, 54. (Lessons 2-2 and 2-7)
12. Find the range.

13. Choose the best interval to form a scale for a frequency table for the data.

14. Find the mean.

15. Find the median.

16. What is the mode?

Write as a decimal. (Lesson 3-1)
17. $\frac{6}{10}$ 18. $\frac{49}{10,000}$

19. thirteen thousandths

State the greater number in each pair. (Lesson 3-3)
20. 0.78 or 0.078   21. 9.7 or 8.688

Estimate. Use any method. (Lesson 3-5)
22. $5.98 + $6.12   23. $0.834 - 0.289$

Add or subtract. (Lesson 3-6)
24. $7.089 + 18.4$ 25. $48 - 7.2$

1. _____
2. _____
3. _____
4. _____
5. _____
6. _____
7. _____
8. _____
9. _____
10. _____
11. _____
12. _____
13. _____
14. _____
15. _____
16. _____
17. _____
18. _____
19. _____
20. _____
21. _____
22. _____
23. _____
24. _____
25. _____

Mathematics: Applications and Connections, Course 1

Form 1A

Page 57

1. A
2. A
3. C
4. B
5. D
6. B
7. D
8. C
9. D
10. C
11. D
12. B

Page 58

13. B
14. C
15. B
16. A
17. D
18. C
19. A
20. B
21. C
22. A
23. B
24. D
25. B

Form 1B

Page 59

1. C
2. D
3. B
4. A
5. A
6. D
7. C
8. B
9. A
10. C
11. D
12. C

Page 60

13. A
14. D
15. B
16. A
17. B
18. B
19. A
20. C
21. C
22. D
23. C
24. A
25. B

Mathematics: Applications and Connections, Course 1

Chapter 3 Answer Key

Form 1C

Page 61		Page 62	
1.	B	13.	D
2.	B	14.	C
3.	A	15.	A
4.	C	16.	B
5.	D	17.	D
6.	A	18.	C
7.	C	19.	C
		20.	B
8.	A	21.	D
9.	C	22.	A
10.	B	23.	B
11.	A	24.	D
12.	D	25.	C

Mathematics: Applications and Connections, Course 1

Chapter 3 Answer Key

Form 2A

Page 63		Page 64	
1.	6.8	17.	0.001
2.	0.05	18.	187.90
3.	0.5217	19.	35,246.2
4.	0.004	20.	$1
5.	235.075		
6.	0.0009	21.	$8 + $5 + $2 + $6 = $21
		22.	0.9 − 0.4 = 0.5
7.	7 cm	23.	6 + 6 + 6 + 6 = 24
8.	2 cm	24.	84 − 10 = 74
		25.	38 − 15 = 23
9.	58 mm	26.	5,349.787
10.	28 mm	27.	212.2158
11.	Sample answer: 25 cm	28.	314.453
		29.	64.488
		30.	$145.54
		31.	10
12.	0.031		
13.	0.7		
14.	2.848	32.	$15
15.	0.007, 0.08, 0.65, 0.7		
16.	98.73, 97.38, 89.73	33.	$4.49

Mathematics: Applications and Connections, Course 1

Chapter 3 Answer Key

Form 2B

1. 2.5
2. 0.029
3. 0.38
4. 0.0123
5. 0.0044
6. 19.003

7. 5 cm
8. 4 cm

9. 42 mm
10. 59 mm
11. Sample answer: 2 m

12. 0.315
13. 0.8
14. 0.30
15. 0.0005, 0.038, 0.35, 0.4
16. 0.090, 0.089, 0.009

17. 0.344
18. 38.9
19. 44
20. $1

21. $5 + $5 + $5 = $15
22. 75 − 13 = 62
23. 3 + 3 + 3 + 3 = 12
24. 70 − 35 = 35
25. 100 + 25 = 125

26. 167.96
27. 80.21
28. 40.7
29. 21.805
30. 12.53
31. 2.7926

32. 3

33. $5.49

Mathematics: Applications and Connections, Course 1

Chapter 3 Answer Key

Form 2C

Page 67		Page 68	
1.	0.29	17.	71.9
2.	0.017	18.	0.93
3.	3.7	19.	19
4.	0.0019	20.	$2
5.	74.019		
6.	0.0307		
		21.	5 + 5 = 10
		22.	$12 − $4 = $8
7.	4 cm	23.	2 + 2 + 2 + 2 = 8
8.	7 cm	24.	5 − 2 = 3
		25.	13 + 3 = 16
9.	56 mm	26.	45.96
10.	68 mm	27.	30.89
11.	Sample answer: 10 cm	28.	82.3
		29.	$115.12
		30.	8.07
		31.	8
12.	0.01		
13.	0.3		
14.	0.65	32.	$3
15.	0.0009, 0.007, 0.08, 0.6		
		33.	$5.50
16.	1.99, 1.9, 1.09		

Mathematics: Applications and Connections, Course 1

Chapter 3 Scoring Guide

Level	Specific Criteria
3 Superior	• Shows thorough understanding of the concepts *modeling, reading, and writing decimals, learning relationships among metric units of lengths and measuring line segments, comparing and ordering a set of decimals, rounding decimals, estimating decimal sums and differences,* and *adding and subtracting decimals.* • Uses appropriate strategies to solve problems. • Computations are correct. • Written explanations are exemplary. • Goes beyond requirements of some or all problems.
2 Satisfactory, with Minor Flaws	• Shows understanding of the concepts *modeling, reading, and writing decimals, learning relationships among metric units of lengths and measuring line segments, comparing and ordering a set of decimals, rounding decimals, estimating decimal sums and differences,* and *adding and subtracting decimals.* • Uses appropriate strategies to solve problems. • Computations are mostly correct. • Written explanations are effective. • Satisfies all requirements of problems.
1 Nearly Satisfactory, with Serious Flaws	• Shows understanding of most of the concepts *modeling, reading, and writing decimals, learning relationships among metric units of lengths and measuring line segments, comparing and ordering a set of decimals, rounding decimals, estimating decimal sums and differences,* and *adding and subtracting decimals.* • May not use appropriate strategies to solve problems. • Computations are mostly correct. • Written explanations are satisfactory. • Satisfies most requirements of problems.
0 Unsatisfactory	• Shows little or no understanding of the *concepts modeling, reading, and writing decimals, learning relationships among metric units of lengths and measuring line segments, comparing and ordering a set of decimals, rounding decimals, estimating decimal sums and differences,* and *adding and subtracting decimals.* • May not use appropriate strategies to solve problems. • Computations are incorrect. • Written explanations are not satisfactory. • Does not satisfy requirements of problems.

Mathematics: Applications and Connections, Course 1

Chapter 3 Answer Key

1. a. 0.0094

b. nitrogen: 0.7802, oxygen: 0.201, other: 0.0094

c. 0.0094, 0.0094, 0.201, 0.7802

d. $0.201 + 0.7802 = 0.9812$

e. $0.201 - 0.0094 = 0.1916$

f. 1. Look at the digit to the right of the place being rounded.

    2. The digit remains the same if the digit to the right is 0, 1, 2, 3, or 4.

    3. Round up if the digit to the right is 5, 6, 7, 8, or 9.

g. Round 0.0094 to 0.01; 0.201 to 0.20; and 0.7802 to 0.78.

2. a. length = 3.5 cm, width = 1.1 cm

b. 10 cm; this would be a reasonable answer because we followed rounding rules so that $3.5 + 3.5 + 1.1 + 1.1 = 4 + 4 + 1 + 1 = 10$.

Mid-Chapter Test
Page 70

1. **371.0005**

2. **0.71**

3. **99.99**

4. **28.0341**

5. **95.46**

6. **4 cm**

7. **2 cm**

8. **27 mm**

9. **32 mm**

10. **2,624 mm**

11. **2.101, 2.121, 3.277, 3.666**

12. **1.478, 1.55, 1.68, 2.1**

13. **5.34, 4.52, 4.319, 2.637**

14. **1.0313, 1.03, 1.003, 1.0003**

15. **9.5999**

16. **159.563, 159.873, 163.638, 170.012 170.146**

Chapter 3 Answer Key

Quiz A, Page 71

1. 0.8
2. 0.003
3. 0.06
4. 0.0004
5. 5 cm
6. 45 mm
7. 19.32
8. 0.29
9. 69.42 mm
10. 42.7 cm

Quiz C, Page 72

1. 3.7
2. 5.193
3. 258.75
4. 72.40
5. $3 + 6 = 9$
6. $0.9 + 0.6 = 1.5$
7. $\$48 - \$30 = \$18$
8. $6.74 < n < 6.85$
9. 19
10. 5.23 lb, 0.96 lb or 3.52 lb, 2.63 lb

Quiz B, Page 71

1. 478.6, 48.68, 48.679, 48.06
2. 8.01, 0.8, 0.083, 0.0095
3. 16.007, 16.07, 16.074, 16.74
4. 50.05, 50.5, 50.55, 50.555
5. Camille, Miriam, Antoine, Margarita

Quiz D, Page 72

1. 16.99
2. 87.74
3. 16.546
4. $3.87
5. 0.3019 gram

Chapter 3 Answer Key

Standardized Test Practice		Cumulative Review
Page 73	Page 74	Page 75

Page 73

1. C
2. A
3. C
4. D
5. B
6. A
7. D
8. C
9. A
10. B

Page 74

11. C
12. B
13. A
14. D
15. C
16. B
17. A
18. A
19. D
20. B

Page 75

1. 500
2. 80
3. 7,000
4. 23
5. 48
6. 15
7. 26
8. 36
9. December
10. Sept. & Nov.
11. $2,750
12. 17
13. 2
14. 43
15. 41
16. 38
17. 0.6
18. 0.0049
19. 0.013
20. 0.78
21. 9.7
22. $6 + $6 = $12
23. 0.8 − 0.3 = 0.5
24. 25.489
25. 40.8

Chapter 4 Test, Form 1A

1. Multiply: 1,320 × 2.06.   1. _____
   A. 271,920   **B.** 27,192   **C.** 27.192   **D.** 2,719.2

2. Multiply: 546 × $3.06.   2. _____
   A. $1,670.76   **B.** $167. 76   **C.** $167,076   **D.** $16.70

3. Find 8 × 2.4 mentally, using the distributive property.   3. _____
   A. 16.32   **B.** 19.2   **C.** 192   **D.** 18.4

4. Find 5.3 × 4 mentally, using the distributive property.   4. _____
   A. 20.2   **B.** 20.12   **C.** 21.2   **D.** 212

5. Multiply: 0.7 × 0.003.   5. _____
   A. 0.21   **B.** 0.021   **C.** 0.0021   **D.** 21

6. Solve $m = 3.45 \times 7.28$.   6. _____
   A. 25.116   **B.** 2,511.6   **C.** 251,160   **D.** 2.5116

7. Find the perimeter of a rectangle with a length of 16 feet and a width of 12 feet.   7. _____
   A. 28 ft   **B.** 192 ft   **C.** 56 ft   **D.** 384 ft

8. Find the area of a square with a side of 2.75 centimeters.   8. _____
   A. 7.5625 cm^2 **B.** 756.25 cm^2
   C. 11 cm^2 **D.** 5.5 cm^2

9. Find the area of the rectangle.   9. _____

   1.8 m

   3.5 m

   A. 5.3 m^2 **B.** 6.3 m^2 **C.** 63 m^2 **D.** 10.6 m^2

10. Find the quotient: 47.6 ÷ 34.   10. _____
    A. 14   **B.** 140   **C.** 0.14   **D.** 1.4

11. Evaluate $a \div b$ if $a = 237.98$ and $b = 73$.   11. _____
    A. 3.26   **B.** 0.326   **C.** 32.6   **D.** 326

12. Round the quotient to the nearest hundredth: $21\overline{)131.38}$.   12. _____
    A. 62.56   **B.** 62.57   **C.** 6.26   **D.** 6.25

13. 0.032 must be multiplied by what power of ten to make a whole number?   13. _____
    A. 10   **B.** 100   **C.** 1,000   **D.** 10,000

       Mathematics: Applications and Connections, Course 1

14. 0.0086 must be multiplied by what power of ten to make a whole number?   14. _____
    A. 10   **B.** 100   **C.** 1,000   **D.** 10,000

15. Evaluate $a \div b$ if $a = 31.54$ and $b = 0.76$.   15. _____
    A. 4.15   **B.** 41.5   **C.** 415   **D.** 0.415

16. Find the quotient: $1.6\overline{)4.944}$.   16. _____
    A. 3.09   **B.** 3.9   **C.** 30.9   **D.** 39

17. Find the quotient: $4.44 \div 0.37$.   17. _____
    A. 1.2   **B.** 12   **C.** 120   **D.** 0.12

18. Twenty-four feet of fencing is sold for $73.80. To the nearest cent, what is   18. _____
 the cost per foot of fencing?
    A. $30.75   **B.** $3.07   **C.** $3.08   **D.** $3.75

19. What unit would you use to measure the mass of a cat?   19. _____
    A. milligram   **B.** gram   **C.** kilogram   **D.** liter

20. What unit would you use to measure the capacity of a watering can?   20. _____
    A. milliliter   **B.** liter   **C.** gram   **D.** kilogram

21. What unit would you use to measure the mass of a truck?   21. _____
    A. milligram   **B.** gram   **C.** liter   **D.** kilogram

22. Change 7.86 liters to milliliters.   22. _____
    A. 0.0786 mL   **B.** 0.786 mL   **C.** 7,860 mL   **D.** 78.6 mL

23. Change 845 millimeters to centimeters.   23. _____
    A. 8,450 cm   **B.** 84.5 cm   **C.** 8.45 cm   **D.** 0.845 cm

24. Marcus needs to spread grass seed on his yard, which is shown below.   24. _____
 What is the area of his yard?

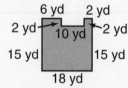

    A. 250 yd²   **B.** 234 yd²   **C.** 286 yd²   **D.** 270 yd²

25. Irma leased a car for $397.41 per month for 24 months. About how much   25. _____
 will the lease cost?
    A. $10,000   **B.** $10,800   **C.** $8,400   **D.** $9,600

Chapter 4 Test, Form 1B

1. Multiply: 0.6×18.
   A. 18.6   B. 12.6   C. 10.8   D. 108

   1. _____

2. Multiply: $\$3.12 \times 86$.
   A. \$24.35   B. \$26.83   C. \$243.51   D. \$268.32

   2. _____

3. Rewrite $8(10 + 7)$ using the distributive property.
   A. $(8 \times 10)(8 \times 7)$ B. $(8 + 10)(8 + 7)$
   C. $8 \times 10 + 8 \times 7$ D. $8 \times 10 + 7$

   3. _____

4. To find 30×4.3 mentally using the distributive property, you would first think:
   A. $30 \times 4.3 = 30(4 + 0.3)$.   B. $30 \times 4.3 = 30 \times 4 + 0.3$.
   C. $30 \times 4.3 = 30 + 4 + 0.3$.   D. $30 \times 4.3 = 30 \times 4 \times 0.3$.

   4. _____

5. Multiply: 0.42×1.8.
   A. 0.756   B. 7.56   C. 75.6   D. 756

   5. _____

6. Solve $a = 0.003 \times 4.1$.
   A. 0.123   B. 0.0123   C. 12.3   D. 1.23

   6. _____

7. Find the perimeter of the square.

   7.6 cm

   A. 15.2 cm   B. 57.76 cm   C. 5.776 cm   D. 30.4 cm

   7. _____

8. Find the area of a rectangle with a length of 6.1 meters and a width of 4.3 meters.
   A. 10.4 m^2 B. 26.23 m^2 C. 2.623 m^2 D. 20.8 m^2

   8. _____

9. Find the perimeter of the triangle.
   A. 18 ft   B. 27 ft
   C. 13.5 ft   D. 36 ft

   7.5 ft
   4.5 ft
   6 ft

   9. _____

10. Find the quotient: $47\overline{)110.92}$.
    A. 2.36   B. 23.6   C. 0.236   D. 236

    10. _____

11. Evaluate $a \div b$ if $a = 104.5$ and $b = 38$.
    A. 0.275   B. 2.75   C. 27.5   D. 275

    11. _____

12. Round the quotient to the nearest hundredth: $34\overline{)172.5}$.
    A. 50.73   B. 5.08   C. 5.07   D. 50.74

    12. _____

Mathematics: Applications and Connections, Course 1

13. 78.35 must be multiplied by what power of ten to make a whole number?   13. _____
    A. 10   **B.** 100   **C.** 1,000   **D.** 10,000

14. 0.348 must be multiplied by what power of ten to make a whole number?   14. _____
    A. 10   **B.** 100   **C.** 1,000   **D.** 10,000

15. Evaluate $a \div b$ if $a = 27.9$ and $b = 0.9$.   15. _____
    A. 31   **B.** 3.1   **C.** 0.31   **D.** 310

16. Find the quotient: $0.72\overline{)11.52}$.   16. _____
    A. 16   **B.** 1.6   **C.** 0.16   **D.** 0.016

17. Find the quotient: $6.09 \div 0.3$.   17. _____
    A. 203   **B.** 0.203   **C.** 2.03   **D.** 20.3

18. The area of a rectangle is 14.245 square meters. The length is 3.5 meters.   18. _____
    What is the width?
    A. 4.7 m   **B.** 4.07 m   **C.** 47 m   **D.** 407 m

19. What unit would you use to measure the mass of an apple?   19. _____
    A. milligram   **B.** gram   **C.** kilogram   **D.** liter

20. What unit would you use to measure the capacity of a hot tub?   20. _____
    A. millimeter   **B.** gram   **C.** liter   **D.** kilogram

21. What unit would you use to measure the mass of a pair of scissors?   21. _____
    A. liter   **B.** milligram   **C.** kilogram   **D.** gram

22. Change 9 grams to milligrams.   22. _____
    A. 0.9 mg   **B.** 0.009 mg   **C.** 900 mg   **D.** 9,000 mg

23. Change 186 millimeters to centimeters.   23. _____
    A. 18.6 cm   **B.** 1.86 cm   **C.** 0.186 cm   **D.** 1,860 cm

24. Oliver needs to mow the lawn shown below. What area will he mow?   24. _____

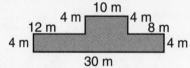

    A. 160 m²   **B.** 68 m²   **C.** 200 m²   **D.** 320 m²

25. Mrs. Jankowski bought 6 videotapes that cost $28.95 each. About how   25. _____
    much did the tapes cost in all?
    A. $120   **B.** $180   **C.** $150   **D.** $100

1. Multiply: 0.9×8.
   A. 72   **B.** 7.2   **C.** 0.72   **D.** 0.072

   1. _____

2. Multiply: $\$1.98 \times 78$.
   A. $15.60   **B.** $15.44   **C.** $145.44   **D.** $154.44

   2. _____

3. Rewrite $7(10 + 3)$ using the distributive property.
   A. $7 \times 10 + 3$ **B.** $7 \times 10 + 7 \times 3$
   C. $(7 + 10)(7 + 3)$ **D.** $(7 \times 10)(7 \times 3)$

   3. _____

4. To find 6×3.2 mentally using the distributive property, you would first think:
   A. $6 \times 3.2 = 6(3 + 0.2)$.   **B.** $6 \times 3.2 = 6 \times 3 + 0.2$.
   C. $6 \times 3.2 = 6 + 3 + 0.2$.   **D.** $6 \times 3.2 = 6 \times 3 \times 0.2$.

   4. _____

5. Multiply: 7.6×1.4.
   A. 1.064   **B.** 106.4   **C.** 1,064   **D.** 10.64

   5. _____

6. Multiply: 1.2×1.2.
   A. 1.44   **B.** 14.4   **C.** 0.144   **D.** 144

   6. _____

7. Find the perimeter of the triangle.
   A. 72 cm   **B.** 42 cm
   C. 432 cm   **D.** 144 cm

   30 cm, 18 cm, 24 cm

   7. _____

8. Find the area of the rectangle.   *0.09 m, 1.9 m*

   A. 1.71 m²   **B.** 17.1 m²   **C.** 0.171 m²   **D.** 3.98 m²

   8. _____

9. Find the perimeter of a square with a side of 1.8 centimeters.
   A. 3.6 cm   **B.** 7.2 cm   **C.** 32.4 cm   **D.** 3.24 cm

   9. _____

10. Find the quotient: $7\overline{)19.6}$.
    A. 28   **B.** 280   **C.** 2.8   **D.** 0.28

    10. _____

11. Evaluate $a \div b$ if $a = 16.8$ and $b = 8$.
    A. 0.21   **B.** 21   **C.** 210   **D.** 2.1

    11. _____

12. Round $154.5 \div 36$ to the nearest tenth.
    A. 4.2   **B.** 4.3   **C.** 42.9   **D.** 0.4

    12. _____

13. 82.4 must be multiplied by what power of ten to make a whole number?   13. _____
    A. 10   **B.** 100   **C.** 1,000   **D.** 10,000

14. 3.015 must be multiplied by what power of ten to make a whole number?   14. _____
    A. 10   **B.** 100   **C.** 1,000   **D.** 10,000

15. Evaluate $a \div b$ if $a = 5.28$ and $b = 0.8$.   15. _____
    A. 0.66   **B.** 6.6   **C.** 66   **D.** 0.066

16. Find the quotient: $7\overline{)4.235}$.   16. _____
    A. 65   **B.** 0.65   **C.** 6.5   **D.** 0.605

17. Find the quotient: $2.736 \div 0.9$.   17. _____
    A. 34   **B.** 3.4   **C.** 3.04   **D.** 30.4

18. The area of a rectangle is 6.09 square meters. The length is 0.3 meter.   18. _____
    What is the width?
    A. 20.3 m   **B.** 2.03 m   **C.** 0.203 m   **D.** 203 m

19. What unit would you use to measure the mass of a grain of sand?   19. _____
    A. milligram   **B.** gram   **C.** kilogram   **D.** liter

20. What unit would you use to measure the capacity of a washing machine?   20. _____
    A. milliliter   **B.** liter   **C.** gram   **D.** kilogram

21. What unit would you use to measure the mass of a cow?   21. _____
    A. milligram   **B.** gram   **C.** kilogram   **D.** liter

22. Change 3 grams to milligrams.   22. _____
    A. 0.3 mg   **B.** 3,000 mg   **C.** 300 mg   **D.** 30 mg

23. Change 2,530 milliliters to liters.   23. _____
    A. 5.3 L   **B.** 2,530,000 L   **C.** 0.0253 L   **D.** 2.53 L

24. Adrian is painting the section of wall shown. What area will he paint?   24. _____

```
    8 ft   10 ft
10 ft ↘ ┌──────┐
       │      │ 16 ft
  8 ft │      │
    ┌──┘      │
    └─────────┘
      20 ft
```

    A. 320 ft²   **B.** 400 ft²   **C.** 240 ft²   **D.** 72 ft²

25. For her new furniture, Rina is making payments of $59.50 per month for   25. _____
    18 months. About how much will she pay in all?
    A. $120   **B.** $1,200   **C.** $1,500   **D.** $80

Chapter 4 Test, Form 2A

1. Estimate: 249×41.　　　　　　　　　　　　　　　1. _____

Multiply.

2. 0.89×48　　　　　　　　　　　　　　　　　　2. _____

3. 428×1.32　　　　　　　　　　　　　　　　　3. _____

4. 3.61×3.61　　　　　　　　　　　　　　　　　4. _____

5. Solve $x = 38.4 \times 5.7$.　　　　　　　　　　　　　5. _____

Find each product mentally. Use the distributive property.

6. 309×9　　　　　　　　　　　　　　　　　　6. _____

7. 40.4×8　　　　　　　　　　　　　　　　　　7. _____

Find the area of each figure.

8. rectangle:
   $l = 4.2$ ft
   $w = 1.8$ ft　　　　　　　　　　　　　　　　　　8. _____

9. ▭ 0.9 cm
   　5.2 cm　　　　　　　　　　　　　　　　　　　9. _____

10. Find the perimeter of a square with sides of 6.5 inches.　　10. _____

Find each quotient.

11. $75.6 \div 42$　　　　　　　　　　　　　　　　　11. _____

12. $47\overline{)145.7}$　　　　　　　　　　　　　　　　12. _____

13. $3.822 \div 0.49$　　　　　　　　　　　　　　　　13. _____

14. $3.6\overline{)273.6}$　　　　　　　　　　　　　　　14. _____

Mathematics: Applications and Connections, Course 1

Find each quotient.

15. $344.28 \div 57$

15. _____

16. $296.805 \div 42.1$

16. _____

17. Evaluate $c \div d$ if $c = 526.64$ and $d = 58$.

17. _____

Round each quotient to the nearest hundredth.

18. $456.7 \div 6$

18. _____

19. $86\overline{)305.9}$

19. _____

Write the unit that you would use to measure each of the following. Then estimate the mass or capacity.

20. capacity of a thimble

20. _____

21. mass of an elephant

21. _____

Complete.

22. $3,428 \text{ mL} = \underline{\ ?\ } \text{ L}$

22. _____

23. $\underline{\ ?\ } \text{ g} = 0.97 \text{ kg}$

23. _____

24. A rectangular room is 12 feet long by 9.5 feet wide. How many feet of wallpaper border are needed to border the ceiling?

24. _____

25. Hiroshi is painting the wall shown. What is the area of the wall he is painting?

25. _____

4 cm · 7 cm
10 cm
6 cm
10 cm
17 cm

Chapter 4 Test, Form 2B

1. Estimate: 4.8×69.

1. _____

Multiply.

2. 0.72×26

2. _____

3. 136×4.32

3. _____

4. 8.97×6.8.

4. _____

5. Solve $m = 0.6 \times 0.09$.

5. _____

Find each product mentally. Use the distributive property.

6. 102×8

6. _____

7. 30.3×4

7. _____

Find the perimeter of each figure.

8. 1.7 m 0.8 m 1.5 m

8. _____

9. 5.6 cm 2.9 cm

9. _____

10. Find the area of the square.

7.5 in.

10. _____

Find each quotient.

11. $8\overline{)28.96}$

11. _____

12. $231.68 \div 32$

12. _____

13. $19.98 \div 0.74$

13. _____

14. $5.9\overline{)48.97}$

14. _____

Chapter 4 Test, Form 2B (continued)

Find each quotient.

15. $73.923 \div 12.3$

15. _____

16. $495.88 \div 98$

16. _____

17. Evaluate $a \div b$ if $a = 38.4$ and $b = 60$.

17. _____

Round each quotient to the nearest tenth.

18. $8.6 \div 7$

18. _____

19. $225.9 \div 42$

19. _____

Write the unit that you would use to measure each of the following. Then estimate the mass or capacity.

20. capacity of a soup bowl

20. _____

21. mass of a sofa

21. _____

Complete.

22. $897 \text{ mL} = \underline{\ ?\ } \text{ L}$

22. _____

23. $\underline{\ ?\ } \text{ g} = 4.6 \text{ kg}$

23. _____

24. A room is 16.5 feet long by 13.7 feet wide. How many square feet of carpeting are needed to cover the room?

24. _____

25. Isidro is fencing his yard. How much fencing does he need?

25. _____

Mathematics: Applications and Connections, Course 1

Chapter 4 Test, Form 2C

1. Estimate: 53×1.8.

1. _____

Multiply.

2. 86×4.1

2. _____

3. 24×3.99

3. _____

4. 6.34×1.5

4. _____

5. Solve $x = 29.3 \times 7.4$.

5. _____

Find each product mentally. Use the distributive property.

6. 104×6

6. _____

7. 20.4×6

7. _____

Find the perimeter of each figure.

8.

25 cm
11 cm
21 cm

8. _____

9. rectangle:
length, 18 m
width, 11 m

9. _____

10. Find the area of the square.

3.5 ft
3.5 ft

10. _____

Find each quotient.

11. $7\overline{)9.45}$

11. _____

12. $61.94 \div 19$

12. _____

13. $3.3 \div 1.1$

13. _____

14. $157.29 \div 32.1$

14. _____

*Mathematics: Applications
and Connections,* Course 1

Find each quotient.
15. $16.362 \div 8.1$

15. _____

16. $208.052 \div 5.2$

16. _____

Round each quotient to the nearest tenth.
17. $7.6 \div 6$

17. _____

18. $148.8 \div 56$

18. _____

19. Evaluate $a \div b$ if $a = 9.64$ and $b = 40$.

19. _____

Write the unit that you would use to measure each of the following. Then estimate the mass or capacity.
20. mass of a pencil

20. _____

21. capacity of a bathtub

21. _____

Complete.
22. $294 \text{ mL} = \underline{\ ?\ } \text{ L}$

22. _____

23. $\underline{\ ?\ } \text{ g} = 7.2 \text{ kg}$

23. _____

24. A room is 20 feet long by 12.5 feet wide. How many square feet of carpeting are needed to cover the floor?

24. _____

25. Barney is seeding his yard. How much area does his yard cover?

25. _____

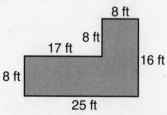

Mathematics: Applications and Connections, Course 1

Name_____ Date _____

Chapter 4 Performance Assessment

Instructions: Demonstrate your knowledge by giving a clear, concise solution to each problem. Be sure to include all relevant drawings and justify your answers. You may show your solutions in more than one way or investigate beyond the requirements of the problems.

1. **a.** Use the 10-by-10 decimal models below to model 2×0.7. Find the product.

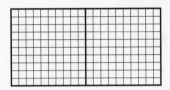

   b. Explain how to multiply 1.5×0.2 using the distributive property. Find the product.

   c. In your own words, tell how to multiply decimals.

2. **a.** Use models to find $2.4 \div 0.8$. Show your work and explain each step.

   b. Estimate $0.15 \div 4$. Then find the product. Show your work.

3. A chef wishes to serve strawberry shortcake for dinner.

   a. Tell how to change from larger units to smaller units of measure in the metric system. Tell how to change from smaller to larger units.

   b. A box of biscuit mix contains 2.26 kilograms. If 23 grams of biscuit mix are required for a shortcake, how many shortcakes can the chef make from each box? Round the quotient to the nearest tenth.

   c. The chef has 5.4 kilograms of strawberries. If he plans to serve 115 grams of strawberries with each shortcake, estimate the number of servings of strawberries he has. Explain each step.

   d. How many servings of strawberries does the chef have in part c?

   e. The front cover of the box of biscuit mix is 20 centimeters wide and 45 centimeters high. What are the perimeter and area of the cover of the box?

Mathematics: Applications and Connections, Course 1

Chapter 4 Mid-Chapter Test

(Lessons 4-1 through 4-5)

Multiply.

1. 0.83×1000

2. 4.38×25

3. 0.092×55

4. Estimate the product of 2.031 and 21.

Find each product mentally. Use the distributive property.

5. 6.22×11 6. 5.07×21

7. Steven bought 12 pairs of socks for $2.96 each. How much did he spend?

8. Brigette jogged around a 440-yard track 5.5 times. How far did she jog?

Multiply.

9. 0.42×1.25 10. 5.1×8.12

Evaluate each expression if a = 3.62, b = 0.05, and c = 1.5.

11. ab 12. $a(b + c)$

13. Find the perimeter of a square with a side of 3.27 yards.

14. Find the area of a rectangle 5.9 feet long and 3.8 feet wide.

15. The Bakers' living room is 13.5 feet by 11.2 feet. The carpet they like is $2.57 per square foot. How much will it cost to carpet the living room, to the nearest cent?

16. Find the area of the figure.

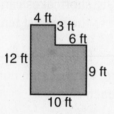

4 ft
3 ft
6 ft
12 ft
9 ft
10 ft

Find each quotient.

17. $0.5 \div 2$ 18. $16\overline{)1.392}$

Round each quotient to the nearest tenth.

19. $57.45 \div 8$ 20. $13.1 \div 12$

1. _____

2. _____

3. _____

4. _____

5. _____

6. _____

7. _____

8. _____

9. _____

10. _____

11. _____

12. _____

13. _____

14. _____

15. _____

16. _____

17. _____

18. _____

19. _____

20. _____

Chapter 4 Quiz A

1. Estimate 8.79 × 58 using rounding.

2. Estimate 248 × 40.3 using compatible numbers.

Find each product mentally. Use the distributive property.
3. 7 × 17   4. 62 × 4   5. 8.1 × 6

Multiply.
6. 9.86 × 124   7. 88 × 0.007

8. Five ballpoint pens cost $0.39 each. How much do they cost in all? Solve mentally using the distributive property.

Solve each equation.
9. $a = 7.2 \times 7.2$ 10. $c = 0.008 \times 0.9$

1. _____

2. _____

3. _____

4. _____

5. _____

6. _____

7. _____

8. _____

9. _____

10. _____

- -

Chapter 4 Quiz B

Find the perimeter of each figure.
1. 65.5 cm 38.2 cm

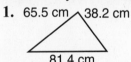

81.4 cm

2. rectangle: length, 4.5 in., width, 3.8 in.

Find the area of each figure.
3. 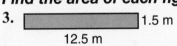1.5 m
   12.5 m

4.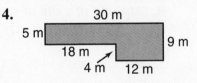

5. a square with sides of 9.1 mm

Find each quotient.
6. 9)25.83   7. 64)492.8   8. 31.74 ÷ 2

Round each quotient to the nearest tenth.
9. 7.059 ÷ 4   10. 35.67 ÷ 15

1. _____

2. _____

3. _____

4. _____

5. _____

6. _____

7. _____

8. _____

9. _____

10. _____

Mathematics: Applications and Connections, Course 1

Chapter 4 Quiz C

(Lessons 4-6 and 4-7)

Find each quotient.

1. $9.2\overline{)79.12}$ 2. $72.5 \div 1.25$

3. $0.86\overline{)2.924}$ 4. $457.6 \div 6.5$

5. $0.9 \div 0.09$ 6. $1.6\overline{)0.08}$

7. $0.2\overline{)40}$ 8. $0.2 \div 40$

9. On a trip, the Juarez family drove 1,585.6 miles and used 58 gallons of gasoline. To the nearest tenth, what was their average number of miles per gallon?

10. Mr. Tanaka paid $8.68 for 1.6 pounds of cashews. To the nearest cent, what was the cost per pound?

1. _____

2. _____

3. _____

4. _____

5. _____

6. _____

7. _____

8. _____

9. _____

10. _____

Chapter 4 Quiz D

(Lessons 4-8 and 4-9)

Write the unit that you would use to measure each of the following. Then estimate the mass or capacity.

1. mass of a television   2. capacity of a water heater

3. mass of a dime   4. capacity of a can of soup

5. mass of a hummingbird

Complete.

6. $2.3 \text{ kg} = \underline{\ ?\ } \text{ g}$ 7. $\underline{\ ?\ } \text{ km} = 678 \text{ m}$

8. $1.27 \text{ L} = \underline{\ ?\ } \text{ mL}$ 9. $4.6 \text{ cm} = \underline{\ ?\ } \text{ mm}$

10. $500 \text{ mg} = \underline{\ ?\ } \text{ kg}$

1. _____

2. _____

3. _____

4. _____

5. _____

6. _____

7. _____

8. _____

9. _____

10. _____

Mathematics: Applications and Connections, Course 1

Chapter 4 Standardized Test Practice

1. Keung rented a car for $19.99 a day plus $0.14 per mile. He kept the car one day and drove 391.8 miles. How much did he pay?
   A. $54.85   **B.** $74.84   **C.** $78.39   **D.** $411.93

   1. _____

2. Dalia is mowing yards to earn money. She decides to charge $0.01 per square foot. If she mows a yard that is 75 feet by 52 feet, how much should she charge?
   A. $390.00   **B.** $2.54   **C.** $25.40   **D.** $39

   2. _____

3. Centuries ago, for their inheritance, farmers would divide their land among their sons. If a farmer had 17.82 acres of land and divided it into 2.97-acre parcels, how many sons did he have?
   A. 5   **B.** 6   **C.** 7   **D.** 8

   3. _____

4. A bottle of window cleaner holds 973 milliliters of liquid. How many liters is that?
   A. 9.73 L   **B.** 0.0973 L   **C.** 97.3 L   **D.** 0.973 L

   4. _____

5. Write *twenty-seven and thirty-nine ten-thousandths* as a decimal.
   A. 27.0039   **B.** 27.39   **C.** 27.039   **D.** 27.3910

   5. _____

6. How many centimeters are in 3.5 kilometers?
   A. 3,500 cm   **B.** 0.0035 cm   **C.** 350,000 cm   **D.** 350 cm

   6. _____

7. Order the set of decimals from least to greatest. 23.2, 22.3, 23.08, 22.8, 22.08
   A. 22.08, 23.2, 23.08, 22.8, 22.3   **B.** 22.08, 22.3, 22.8, 23.08, 23.2
   C. 23.2, 22.3, 22.8, 22.08, 23.08   **D.** 22.3, 22.08, 22.8, 23.2, 23.08

   7. _____

8. Joshua and Sam are going to the movies. Joshua has $7.28 and Sam has $6.83. How much do they have together?
   A. $14.11   **B.** $13.01   **C.** $14.01   **D.** $13.11

   8. _____

9. Latoya is making a circle graph as part of a report. If the parts of the graph are in percents, what number should she get when she adds all of the parts?
   A. 50%   **B.** 1   **C.** 100%   **D.** can't tell

   9. _____

10. On the last math test, Jamil's class had the following scores: 98, 72, 65, 83, 91, 84, 90, 77, 96, 72, 91, 79, 85, 76, 97. When rounded to the nearest ones place, which two measures are equal?
    A. mean and mode   **B.** mean and median
    C. median and mode   **D.** none are equal

    10. _____

Mathematics: Applications and Connections, Course 1

11. On a coordinate system, what three things must be labeled?
    A. origin, *x*-coordinate, *y*-coordinate
    B. data point, ordered pair, grid
    C. title, horizontal axis, vertical axis
    D. origin, *x*-axis, *y*-axis

11. _____

12. Simplify: $28 \div 7 + 7 \times 6 - 2$.
    A. 44   B. 64   C. 8   D. 10

12. _____

13. Simplify: $25 - 4 \times 3 + 12 \div 6$.
    A. 12   B. 15   C. 52.5   D. 12.5

13. _____

14. Althea rented a car for $21 plus $0.12 per mile. If *m* represents the number of miles driven, then the algebraic expression $21 + $0.12*m* gives the cost for the car. Find the cost if Althea drove 342 miles.
    A. $7,223.04   B. $41.04   C. $62.04   D. $83.04

14. _____

15. The volume of a cube can be found by using the expression $V = s^3$, where *s* is the length of a side. A shipping box is a cube with a side length of 2 feet. What is the volume of the box?
    A. 4 ft³   B. 8 ft³   C. 6 ft³   D. 10 ft³

15. _____

16. The Hope diamond is a 45.52-carat blue diamond that is believed to have been cut from a 112-carat stone found in India in the 1600s. How many carats remained of the original stone after the Hope diamond was cut?
    A. 66.48   B. 157.52   C. 45.78   D. 44.40

16. _____

17. Dominic purchased a shirt for $7.64. To the nearest dollar, how much is this?
    A. $7   B. $7.50   C. $8   D. $7.60

17. _____

18. Estimate $43.768 - 37.419$ using rounding.
    A. 6   B. 6.249   C. 7   D. 6.4

18. _____

19. Rewrite 7(37) using the distributive property.
    A. 7(3) + 7(7)   B. 7(30) + 7(7)
    C. 7(3 + 7)   D. 7 + (3) + 7 + (7)

19. _____

20. Christy and three friends went in together on a gift for their teacher. If the gift cost $23.49, how much does each friend owe to the nearest cent?
    A. $5.88   B. $7.83   C. $5.90   D. $5.87

20. _____

102   *Mathematics: Applications and Connections,* Course 1

Cumulative Review, Chapters 1–4

Perform the indicated operation. (Lessons 4-3, 3-6, 4-5, and 4-6)

1. 3.8×2.5

2. $7.66 + 1.5$

3. $38\overline{)53.2}$

4. $0.27\overline{)0.999}$

Evaluate. (Lessons 1-4, 1-6, and 1-5)

5. $7 + 6 \times 3 + 6$ 6. 7^4

7. mn if $m = 8$ and $n = 25$ 8. x^6 if $x = 10$

9. Order the following decimals from least to greatest: 0.003, 0.95, 0.2, 0.0056. (Lesson 3-3)

Golf Scores: 78, 136, 92, 100, 134, 92

10. What is the range of the golf scores? (Lesson 2-7)

11. What is the median of the golf scores? (Lesson 2-7)

12. Refer to the circle graph at the right. Which two flavors received about the same number of votes? (Lesson 2-4)

Favorite Flavors

13. The equation for finding the perimeter of a hexagon with six equal sides is $P = 6s$. If the length (s) of each side of a hexagon is 18 centimeters, find the perimeter. (Lesson 4-4)

Estimate. (Lessons 3-5 and 1-3)

14. $0.716 + 0.855$ 15. 49×86

16. $355 \div 7$ 17. $166 + 299$

18. Change 1.9 kilograms to grams. (Lesson 4-9)

19. Find the area of the figure at the right. (Lesson 4-4)

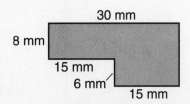

20. Round $18.65 \div 3.8$ to the nearest hundredth. (Lesson 4-7)

1. _____
2. _____
3. _____
4. _____
5. _____
6. _____
7. _____
8. _____
9. _____
10. _____
11. _____
12. _____
13. _____
14. _____
15. _____
16. _____
17. _____
18. _____
19. _____
20. _____

Chapter 4 Answer Key

Form 1A

Page 85

1. D
2. A
3. B
4. C
5. C
6. A
7. C
8. A
9. B
10. D
11. A
12. C
13. C

Page 86

14. D
15. B
16. A
17. B
18. C
19. C
20. B
21. D
22. C
23. B
24. A
25. D

Form 1B

Page 87

1. C
2. D
3. C
4. A
5. A
6. B
7. D
8. B
9. A
10. A
11. B
12. C

Page 88

13. B
14. C
15. A
16. A
17. D
18. B
19. B
20. C
21. D
22. D
23. A
24. A
25. B

Mathematics: Applications and Connections, Course 1

4

Chapter 4 Answer Key

Page 89

1. B
2. D
3. B
4. A
5. D
6. A
7. A
8. C
9. B
10. C
11. D
12. B

Page 90

13. A
14. C
15. B
16. D
17. C
18. A
19. A
20. B
21. C
22. B
23. D
24. C
25. B

Chapter 4 Answer Key

Form 2A

Page 91

$250 \times 40 =$
1. _____ 10,000 _____

2. _____ 42.72 _____

3. _____ 564.96 _____

4. _____ 13.0321 _____

5. _____ 218.88 _____

6. _____ 2, 781 _____

7. _____ 323.2 _____

8. _____ 7.56 ft^2 _____

9. _____ 4.68 cm^2 _____

10. _____ 26 in. _____

11. _____ 1.8 _____

12. _____ 3.1 _____

13. _____ 7.8 _____

14. _____ 76 _____

Page 92

15. _____ 6.04 _____

16. _____ 7.05 _____

17. _____ 9.08 _____

18. _____ 76.12 _____

19. _____ 3.56 _____

20. _____ mL, 10 mL _____

21. _____ kg, 3,600 kg _____

22. _____ 3.428 _____

23. _____ 970 _____

24. _____ 43 ft _____

25. _____ 130 cm^2 _____

Chapter 4 Answer Key

Page 93

1. $5 \times 70 = 350$

2. 18.72

3. 587.52

4. 60.996

5. 0.054

6. 816

7. 121.2

8. 4 m

9. 17 cm

10. 56.25 in^2

11. 3.62

12. 7.24

13. 27

14. 8.3

Page 94

15. 6.01

16. 5.06

17. 0.64

18. 1.2

19. 5.4

20. mL, 300 mL

21. kg, 40 kg

22. 0.897

23. 4,600

24. 226.05 ft^2

25. 64 m

Mathematics: Applications and Connections, Course 1

Chapter 4 Answer Key

Page 95

1. $50 \times 2 = 100$

2. 352.6

3. 95.76

4. 9.51

5. 216.82

6. 624

7. 122.4

8. 57 cm

9. 58 m

10. 12.25 ft²

11. 1.35

12. 3.26

13. 3

14. 4.9

Page 96

15. 2.02

16. 40.01

17. 1.3

18. 2.7

19. 0.241

20. g, 7 g

21. L, 150 L

22. 0.294

23. 7,200

24. 250 ft²

25. 264 ft²

Mathematics: Applications and Connections, Course 1

Chapter 4 Scoring Guide

Level	Specific Criteria
3 Superior	• Shows thorough understanding of the concepts *estimating, modeling, and finding products and quotients of decimals, finding perimeter and area,* and *changing units and solving problems in the metric system.* • Uses appropriate strategies to solve problems. • Computations are correct. • Written explanations are exemplary. • Diagrams are accurate and appropriate. • Goes beyond requirements of some or all problems.
2 Satisfactory, with Minor Flaws	• Shows understanding of the concepts *estimating, modeling, and finding products and quotients of decimals, finding perimeter and area,* and *changing units and solving problems in the metric system.* • Uses appropriate strategies to solve problems. • Computations are mostly correct. • Diagrams are mostly accurate and appropriate. • Written explanations are effective. • Satisfies all requirements of problems.
1 Nearly Satisfactory, with Serious Flaws	• Shows understanding of most of the concepts *estimating, modeling, and finding products and quotients of decimals, finding perimeter and area,* and *changing units and solving problems in the metric system.* • May not use appropriate strategies to solve problems. • Computations are mostly correct. • Diagrams are mostly accurate or appropriate. • Written explanations are satisfactory. • Satisfies most requirements of problems.
0 Unsatisfactory	• Shows little or no understanding of the concepts *estimating, modeling, and finding products and quotients of decimals, finding perimeter and area,* and *changing units and solving problems in the metric system.* • May not use appropriate strategies to solve problems. • Computations are incorrect. • Diagrams are not accurate or appropriate. • Written explanations are not satisfactory. • Does not satisfy requirements of problems.

Chapter 4 Answer Key

Performance Assessment Sample Answers
Page 97

1. a. $2 \times 0.7 = 1.4$

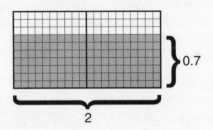

b. $1.5 \times 0.2 = (1 + 0.5) \times 0.2$
$= (1 \times 0.2) + (0.5 \times 0.2)$
$= 0.2 + 0.1$
$= 0.3$

c. Multiply as with whole numbers. Add the number of decimal places in each factor. The product will have this number of decimal places.

2. a. 2.4 is represented by 2 ones blocks and 4 tenths strips.
0.8 is represented by 8 tenths strips.
Replace each ones block with 10 tenths. Divide the tenths strips into groups with 8 tenths strips.
$2.4 \div 0.8 = 3$

  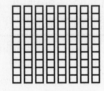

b. $0.15 \div 4 \approx 0.16 \div 4 = 0.04$
$0.15 \div 4 = 0.0375$

3. a. Multiply to change from larger units to smaller units. Divide to change from smaller units to larger units.

b. 2.26 kg = 2260 g
$2{,}260 \div 23 \approx 98.3$ shortcakes

c. Change 5.4 kg to 5,400 g. Round 5,400 to 5,000 and 115 to 100.
$5{,}000 \div 100 = 50$
There are about 50 servings.

d. $5{,}400 \div 115 \approx 47$ servings

e. $P = 2(20) + 2(45) = 130$ cm
$A = 20 \times 45 = 900$ cm^2

Mid-Chapter Test
Page 98

1. 830
2. 109.5
3. 5.06
4. $2 \times 20 = 40$
5. 68.42
6. 106.47
7. $35.52
8. 2,420 yd
9. 0.525
10. 41.412
11. 0.181
12. 5.611
13. 13.08 yd
14. 22.42 ft^2
15. $388.58
16. 102 ft^2
17. 0.25
18. 0.087
19. 7.2
20. 1.1

Mathematics: Applications and Connections, Course 1

Chapter 4 Answer Key

Quiz A, Page 99

1. $9 \times 60 = 540$
   $250 \times 40 =$
2. $10,000$
3. 119
4. 248
5. 48.6
6. $1,222.64$
7. 0.616
8. $\$1.95$
9. 51.84
10. 0.0072

Quiz B, Page 99

1. 185.1 cm
2. 16.6 in.
3. 18.75 m^2
4. 198 m^2
5. 82.81 mm^2
6. 2.87
7. 7.7
8. 15.87
9. 1.8
10. 2.4

Quiz C, Page 100

1. 8.6
2. 58
3. 3.4
4. 70.4
5. 10
6. 0.05
7. 200
8. 0.005
9. 27.3
10. $\$5.43$

Quiz D, Page 100

1. kg, 25 kg
2. L, 200 L
3. g, 1 g
4. mL, 350 mL
5. g, 4 g
6. $2,300$
7. 0.678
8. $1,270$
9. 46
10. 0.0005

Chapter 4 Answer Key

Standardized Test Practice		Cumulative Review

Page 101

1. B
2. D
3. B
4. D
5. A
6. C
7. B
8. A
9. C
10. B

Page 102

11. D
12. A
13. B
14. C
15. B
16. A
17. C
18. C
19. B
20. D

Page 103

1. 9.5
2. 9.16
3. 1.4
4. 3.7
5. 31
6. 2,401
7. 200
8. 1,000,000
9. 0.003, 0.0056, 0.2, 0.95
10. 58
11. 96
12. chocolate and vanilla
13. 108 cm
14. $0.7 + 0.9 = 1.6$
15. $50 \times 90 = 4,500$
16. $350 \div 7 = 50$
17. $170 + 300 = 470$
18. 1,900 g
19. 330 mm^2
20. 4.91

Mathematics: Applications and Connections, Course 1

Chapter 5 Test, Form 1A

1. 345 is divisible by which of these numbers?   1. _____
  A. 3, 4, and 5   **B.** 3, 5, and 25
  C. 3, 5, and 13   **D.** 3, 5, and 23

2. 536 is divisible by which of these numbers?   2. _____
  A. 3, 5, and 6   **B.** 2, 3, and 67
  C. 2^3 and 67   **D.** 2^4 and 56

3. Which numbers are factors of 68?   3. _____
  A. 2, 4, 5, 18, and 36   **B.** 2, 4, 17, and 34
  C. 2, 5, and 10   **D.** 4, 5, 6, 12, and 32

4. Find the prime factorization of 540.   4. _____
  A. $4 \times 15 \times 9$ **B.** $4 \times 3 \times 5 \times 9$
  C. $2 \times 2 \times 3 \times 3 \times 3 \times 5$ **D.** $2 \times 3 \times 3 \times 5 \times 6$

5. Which number is prime?   5. _____
  A. 67   **B.** 27   **C.** 87   **D.** 81

6. What is the GCF of 34 and 51?   6. _____
  A. 15   **B.** 13   **C.** 19   **D.** 17

7. What is the GCF of 12, 36, and 54?   7. _____
  A. 12   **B.** 6   **C.** 9   **D.** 3

8. Which fraction is in simplest form?   8. _____
  A. $\frac{31}{65}$ **B.** $\frac{11}{55}$ **C.** $\frac{9}{27}$ **D.** $\frac{16}{32}$

9. Which ratio is in simplest form?   9. _____
  A. 10 to 730   **B.** 11 to 550   **C.** 12 to 480   **D.** 13 to 660

10. Which fraction is *not* in simplest form?   10. _____
  A. $\frac{13}{15}$ **B.** $\frac{9}{11}$ **C.** $\frac{81}{84}$ **D.** $\frac{32}{93}$

11. Express $9\frac{7}{8}$ as an improper fraction.   11. _____
  A. $\frac{7}{98}$ **B.** $\frac{79}{8}$ **C.** $\frac{97}{8}$ **D.** $\frac{24}{8}$

12. Express $\frac{152}{9}$ as a mixed number.   12. _____
  A. $16\frac{8}{9}$ **B.** $16\frac{7}{9}$ **C.** $15\frac{8}{9}$ **D.** $16\frac{8}{152}$

13. Find the length of the segment to the nearest fourth inch.   13. _____

   A. 2 in.   **B.** $2\frac{1}{4}$ in.   **C.** 3 in.   **D.** $2\frac{1}{2}$ in.

14. Complete: 105 in. = _?_ ft.   14. _____
   A. 3   **B.** 8   **C.** $8\frac{3}{4}$ **D.** 35

15. Find the LCM for 42 and 50.   15. _____
   A. 2,100   **B.** 1,050   **C.** 2   **D.** 92

16. Which number is a multiple of 19?   16. _____
   A. 9   **B.** 105   **C.** 85   **D.** 95

17. What is the LCD for $\frac{5}{12}$ and $\frac{7}{18}$?   17. _____
   A. 6   **B.** 12   **C.** 72   **D.** 36

18. Which sentence is true?   18. _____
   A. $\frac{41}{48} < \frac{7}{8}$ **B.** $\frac{41}{48} = \frac{7}{8}$ **C.** $\frac{41}{48} > \frac{7}{8}$ **D.** $\frac{7}{8} < \frac{41}{48}$

19. Which fraction is the greatest?   19. _____
   A. $\frac{13}{36}$ **B.** $\frac{5}{12}$ **C.** $\frac{7}{18}$ **D.** $\frac{5}{6}$

20. Express 0.78 as a fraction in simplest form.   20. _____
   A. $\frac{78}{100}$ **B.** $\frac{4}{5}$ **C.** $\frac{39}{50}$ **D.** $\frac{19}{25}$

21. Express 15.85 as a fraction in simplest form.   21. _____
   A. $15\frac{85}{100}$ **B.** $15\frac{17}{20}$ **C.** $15\frac{4}{5}$ **D.** $15\frac{5}{20}$

22. Express $11\frac{7}{8}$ as a decimal.   22. _____
   A. 11.875   **B.** 11.78   **C.** 0.875   **D.** 11.7

23. Express $\frac{5}{11}$ as a decimal. Use bar notation to show a repeating decimal.   23. _____
   A. $0.\overline{45}$ **B.** 0.045   **C.** $0.\overline{45}$ **D.** 0.45

24. Alfonso and Nick were choosing movies. They each found three they   24. _____
   liked, but only have time to watch two. How many combinations of
   movies are possible?
   A. 3   **B.** 15   **C.** 6   **D.** 12

25. Jessica has two pieces of wood that she needs to cut into equal length   25. _____
   pieces. One piece is 108 inches long, and the other is 144 inches long.
   What is the longest length each piece of wood can be?
   A. 12 in.   **B.** 18 in.   **C.** 72 in.   **D.** 36 in.

Chapter 5 Test, Form 1B

1. 216 is divisible by which of these numbers?
   A. 2, 3, 5, 6, and 9   B. 2, 3, 6, and 9
   C. 5, 6, and 10   D. 9 and 10

2. 144 is divisible by which of these numbers?
   A. 2, 3, 5, 6, and 9   B. 3, 6, and 10
   C. 9 and 10   D. 2, 3, 6, and 9

3. Which numbers are factors of 54?
   A. 2, 3, 6, and 12   B. 5, 6, and 9
   C. 10 and 27   D. 2, 3, 9, 18, and 27

4. Find the prime factorization of 84.
   A. $3 \times 4 \times 7$ B. $2 \times 2 \times 3 \times 7$
   C. 2×42 D. 7×12

5. Which number is prime?
   A. 15   B. 28   C. 31   D. 33

6. What is the GCF of 28 and 36?
   A. 2   B. 4   C. 7   D. 9

7. What is the GCF of 8, 12, and 30?
   A. 2   B. 3   C. 4   D. 6

8. Which fraction is in simplest form?
   A. $\frac{18}{27}$ B. $\frac{50}{100}$ C. $\frac{32}{34}$ D. $\frac{21}{25}$

9. Which ratio is in simplest form?
   A. 10 to 18   B. 27 to 36   C. 15 to 19   D. 18 to 20

10. Which fraction is *not* in simplest form?
    A. $\frac{5}{18}$ B. $\frac{25}{50}$ C. $\frac{3}{100}$ D. $\frac{11}{12}$

11. Express $3\frac{2}{5}$ as an improper fraction.
    A. $\frac{17}{5}$ B. $\frac{11}{5}$ C. $\frac{10}{5}$ D. $\frac{30}{5}$

12. Express $\frac{35}{4}$ as a mixed number.
    A. $8\frac{3}{4}$ B. $8\frac{2}{4}$ C. $\frac{3}{4}$ D. $8\frac{3}{35}$

13. Find the length of the segment to the nearest fourth inch.

    A. 2 in.   B. $2\frac{2}{4}$ in.   C. $1\frac{3}{4}$ in.   D. $2\frac{1}{4}$ in.

1. _____
2. _____
3. _____
4. _____
5. _____
6. _____
7. _____
8. _____
9. _____
10. _____
11. _____
12. _____
13. _____

Mathematics: Applications and Connections, Course 1

14. Complete: 18 in. = __?__ ft.
    A. $\frac{1}{2}$ **B.** 1   **C.** $1\frac{1}{2}$ **D.** 2

14. _____

15. Find the LCM for 18 and 24.
    A. 36   **B.** 48   **C.** 54   **D.** 72

15. _____

16. Which number is a multiple of 18?
    A. 9   **B.** 36   **C.** 52   **D.** 6

16. _____

17. What is the LCD for $\frac{5}{6}$ and $\frac{3}{4}$?
    A. 2   **B.** 4   **C.** 12   **D.** 24

17. _____

18. Which sentence is true?
    A. $\frac{21}{25} = \frac{4}{5}$ **B.** $\frac{21}{25} < \frac{4}{5}$ **C.** $\frac{21}{25} > \frac{4}{5}$ **D.** $\frac{4}{5} > \frac{21}{25}$

18. _____

19. Which fraction is the greatest?
    A. $\frac{3}{4}$ **B.** $\frac{7}{8}$ **C.** $\frac{13}{16}$ **D.** $\frac{25}{32}$

19. _____

20. Express 0.48 as a fraction in simplest form.
    A. $\frac{48}{100}$ **B.** $\frac{24}{50}$ **C.** $\frac{12}{25}$ **D.** $\frac{12}{50}$

20. _____

21. Express 3.64 as a fraction in simplest form.
    A. $3\frac{16}{25}$ **B.** $3\frac{32}{50}$ **C.** $3\frac{64}{100}$ **D.** $\frac{16}{25}$

21. _____

22. Express $6\frac{11}{20}$ as a decimal.
    A. 6.5   **B.** 6.55   **C.** 0.55   **D.** 6.11

22. _____

23. Express $\frac{5}{18}$ as a decimal. Use bar notation to show a repeating decimal.
    A. $0.2\overline{7}$ **B.** $0.\overline{27}$ **C.** 0.027   **D.** 27.7

23. _____

24. At an ice cream store, three flavors of ice cream are available: chocolate,
    vanilla, and strawberry. Three types of toppings are available: marshmallow,
    pineapple, and hot fudge. If you choose one ice cream and one topping,
    how many combinations are possible?
    A. 3   **B.** 9   **C.** 6   **D.** 5

24. _____

25. Raleigh has two lengths of cord for making bead bracelets. One is 18 inches
    long, and the other is 45 inches long. He wants to cut both cords into pieces,
    all having the same length. What is the longest length each cord can be?
    A. 3 in.   **B.** 6 in.   **C.** 5 in.   **D.** 9 in.

25. _____

Chapter 5 Test, Form 1C

1. 200 is divisible by which of these numbers?
   A. 2, 5, and 10
   B. 2, 3, 5, 6, and 10
   C. 5, 6, and 10
   D. 9 and 10

   1. _____

2. 135 is divisible by which of these numbers?
   A. 5 and 10
   B. 5, 9, and 10
   C. 2, 3, and 5
   D. 3, 5, and 9

   2. _____

3. Which numbers are factors of 36?
   A. 2, 3, 5, and 6
   B. 2, 4, 9, 12, and 18
   C. 6 and 10
   D. 5 and 9

   3. _____

4. Find the prime factorization of 40.
   A. $2 \times 2 \times 10$
   B. 8×5
   C. $2 \times 2 \times 2 \times 5$
   D. 2×20

   4. _____

5. Which number is prime?
   A. 16
   B. 17
   C. 18
   D. 20

   5. _____

6. What is the GCF of 8 and 20?
   A. 4
   B. 2
   C. 5
   D. 10

   6. _____

7. What is the GCF of 6, 15, and 18?
   A. 2
   B. 3
   C. 6
   D. 9

   7. _____

8. Which fraction is in simplest form?
   A. $\frac{7}{18}$
   B. $\frac{12}{16}$
   C. $\frac{8}{10}$
   D. $\frac{10}{15}$

   8. _____

9. Which ratio is in simplest form?
   A. 15 to 20
   B. 14 to 16
   C. 3 to 10
   D. 25 to 100

   9. _____

10. Which fraction is *not* in simplest form?
    A. $\frac{18}{36}$
    B. $\frac{19}{20}$
    C. $\frac{4}{13}$
    D. $\frac{9}{10}$

    10. _____

11. Express $5\frac{1}{6}$ as an improper fraction.
    A. $\frac{11}{6}$
    B. $\frac{31}{6}$
    C. $\frac{30}{6}$
    D. $\frac{6}{31}$

    11. _____

12. Express $\frac{29}{3}$ as a mixed number.
    A. 9
    B. $9\frac{2}{3}$
    C. $\frac{2}{3}$
    D. $9\frac{2}{29}$

    12. _____

13. Find the length of the segment to the nearest fourth inch.

    13. _____

    A. 1 in.   **B.** $1\frac{2}{4}$ in.   **C.** $1\frac{3}{4}$ in.   **D.** 2 in.

14. Complete: 2 ft = __?__ in.

    14. _____

    A. 24   **B.** $\frac{2}{3}$ **C.** 72   **D.** 12

15. Find the LCM for 6 and 10.

    15. _____

    A. 2   **B.** 60   **C.** 30   **D.** 8

16. Which number is a multiple of 25?

    16. _____

    A. 5   **B.** 10   **C.** 40   **D.** 75

17. What is the LCD for $\frac{2}{3}$ and $\frac{5}{9}$?

    17. _____

    A. 3   **B.** 6   **C.** 9   **D.** 18

18. Which sentence is true?

    18. _____

    A. $\frac{3}{21} = \frac{1}{7}$ **B.** $\frac{3}{21} < \frac{1}{7}$ **C.** $\frac{3}{21} > \frac{1}{7}$ **D.** $\frac{1}{7} < \frac{3}{21}$

19. Which fraction is the greatest?

    19. _____

    A. $\frac{1}{2}$ **B.** $\frac{2}{5}$ **C.** $\frac{7}{10}$ **D.** $\frac{7}{20}$

20. Express 0.08 as a fraction in simplest form.

    20. _____

    A. $\frac{8}{100}$ **B.** $\frac{4}{50}$ **C.** $\frac{8}{10}$ **D.** $\frac{2}{25}$

21. Express 1.25 as a fraction in simplest form.

    21. _____

    A. $1\frac{25}{100}$ **B.** $1\frac{1}{4}$ **C.** $\frac{1}{4}$ **D.** $1\frac{5}{20}$

22. Express $\frac{9}{16}$ as a decimal.

    22. _____

    A. 0.5625   **B.** 56.25   **C.** 4.57   **D.** 0.05625

23. Express $\frac{5}{6}$ as a decimal. Use bar notation to show a repeating decimal.

    23. _____

    A. 0.83   **B.** $0.\overline{83}$ **C.** 0.083   **D.** $0.8\overline{3}$

24. How many two-digit numbers can you make using the digits 3, 5, and 7 if the same digit can be repeated?

    24. _____

    A. 9   **B.** 8   **C.** 6   **D.** 5

25. Tawanda has two wooden dowels that she is using for a craft project. One is 40 inches long, and the other is 50 inches long. She plans to cut the dowels into pieces, all having the same length. What is the longest length possible for the pieces?

    25. _____

    A. 2 in.   **B.** 5 in.   **C.** 10 in.   **D.** 20 in.

Chapter 5 Test, Form 2A

State whether each number is divisible by 2, 3, 5, 6, 9, or 10 for Questions 1–3.

1. 810

2. 2,835

3. 402

4. How many 4-digit numbers can you make using the digits 4, 5, 8, and 9 if digits can be repeated?

Find the prime factorization of each number for Questions 5–7.

5. 124

6. 336

7. 175

8. List all of the factors of 90.

Find the GCF of each pair of numbers.

9. 18, 84

10. 24, 42

State whether each fraction or ratio is in simplest form. If not, write each fraction or ratio in simplest form.

11. $\frac{84}{128}$

12. 14:63

13. $\frac{18}{27}$

14. 27:45

Express each fraction as a mixed number.

15. $\frac{213}{12}$

16. $\frac{789}{9}$

1. _____

2. _____

3. _____

4. _____

5. _____

6. _____

7. _____

8. _____

_____

_____

9. _____

10. _____

11. _____

12. _____

13. _____

14. _____

15. _____

16. _____

Mathematics: Applications and Connections, Course 1

Express each mixed number as an improper fraction for Questions 17–18.

17. $403\frac{2}{9}$

18. $28\frac{2}{3}$

17. _____

19. Find the length of the segment to the nearest eighth inch.

18. _____

19. _____

20. Complete: 325 feet = ___?___ yards.

20. _____

Find the LCM for each set of numbers.

21. 8, 18

21. _____

22. 6, 14, 48

22. _____

23. 30, 50

23. _____

Replace each ● with < , > , or = to make a true sentence.

24. $\frac{5}{7}$ ● $\frac{7}{12}$

24. _____

25. $\frac{4}{19}$ ● $\frac{16}{76}$

25. _____

26. $\frac{9}{25}$ ● $\frac{19}{50}$

26. _____

Express each decimal as a fraction in simplest form.

27. 0.876

27. _____

28. 23.48

28. _____

29. 0.36

29. _____

Express each fraction as a decimal for Questions 30–32. Use bar notation to show a repeating decimal.

30. $\frac{43}{80}$

30. _____

31. $\frac{7}{11}$

31. _____

32. $\frac{1}{9}$

32. _____

33. Jacob has to read two books for English. One book is 132 pages, and the other is 176 pages. He wants to read the same number of pages in both books each night until the books are finished. How many pages per night should he read?

33. _____

Mathematics: Applications and Connections, Course 1

Chapter 5 Test, Form 2B

State whether each number is divisible by 2, 3, 5, 6, 9, or 10 for Questions 1–3.

1. 225

2. 351

3. 135

4. How many 3-digit numbers can you make using the digits 3, 6, and 9 if digits can be repeated?

1. _____

2. _____

3. _____

4. _____

Find the prime factorization of each number for Questions 5–7.

5. 70

6. 192

7. 54

8. List all of the factors of 60.

5. _____

6. _____

7. _____

8. _____

Find the GCF of each pair of numbers.

9. 32, 36

10. 33, 55

9. _____

10. _____

State whether each fraction or ratio is in simplest form. If not, write each fraction or ratio in simplest form.

11. $\frac{45}{80}$

12. 5 to 32

13. 15:35

14. $\frac{9}{12}$

11. _____

12. _____

13. _____

14. _____

Express each fraction as a mixed number.

15. $\frac{32}{7}$

16. $\frac{50}{9}$

15. _____

16. _____

Mathematics: Applications and Connections, Course 1

Chapter 5 Test, Form 2B (continued)

Express each mixed number as an improper fraction for Questions 17–18.

17. $5\frac{7}{12}$

17. _____

18. $10\frac{3}{20}$

18. _____

19. Find the length of the segment to the nearest eighth inch.

19. _____

20. Complete: 76 inches = __?__ feet.

20. _____

Find the LCM for each pair of numbers.

21. 18, 10

21. _____

22. 21, 35

22. _____

23. 25, 30

23. _____

Replace each ● with , <, >, or = to make a true sentence.

24. $\frac{4}{7}$ ● $\frac{3}{8}$

24. _____

25. $\frac{20}{30}$ ● $\frac{4}{6}$

25. _____

26. $\frac{73}{100}$ ● $\frac{23}{50}$

26. _____

Express each decimal as a fraction in simplest form.

27. 0.82   28. 2.4   29. 0.45

27. _____

28. _____

Express each fraction as a decimal for Questions 30–32. Use bar notation to show a repeating decimal.

29. _____

30. $\frac{39}{50}$

30. _____

31. $\frac{7}{9}$

31. _____

32. $\frac{2}{9}$

32. _____

33. One ribbon is 80 inches long, and another ribbon is 32 inches long. The ribbons are to be cut into pieces of equal length. What is the longest length possible for the pieces if there is to be no leftover ribbon?

33. _____

Chapter 5 Test, Form 2C

State whether each number is divisible by 2, 3, 5, 6, 9, or 10 for Questions 1–3.

1. 110

1. _____

2. 204

2. _____

3. 108

3. _____

4. How many 3-digit numbers can you make using the digits 6, 7, and 8 if digits can be repeated?

4. _____

Find the prime factorization of each number for Questions 5–7.

5. 80

5. _____

6. 105

6. _____

7. 30

7. _____

8. List all of the factors of 44.

8. _____

Find the GCF of each pair of numbers.

9. 40, 60

9. _____

10. 35, 56

10. _____

State whether each fraction or ratio is in simplest form. If not, write each fraction or ratio in simplest form.

11. $\frac{62}{100}$

11. _____

12. 18 to 25

12. _____

13. 3:16

13. _____

14. $\frac{40}{50}$

14. _____

Express each fraction as a mixed number.

15. $\frac{41}{5}$

15. _____

16. $\frac{27}{8}$

16. _____

Mathematics: Applications and Connections, Course 1

Express each mixed number as an improper fraction for Questions 17–18.

17. $3\frac{7}{8}$ 18. $10\frac{2}{3}$

19. Find the length of the segment to the nearest eighth inch.

20. Complete: 36 inches = __?__ yard(s).

Find the LCM for each pair of numbers.

21. 15, 25

22. 16, 20

23. 6, 15

Replace each ● with <, >, or = to make a true sentence.

24. $\frac{25}{50}$ ● $\frac{5}{10}$

25. $\frac{5}{12}$ ● $\frac{3}{8}$

26. $\frac{3}{10}$ ● $\frac{9}{25}$

Express each decimal as a fraction in simplest form.

27. 0.16

28. 1.35

29. 0.9

Express each fraction as a decimal for Questions 30–32. Use bar notation to show a repeating decimal.

30. $\frac{21}{25}$

31. $\frac{1}{18}$

32. $\frac{23}{50}$

33. One board is 48 inches long and another board is 36 inches long. Both boards are to be cut into pieces having the same length. What is the longest length possible for the pieces if both entire boards are used?

17. _____

18. _____

19. _____

20. _____

21. _____

22. _____

23. _____

24. _____

25. _____

26. _____

27. _____

28. _____

29. _____

30. _____

31. _____

32. _____

33. _____

Chapter 5 Performance Assessment

Instructions: Demonstrate your knowledge by giving a clear, concise solution to each problem. Be sure to include all relevant drawings and justify your answers. You may show your solutions in more than one way or investigate beyond the requirements of the problems.

1. Mr. Berkowitz is planning the half-time show for the first football game of the season. He expects 120 band members this year and needs to determine possible marching formations.

   a. Tell how to find the prime factorization of a number.

   b. Find the prime factorization of 120. Show your work.

   c. Give all possible rectangular formations the band can make.

   d. At one point in the show, the woodwind and brass sections of the band will march toward each other from the end zones in rows across the field of equal length. If there are 30 woodwinds and 50 in the brass section, what is the longest row possible? What is this number called?

   e. In the finale, band members in rows of 10 perform with members of the flag corp in rows of 6. What is the LCM of 6 and 10? If he wishes to use the same number of band members as flag corp members, what is the least number of rows of each that he can use?

2. A restaurant owner is planning a menu for the next day.

   a. She has $2\frac{5}{6}$ apple pies left. If each serving is one-sixth of a pie, how many servings does she have left? Write the answer as an improper fraction and as a decimal.

   b. She sells about 50 servings of pecan pie a day. How many pecan pies does she usually sell a day?

   c. If she is sold out of pecan pie, how many pies should she order for the next day?

   d. Write a word problem that uses mixed numbers. Solve and give the meaning of the answer.

3. Dominique is trimming a picture to fit in a frame. The frame measures 0.75 foot by 0.5 foot.

   a. Change the decimals to fractions.

   b. What are the measurements of the frame in inches? Show how you determine this.

Mathematics: Applications and Connections, Course 1

Chapter 5 Mid-Chapter Test

(Lessons 5-1 through 5-5)

Determine whether the first number is divisible by the second number.

1. 2,233; 9

2. 134; 2

1. _____

2. _____

State whether each number is divisible by 2, 3, 5, 6, 9, or 10.

3. 945

4. 324

3. _____

4. _____

Tell whether each number is prime, composite, or neither.

5. 221

6. 0

5. _____

6. _____

Find the prime factorization of each number for Questions 7–8.

7. 162

8. 140

7. _____

9. Fernando's grocery store has powdered, glazed, and iced donuts. These come in holes, mini, and regular sizes. How many different options are available to the customers?

8. _____

9. _____

Find the GCF of each set of numbers.

10. 77, 35

11. 88, 104, 136

10. _____

12. 17, 153, 187

11. _____

12. _____

Replace each ▥ with a number so that the fractions are equivalent.

13. $\frac{7}{9} = \frac{42}{▥}$

14. $\frac{10}{11} = \frac{▥}{66}$

13. _____

14. _____

State whether each fraction or ratio is in simplest form. If not, write each fraction or ratio in simplest form.

15. 39 to 270

16. $\frac{21}{55}$

15. _____

16. _____

17. _____

Express each mixed number as an improper fraction.

17. $15\frac{2}{7}$

18. $6\frac{11}{15}$

18. _____

19. _____

Express each improper fraction as a mixed number.

19. $\frac{155}{20}$

20. $\frac{72}{5}$

20. _____

Mathematics: Applications and Connections, Course 1

Chapter 5 Quiz A

(Lessons 5-1 through 5-3)

State whether each number is divisible by 2, 3, 5, 6, 9, or 10 for Questions 1–2.

1. 72   2. 315

3. Find the prime factorization of 150.

4. Is 51 prime, composite, or neither?

5. Find the prime factorization of 40.

6. A sweatshirt is available in white, black, or red and in three sizes: small, medium, and large. How many different types of sweatshirts are available?

Find the GCF of each set of numbers.

7. 35, 45   8. 52, 72

9. 15, 40   10. 27, 105, 126

1. _____

2. _____

3. _____

4. _____

5. _____

6. _____

7. _____

8. _____

9. _____

10. _____

Chapter 5 Quiz B

(Lessons 5-4 and 5-5)

State whether each fraction or ratio is in simplest form. If not, write each fraction or ratio in simplest form.

1. $\frac{9}{35}$ 2. 54 to 60

3. 23:69   4. 8 out of 128

Express each mixed number as an improper fraction.

5. $6\frac{3}{8}$ 6. $22\frac{1}{4}$

7. $2\frac{7}{9}$ 8. $40\frac{2}{3}$

Express each improper fraction as a mixed number.

9. $\frac{53}{9}$ 10. $\frac{165}{40}$

1. _____

2. _____

3. _____

4. _____

5. _____

6. _____

7. _____

8. _____

9. _____

10. _____

Mathematics: Applications and Connections, Course 1

Chapter 5 Quiz C

1. Measure the following segment to the nearest eighth inch.

2. Complete: 7 miles = _?_ feet.

3. Complete: 66 inches = _?_ feet.

Find the LCM of each set of numbers.

4. 30, 45   **5.** 22, 33   **6.** 15, 25, 45

Replace each ● with <, >, or = to make a true sentence.

7. $\frac{5}{18}$ ● $\frac{1}{3}$ **8.** $\frac{32}{64}$ ● $\frac{5}{10}$

9. $\frac{5}{6}$ ● $\frac{7}{8}$ **10.** $\frac{5}{12}$ ● $\frac{7}{20}$

1. _____
2. _____
3. _____
4. _____
5. _____
6. _____
7. _____
8. _____
9. _____
10. _____

Chapter 5 Quiz D

Express each decimal as a fraction in simplest form.

1. 0.78   **2.** 1.45

3. 12.06   **4.** 0.008

Express each fraction or mixed number as a decimal. Use bar notation to show a repeating decimal.

5. $\frac{4}{9}$

6. $\frac{19}{25}$

7. $\frac{272}{15}$

8. $2\frac{4}{11}$

9. $\frac{5}{6}$

10. $9\frac{3}{8}$

1. _____
2. _____
3. _____
4. _____
5. _____
6. _____
7. _____
8. _____
9. _____
10. _____

Name_____ Date _____

Chapter 5 Standardized Test Practice

1. The volume of a box is found by multiplying its height, length, and width. If the measure of the volume of a box is 175, what could its dimensions be?
   A. $3 \times 5 \times 9$ B. $3 \times 5 \times 7$ C. $5 \times 5 \times 7$ D. $5 \times 5 \times 9$

   1._____

2. Find the GCF of 16, 36, and 40.
   A. 4   B. 2   C. 6   D. 1

   2._____

3. Ethan is training for a race. He ran $\frac{17}{4}$ miles. Express this distance as a mixed number.
   A. $1\frac{7}{4}$ B. $4\frac{1}{4}$ C. $3\frac{5}{4}$ D. $4\frac{1}{17}$

   3._____

4. Taro feeds his kitten 0.625 of a can of food. What fraction is this in simplest form?
   A. $6\frac{2}{5}$ B. $\frac{3}{5}$ C. $62\frac{1}{2}$ D. $\frac{5}{8}$

   4._____

5. Rosario is taking trombone lessons for $22 per week. If he takes 8 weeks of lessons, how much do they cost?
   A. $17.60   B. $30   C. $176   D. $200

   5._____

6. Jacqueline bought 8 yards of ribbon for $4.96. How much was the ribbon per yard?
   A. $0.62   B. $0.40   C. $0.71   D. $0.58

   6._____

7. Mistyville received 24.72 inches of rain in 24 hours. How much did it rain per hour?
   A. 1.03 in.   B. 1.3 in.   C. 0.103 in.   D. 10.3 in.

   7._____

8. The distance horses run in the Kentucky Derby is $1\frac{1}{4}$ miles. Write this distance as a decimal.
   A. 1.025   B. 1.40   C. 1.25   D. 0.0125

   8._____

9. One mile equals 1.609 kilometers. Round this measurement to the nearest tenth.
   A. 1.6 km   B. 1.61 km   C. 1.7 km   D. 2 km

   9._____

10. A photo is 3.5 inches high. The frame is 7.77 inches high. Estimate how much total extra space there will be between the photo and the frame.
    A. 3.5 in.   B. 3 in.   C. 4 in.   D. 5 in.

    10._____

Mathematics: Applications and Connections, Course 1

11. Choose the best interval for a frequency table for the data shown.
51, 87, 42, 53, 28, 12, 17, 72, 43
A. 4   **B.** 10   **C.** 5   **D.** 20

11. _____

12. Bobbie's science project requires her to track her plant's growth. Refer to the graph and predict the plant's height at 12 weeks.
A. 15 in.   **B.** 25 in.
C. 18 in.   **D.** 20 in.

Plant Growth

Ht. (in.)

Week

12. _____

13. Determine the stems for the data shown.
5, 1, 22, 18, 7, 24, 41
A. 0, 1, 2, 3, 4   **B.** 1, 2, 4
C. 1, 2, 3, 4   **D.** 0, 1, 2, 4

13. _____

14. The distance from Berlin to Moscow is 996 miles. The distance from Moscow to Tokyo is 4,650 miles. About how far is it from Berlin to Tokyo if you go through Moscow?
A. 1,000 miles   **B.** 4,700 miles
C. 5,700 miles   **D.** 6,000 miles

14. _____

15. Evaluate $3a + 2b - 4 \div c$ if $a = 4$, $b = 5$, and $c = 2$.
A. 9   **B.** 20   **C.** 33   **D.** 28

15. _____

16. Joanne orders a T-shirt for a total cost of $15. Shipping and handling is $2.50. If t stands for the cost of the T-shirt, the equation $15 = 2.50 + t$ results. Find the cost of the T-shirt.
A. $17.50   **B.** $10.00   **C.** $2.50   **D.** $12.50

16. _____

17. A bank is paying 5% interest. Use prt to find the interest on $500 invested for 3.5 years. Use $p = \$500$, $r = 0.5$, and $t = 3.5$.
A. $87.50   **B.** $875   **C.** $8.75   **D.** $75

17. _____

18. A pygmy shrew weighs 4.53 grams and a mouse weighs 22.40 grams. What is the difference in their weights?
A. 22.9 g   **B.** 17.87 g   **C.** 67.7 g   **D.** 93 g

18. _____

19. Shayla purchased $7\frac{7}{8}$ yards of material. Find the decimal equivalent for the amount of material purchased.
A. 7.75 yd   **B.** 7.85 yd   **C.** 7.78 yd   **D.** 7.875 yd

19. _____

20. Find the mean distance from the Sun in millions of miles if Venus is 67 million miles, Earth is 93 million miles, and Mars is 142 million miles from the Sun.
A. 100.67 million mi   **B.** 116 million mi
C. 96.5 million mi   **D.** 93 million mi

20. _____

Cumulative Review, Chapters 1–5

Perform the indicated operation.

1. $56\overline{)190.4}$

2. 18×3.52

3. $7.284 \div 1.2$

Evaluate.

4. $7 \times 12 + 6 \times 12$

5. n^3 if $n = 13$

Estimate.

6. $\$3.98 + \$5.13$

7. 9.2×28.3

8. Find the best interval for a frequency table for these scores: 91, 88, 83, 83, 90.

9. Find the median of the following scores: 17, 13, 25, 22, 13.

10. A United States one-dollar bill is 15.7 centimeters long and 6.6 centimeters wide. Find the perimeter.

11. Complete: 63 in. = _?_ ft.

12. Change 3.8 kilograms to grams.

13. Express $\frac{31}{5}$ as a mixed number.

Write as a decimal.

14. $\frac{81}{10,000}$

15. $\frac{15}{16}$

Order from least to greatest for Questions 16–17.

16. 0.006, 0.2, 0.03, 0.0008

17. $\frac{3}{8}, \frac{1}{4}, \frac{15}{16}, \frac{1}{2}$

18. Find the GCF of 18 and 30.

19. Express 0.06 as a fraction in simplest form.

20. Find the LCM for 14, 15, and 21.

1. _____

2. _____

3. _____

4. _____

5. _____

6. _____

7. _____

8. _____

9. _____

10. _____

11. _____

12. _____

13. _____

14. _____

15. _____

16. _____

17. _____

18. _____

19. _____

20. _____

Mathematics: Applications and Connections, Course 1

Chapter 5 Answer Key

Form 1A

Page 113	Page 114
1. D	13. D
2. C	14. C
3. B	15. B
4. C	16. D
	17. D
5. A	18. A
6. D	19. D
7. B	20. C
8. A	21. B
9. D	22. A
10. C	23. C
11. B	24. B
12. A	25. D

Form 1B

Page 115	Page 116
1. B	14. C
2. D	15. D
3. D	16. B
4. B	17. C
5. C	18. C
6. B	19. B
7. A	20. C
8. D	21. A
9. C	22. B
10. B	23. A
11. A	24. B
12. A	25. D
13. D	

Mathematics: Applications and Connections, Course 1

Chapter 5 Answer Key

Form 1C

Page 117		Page 118	
1.	A	13.	C
2.	D	14.	A
		15.	C
3.	B	16.	D
4.	C	17.	C
		18.	A
5.	B	19.	C
6.	A	20.	D
7.	B	21.	B
8.	A	22.	A
9.	C	23.	D
10.	A	24.	A
11.	B	25.	C
12.	B		

Mathematics: Applications and Connections, Course 1

Chapter 5 Answer Key

Form 2A

Page 119

1. 2, 3, 5, 6, 9, 10

2. 3, 5, 9

3. 2, 3, 6

4. 256

5. $2^2 \times 31$

6. $2^4 \cdot 3 \cdot 7$

7. $5^2 \cdot 7$

8. 1, 2, 3, 5, 6, 9,
   10, 15, 18,
   30, 45, 90

9. 6

10. 6

11. no, $\frac{21}{32}$

12. no, 2 to 9

13. no, $\frac{2}{3}$

14. no, 3:5

15. $17\frac{3}{4}$

16. $87\frac{2}{3}$

Page 120

17. $\frac{3,629}{9}$

18. $\frac{86}{3}$

19. $\frac{5}{8}$ in.

20. $108\frac{1}{3}$

21. 72

22. 336

23. 150

24. >

25. =

26. <

27. $\frac{219}{250}$

28. $23\frac{12}{25}$

29. $\frac{9}{25}$

30. 0.5375

31. $0.\overline{63}$

32. $0.\overline{1}$

33. 44

Mathematics: Applications
and Connections, Course 1

Chapter 5 Answer Key

Form 2B

Page 121		Page 122	
1.	3, 5, 9	17.	$\frac{67}{12}$
2.	3, 9	18.	$\frac{203}{20}$
3.	3, 5, 9	19.	$1\frac{6}{8}$ in.
4.	27	20.	$6\frac{1}{3}$
5.	$2 \times 5 \times 7$	21.	90
6.	$2^6 \times 3$	22.	105
7.	$2 \cdot 3^3$	23.	150
8.	1, 2, 3, 4, 5, 6, 10, 12, 15, 20, 30, 60	24.	>
9.	4	25.	=
10.	11	26.	>
11.	no, $\frac{9}{16}$	27.	$\frac{41}{50}$
12.	yes	28.	$2\frac{2}{5}$
13.	no, 3:7	29.	$\frac{9}{20}$
14.	no, $\frac{3}{4}$	30.	0.78
15.	$4\frac{4}{7}$	31.	$0.\overline{7}$
16.	$5\frac{5}{9}$	32.	$0.\overline{2}$
		33.	16 in.

Mathematics: Applications and Connections, Course 1

Chapter 5 Answer Key

Form 2C

Page 123		Page 124	
1.	2, 5, 10	17.	$\frac{31}{8}$
2.	2, 3, 6	18.	$\frac{32}{3}$
3.	2, 3, 6, 9	19.	$1\frac{1}{8}$ in.
4.	27	20.	1
		21.	75
		22.	80
5.	$2^4 \cdot 5$	23.	30
6.	$3 \cdot 5 \cdot 7$		
7.	$2 \cdot 3 \cdot 5$	24.	=
8.	1, 2, 4, 11, 22, 44	25.	>
		26.	<
9.	20		
10.	7	27.	$\frac{4}{25}$
		28.	$1\frac{7}{20}$
		29.	$\frac{9}{10}$
11.	no, $\frac{31}{50}$		
12.	yes		
13.	yes	30.	0.84
14.	no, $\frac{4}{5}$	31.	$0.0\overline{5}$
		32.	0.46
15.	$8\frac{1}{5}$	33.	12 in.
16.	$3\frac{3}{8}$		

Mathematics: Applications and Connections, Course 1

Chapter 5 Scoring Guide

Level	Specific Criteria
3 Superior	• Shows thorough understanding of the concepts *prime factorization, greatest common factor, least common multiple, expression of mixed numbers as improper fractions and vice versa,* and *expression of decimals as fractions and vice versa.* • Uses appropriate strategies to solve problems. • Computations are correct. • Written explanations are exemplary. • Word problem concerning mixed numbers is appropriate and makes sense. • Diagram is accurate and appropriate. • Goes beyond requirements of some or all problems.
2 Satisfactory, with Minor Flaws	• Shows understanding of the concepts *prime factorization, greatest common factor, least common multiple, expression of mixed numbers as improper fractions and vice versa,* and *expression of decimals as fractions and vice versa.* • Uses appropriate strategies to solve problems. • Computations are mostly correct. • Written explanations are effective. • Word problem concerning mixed numbers is appropriate and makes sense. • Diagram is accurate and appropriate. • Satisfies all requirements of problems.
1 Nearly Satisfactory, with Serious Flaws	• Shows understanding of most of the concepts *prime factorization, greatest common factor, least common multiple, expression of mixed numbers as improper fractions and vice versa,* and *expression of decimals as fractions and vice versa.* • May not use appropriate strategies to solve problems. • Computations are mostly correct. • Written explanations are satisfactory. • Word problem concerning mixed numbers is mostly appropriate and sensible. • Diagram is mostly accurate and appropriate. • Satisfies most requirements of problems.
0 Unsatisfactory	• Shows little or no understanding of the concepts *prime factorization, greatest common factor, least common multiple, expression of mixed numbers as improper fractions and vice versa,* and *expression of decimals as fractions and vice versa.* • May not use appropriate strategies to solve problems. • Computations are incorrect. • Written explanations are not satisfactory. • Word problem concerning mixed numbers is not appropriate and sensible. • Diagram is not accurate or appropriate. • Does not satisfy requirements of problems.

Chapter 5 Answer Key

Performance Assessment Sample Answers
Page 125

1. a. Use a factor tree to find two factors of a number. Then find factors of these factors and subsequent factors until all factors are prime.

b.

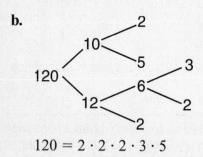

$120 = 2 \cdot 2 \cdot 2 \cdot 3 \cdot 5$

c. 2 by 60, 3 by 40, 4 by 30, 5 by 24, 6 by 20, 8 by 15, 10 by 12

d. 10; It is called the greatest common factor.

e. The LCM is 30. Three rows of band members and five rows of flag corps members.

2. a. 17 servings, $\frac{17}{6}$, $2.8\overline{3}$

b. $8\frac{1}{3}$ pies

c. 9 pies

d. Kareem sold 5 half-pound tins of nuts. How many pounds of nuts did he sell? Kareem sold $\frac{5}{2}$ or $2\frac{1}{2}$ pounds of nuts.

3. a. $0.75 = \frac{75}{100}$ or $\frac{3}{4}$

$0.5 = \frac{5}{10}$ or $\frac{1}{2}$

b. $\frac{3}{4}$ ft $= \frac{3}{4} \times 12$ or 9 in.

$\frac{1}{2}$ ft $= \frac{1}{2} \times 12$ or 6 in.

Mid-Chapter Test
Page 126

1. no
2. yes
3. 3, 5, 9
4. 2, 3, 6, 9
5. composite
6. neither
7. 2×3^4
8. $2^2 \times 5 \times 7$
9. 9
10. 7
11. 8
12. 17
13. 54
14. 60
15. no, 13 to 90
16. yes
17. $\frac{107}{7}$
18. $\frac{101}{15}$
19. $7\frac{3}{4}$
20. $14\frac{2}{5}$

Mathematics: Applications and Connections, Course 1

Chapter 5 Answer Key

Quiz A, Page 127

1. $2, 3, 6, 9$
2. $3, 5, 9$
3. $2 \times 3 \times 5 \times 5$
4. composite
5. $2^3 \times 5$
6. 9
7. 5
8. 4
9. 5
10. 3

Quiz B, Page 127

1. yes
2. no, 9 to 10
3. no, 1:3
4. no, 1 out of 16
5. $\frac{51}{8}$
6. $\frac{89}{4}$
7. $\frac{25}{9}$
8. $\frac{122}{3}$
9. $5\frac{8}{9}$
10. $4\frac{1}{8}$

Quiz C, Page 128

1. $2\frac{5}{8}$ in.
2. $36{,}960$
3. $5\frac{1}{2}$
4. 90
5. 66
6. 225
7. $<$
8. $=$
9. $<$
10. $>$

Quiz D, Page 128

1. $\frac{39}{50}$
2. $1\frac{9}{20}$
3. $12\frac{3}{50}$
4. $\frac{1}{125}$
5. $0.\overline{4}$
6. 0.76
7. $18.1\overline{3}$
8. $2.\overline{36}$
9. $0.8\overline{3}$
10. 9.375

Mathematics: Applications and Connections, Course 1

Chapter 5 Answer Key

Standardized Test Practice		Cumulative Review
Page 129	Page 130	Page 131

Page 129

1. C
2. A
3. B
4. D
5. C
6. A
7. A
8. C
9. A
10. C

Page 130

11. B
12. D
13. A
14. C
15. B
16. D
17. A
18. B
19. D
20. A

Page 131

1. 3.4
2. 63.36
3. 6.07
4. 156
5. 2,197
6. $4 + $5 = $9
7. 9 × 30 = 270
8. 2
9. 17
10. 44.6 cm
11. $5\frac{1}{4}$ ft
12. 3,800 g
13. $6\frac{1}{5}$
14. 0.0081
15. 0.9375
16. 0.0008, 0.006, 0.03, 0.2
17. $\frac{1}{4}, \frac{3}{8}, \frac{1}{2}, \frac{15}{16}$
18. 6
19. $\frac{3}{50}$
20. 210

Mathematics: Applications and Connections, Course 1

Chapter 6 Test, Form 1A

1. Round $\frac{29}{32}$ to the nearest half.   1. _____
   A. 0   B. $\frac{1}{2}$ C. 1   D. none of these

2. Round $9\frac{3}{8}$ to the nearest half.   2. _____
   A. 9   B. $9\frac{1}{2}$ C. 10   D. none of these

3. Estimate $15\frac{6}{11} + 7\frac{3}{4}$.   3. _____
   A. 22   B. $22\frac{1}{2}$ C. 23   D. $23\frac{1}{2}$

4. Estimate $\frac{9}{10} - \frac{62}{71}$.   4. _____
   A. 0   B. $\frac{1}{2}$ C. 1   D. $\frac{1}{4}$

5. Rose's tallest books are $12\frac{3}{4}$ inches tall. When she adjusts the shelf   5. _____
   height for them, what is her best choice?
   A. 12 in.   B. $12\frac{1}{2}$ in.   C. 13 in.   D. none of these

6. Add: $\frac{17}{50} + \frac{23}{50}$.   6. _____
   A. $\frac{3}{25}$ B. $\frac{4}{5}$ C. $\frac{41}{50}$ D. 10

7. Subtract: $\frac{73}{82} - \frac{51}{82}$.   7. _____
   A. $\frac{11}{41}$ B. $1\frac{21}{41}$ C. 22   D. $\frac{23}{82}$

8. A tablecloth is $\frac{35}{36}$ yard long. The border is $\frac{7}{36}$ yard and is cut off. How   8. _____
   much material remains?
   A. $1\frac{1}{6}$ yard   B. 1 yard   C. $\frac{29}{36}$ yard   D. $\frac{7}{9}$ yard

9. Solve $\frac{47}{62} - \frac{33}{62} = b$.   9. _____
   A. $\frac{7}{62}$ B. $\frac{20}{31}$ C. $\frac{7}{31}$ D. $1\frac{9}{31}$

10. Add: $\frac{5}{16} + \frac{7}{12}$.   10. _____
    A. $\frac{43}{48}$ B. $\frac{3}{7}$ C. $\frac{1}{2}$ D. none of these

11. Subtract: $\frac{2}{3} - \frac{5}{9}$.   11. _____
    A. $\frac{1}{2}$ B. $\frac{1}{9}$ C. $\frac{7}{12}$ D. $\frac{7}{6}$

12. Add: $\frac{1}{2} + \frac{2}{3} + \frac{7}{18}$.   12. _____
    A. $1\frac{1}{2}$ B. $\frac{10}{23}$ C. $\frac{5}{9}$ D. $1\frac{5}{9}$

13. Solve $m = \frac{11}{20} - \frac{3}{8}$.   13. _____
    A. $\frac{1}{2}$ B. $\frac{2}{3}$ C. $\frac{7}{40}$ D. none of these

Mathematics: Applications and Connections, Course 1

14. Subtract: $7\frac{11}{12} - 2\frac{5}{6}$.

    A. $5\frac{1}{12}$ **B.** $5\frac{1}{2}$ **C.** 5   **D.** $9\frac{8}{9}$

14. _____

15. Add: $6\frac{3}{8} + 2\frac{2}{3}$.

    A. $8\frac{1}{24}$ **B.** $9\frac{1}{24}$ **C.** $8\frac{5}{11}$ **D.** $8\frac{25}{48}$

15. _____

16. Evaluate $r - s$ if $r = 9\frac{2}{7}$ and $s = 5\frac{1}{10}$.

    A. $14\frac{3}{17}$ **B.** $4\frac{1}{3}$ **C.** $4\frac{13}{70}$ **D.** $14\frac{27}{70}$

16. _____

17. Evaluate $c + d$ if $c = 11\frac{13}{24}$ and $d = 12\frac{1}{8}$.

    A. $1\frac{3}{4}$ **B.** $23\frac{2}{3}$ **C.** $23\frac{7}{16}$ **D.** none of these

17. _____

18. Subtract: $18 - 5\frac{4}{15}$.

    A. $13\frac{4}{15}$ **B.** $12\frac{4}{15}$ **C.** $13\frac{11}{15}$ **D.** $12\frac{11}{15}$

18. _____

19. Subtract: $15\frac{1}{12} - 7\frac{7}{8}$.

    A. $7\frac{1}{2}$ **B.** $8\frac{5}{24}$ **C.** $7\frac{5}{24}$ **D.** $8\frac{1}{2}$

19. _____

20. A shelf is $30\frac{1}{4}$ inches long. The space for the shelf is $29\frac{1}{3}$ inches long. How much longer is the shelf than the space?

    A. 1 in.   **B.** $\frac{1}{2}$ in.   **C.** $\frac{11}{12}$ in.   **D.** $1\frac{11}{12}$ in.

20. _____

21. Subtract: $9 - 3\frac{6}{13}$.

    A. $6\frac{6}{13}$ **B.** $5\frac{7}{13}$ **C.** $6\frac{7}{13}$ **D.** $5\frac{6}{13}$

21. _____

22. Add: 5 min 49 s + 9 min 51 s.

    A. 14 min 40 s   **B.** 15 min

    C. 15 min 40 s   **D.** 14 min

22. _____

23. Subtract: 12 h − 8 h 15 min 29 s.

    A. 4 h 15 min 29 s   **B.** 4 h 45 min 31 s

    C. 3 h 44 min 31 s   **D.** 3 h 45 min 31 s

23. _____

24. Tanika went shopping from 4:25 P.M. to 8:55 P.M. How long was Tanika shopping?

    A. 4 h 30 min   **B.** 4 h   **C.** 5 h 30 min   **D.** 4 h 25 min

24. _____

25. At the cross country meet, Tony's time was 1 hour 37 minutes and 41 seconds. Scott's time was 1 hour 36 minutes and 57 seconds. What was the difference in their times?

    A. 44 s   **B.** 1 min 16 s   **C.** 16 s   **D.** none of these

25. _____

Chapter 6 Test, Form 1B

1. Round $\frac{15}{18}$ to the nearest half.
   A. 0   B. $\frac{1}{2}$ C. 1   D. none of these

   1. _____

2. Round $2\frac{1}{8}$ to the nearest half.
   A. 2   B. $2\frac{1}{2}$ C. 3   D. none of these

   2. _____

3. Estimate $4\frac{7}{8} + 6\frac{3}{4}$.
   A. 10   B. 11   C. 12   D. 13

   3. _____

4. Estimate $\frac{3}{32} - \frac{1}{16}$.
   A. 0   B. $\frac{1}{2}$ C. 1   D. $\frac{1}{4}$

   4. _____

5. Roberto is buying blinds for a window that is $28\frac{3}{4}$ inches wide. Which is the best choice if the blinds come in these widths?
   A. 28 in.   B. $28\frac{1}{2}$ in.   C. 29 in.   D. 30 in.

   5. _____

6. Add: $\frac{13}{20} + \frac{3}{20}$.
   A. $\frac{4}{5}$ B. $\frac{2}{5}$ C. $\frac{16}{40}$ D. $\frac{8}{20}$

   6. _____

7. Subtract: $\frac{14}{15} - \frac{2}{15}$.
   A. $\frac{12}{30}$ B. $\frac{4}{5}$ C. $\frac{6}{15}$ D. $\frac{2}{5}$

   7. _____

8. A sheet of wood is $\frac{5}{32}$ inch thick. A planing machine will remove a $\frac{1}{32}$-inch layer of wood. How thick will the sheet be after the planing?
   A. $\frac{6}{32}$ inch   B. $\frac{1}{8}$ inch   C. $\frac{3}{16}$ inch   D. $\frac{1}{4}$ inch

   8. _____

9. Solve $m = \frac{9}{25} - \frac{3}{25}$.
   A. $\frac{6}{25}$ B. $\frac{12}{25}$ C. $\frac{12}{50}$ D. $\frac{6}{50}$

   9. _____

10. Add: $\frac{7}{20} + \frac{3}{10}$.
    A. $\frac{10}{30}$ B. $\frac{10}{15}$ C. $\frac{1}{3}$ D. none of these

    10. _____

11. Subtract: $\frac{2}{15} - \frac{1}{10}$.
    A. $\frac{1}{30}$ B. $\frac{3}{25}$ C. $\frac{7}{60}$ D. $\frac{3}{30}$

    11. _____

12. Add: $\frac{4}{15} + \frac{1}{3} + \frac{1}{5}$.
    A. $\frac{6}{23}$ B. $\frac{2}{5}$ C. $\frac{4}{225}$ D. $\frac{4}{5}$

    12. _____

13. Solve $c = \frac{1}{2} - \frac{1}{7}$.
    A. $\frac{1}{7}$ B. $\frac{3}{7}$ C. $\frac{1}{3}$ D. none of these

    13. _____

14. Subtract: $5\frac{12}{25} - 2\frac{2}{25}$.

  A. $3\frac{2}{5}$ **B.** $2\frac{2}{5}$ **C.** $3\frac{10}{50}$ **D.** $3\frac{1}{5}$

14. _____

15. Add: $9\frac{3}{8} + 2\frac{5}{6}$.

  A. $11\frac{5}{24}$ **B.** $12\frac{5}{24}$ **C.** $11\frac{29}{48}$ **D.** $11\frac{4}{7}$

15. _____

16. Evaluate $x - y$ if $x = 9\frac{5}{8}$ and $y = 4\frac{3}{16}$.

  A. $5\frac{7}{16}$ **B.** $4\frac{7}{16}$ **C.** $13\frac{13}{16}$ **D.** $13\frac{1}{4}$

16. _____

17. Evaluate $a + b$ if $a = 7\frac{1}{3}$ and $b = 8\frac{1}{2}$.

  A. $15\frac{1}{3}$ **B.** $15\frac{5}{6}$ **C.** $1\frac{1}{6}$ **D.** none of these

17. _____

18. Subtract: $9\frac{1}{12} - 2\frac{3}{4}$.

  A. $7\frac{2}{3}$ **B.** $6\frac{1}{3}$ **C.** $7\frac{3}{48}$ **D.** $7\frac{1}{4}$

18. _____

19. Subtract: $20 - 6\frac{9}{10}$.

  A. $13\frac{9}{10}$ **B.** $14\frac{9}{10}$ **C.** $14\frac{1}{10}$ **D.** $13\frac{1}{10}$

19. _____

20. A metal pipe is $26\frac{3}{16}$ inches long. A plumber needs a $25\frac{1}{2}$-inch-long pipe. How much of the pipe does the plumber need to cut off?

  A. $\frac{11}{16}$ in. **B.** $1\frac{11}{16}$ in. **C.** $51\frac{11}{16}$ in. **D.** $1\frac{1}{7}$ in.

20. _____

21. Subtract: $5 - 1\frac{1}{3}$.

  A. $4\frac{2}{3}$ **B.** $4\frac{1}{3}$ **C.** $3\frac{2}{3}$ **D.** none of these

21. _____

22. Add: 16 min 43 s
         + 9 min 17 s

  A. 25 min **B.** 26 min
  C. 26 min 10 s **D.** 25 min 50 sec

22. _____

23. Subtract: 6 h
          − 2 h 28 min 41 s

  A. 4 h 28 min 41 s **B.** 3 h 28 min 41 s
  C. 3 h 31 min 19 s **D.** 3 h 32 min 19 s

23. _____

24. Jack baby-sat for his sister from 6:45 P.M. to 11:30 P.M. How long did he baby-sit?

  A. 5 h 15 min **B.** 4 h 15 min **C.** 4 h 45 min **D.** 5 h 45 min

24. _____

25. The science class set off two rockets. Rocket A was in the air 2 minutes 56 seconds. Rocket B was in the air 3 minutes 4 seconds. What was the difference in the air times of the rockets?

  A. 1 min 52 s **B.** 52 s **C.** 8 s **D.** 1 min 8 s

25. _____

Mathematics: Applications and Connections, Course 1

Chapter 6 Test, Form 1C

1. Round $\frac{1}{12}$ to the nearest half.
   A. 0   B. $\frac{1}{2}$ C. 1   D. none of these

   1. _____

2. Round $4\frac{9}{10}$ to the nearest half.
   A. 4   B. $4\frac{1}{2}$ C. 5   D. none of these

   2. _____

3. Estimate $3\frac{1}{5} + 4\frac{9}{10}$.
   A. 7   B. 8   C. 9   D. 10

   3. _____

4. Estimate $\frac{15}{16} - \frac{1}{8}$.
   A. 0   B. $\frac{1}{2}$ C. 1   D. $\frac{1}{4}$

   4. _____

5. Janelle is buying a board to make a shelf that is $28\frac{3}{4}$ inches long. Which length of board would be the best choice?
   A. 28 in.   B. $28\frac{1}{2}$ in.   C. 29 in.   D. 25 in.

   5. _____

6. Add: $\frac{9}{15} + \frac{1}{15}$.
   A. $\frac{10}{30}$ B. $\frac{1}{3}$ C. $\frac{2}{3}$ D. $\frac{9}{15}$

   6. _____

7. Subtract: $\frac{9}{10} - \frac{1}{10}$.
   A. $\frac{8}{20}$ B. 0   C. $\frac{9}{100}$ D. $\frac{4}{5}$

   7. _____

8. A recipe calls for $\frac{3}{8}$ cup of milk and $\frac{3}{8}$ cup of syrup. What is the total amount of milk and syrup in the recipe?
   A. $\frac{3}{8}$ cup   B. $\frac{3}{4}$ cup   C. $\frac{9}{16}$ cup   D. $\frac{9}{64}$ cup

   8. _____

9. Solve $a = \frac{12}{16} - \frac{7}{16}$.
   A. $\frac{5}{16}$ B. $\frac{19}{16}$ C. $\frac{5}{8}$ D. $\frac{5}{32}$

   9. _____

10. Add: $\frac{3}{10} + \frac{1}{5}$.
    A. $\frac{4}{15}$ B. $\frac{1}{2}$ C. $\frac{3}{15}$ D. $\frac{1}{4}$

    10. _____

11. Subtract: $\frac{5}{6} - \frac{1}{4}$.
    A. 2   B. $\frac{7}{24}$ C. $\frac{7}{12}$ D. $\frac{1}{2}$

    11. _____

12. Add: $\frac{1}{2} + \frac{1}{10} + \frac{1}{5}$.
    A. $\frac{3}{17}$ B. $\frac{8}{30}$ C. $\frac{4}{15}$ D. $\frac{4}{5}$

    12. _____

13. Solve $b = \frac{3}{10} - \frac{1}{5}$.
    A. $\frac{1}{10}$ B. $\frac{2}{5}$ C. $\frac{2}{10}$ D. none of these

    13. _____

14. Subtract: $7\frac{9}{16} - 3\frac{1}{16}$.   14. _____
   A. $4\frac{1}{2}$ **B.** $4\frac{1}{4}$ **C.** $4\frac{8}{32}$ **D.** $4\frac{9}{32}$

15. Add: $6\frac{1}{2} + 3\frac{1}{4}$.   15. _____
   A. $3\frac{1}{4}$ **B.** $9\frac{1}{2}$ **C.** $9\frac{3}{4}$ **D.** none of these

16. Evaluate $w - x$ if $w = 7\frac{9}{20}$ and $x = 3\frac{3}{10}$.   16. _____
   A. $10\frac{12}{30}$ **B.** $4\frac{6}{10}$ **C.** $4\frac{3}{40}$ **D.** $4\frac{3}{20}$

17. Evaluate $b + c$ if $b = 1\frac{1}{2}$ and $c = 2\frac{1}{4}$.   17. _____
   A. $3\frac{2}{3}$ **B.** $1\frac{1}{4}$ **C.** $3\frac{3}{4}$ **D.** none of these

18. Subtract: $7\frac{3}{10} - 2\frac{4}{5}$.   18. _____
   A. $5\frac{1}{5}$ **B.** $4\frac{1}{2}$ **C.** $5\frac{1}{2}$ **D.** $4\frac{1}{4}$

19. Subtract: $10 - 5\frac{1}{2}$.   19. _____
   A. $4\frac{1}{2}$ **B.** $5\frac{1}{2}$ **C.** 5   **D.** none of these

20. In a science experiment, a plant was $4\frac{7}{8}$ inches tall at the beginning of the   20. _____
   week. By the end of the week, the plant was $6\frac{1}{4}$ inches tall. How much did
   the plant grow during the week?
   A. $11\frac{8}{12}$ in.   **B.** $1\frac{3}{8}$ in.   **C.** $2\frac{3}{8}$ in.   **D.** $11\frac{1}{8}$ in.

21. Subtract: $3 - 1\frac{1}{3}$.   21. _____
   A. $1\frac{4}{3}$ **B.** $2\frac{1}{3}$ **C.** $2\frac{2}{3}$ **D.** $1\frac{2}{3}$

22. Add: 4 h 22 min 12 s   22. _____
         + 2 h 13 min 41 s
   A. 6 h 9 min 53 s   **B.** 6 h 35 min 53 s
   C. 4 h 35 min 53 s   **D.** 6 h 35 min 41 s

23. Subtract: 6 h 51 min 21 s   23. _____
            − 3 h 46 min 19 s
   A. 2 h 5 min 3 s   **B.** 3 h 9 min 3 s
   C. 3 h 5 min 2 s   **D.** 3 h 5 min 3 s

24. A play starts at 7:30 P.M. and ends at 10:15 P.M. How long does the play last?   24. _____
   A. 3 h 15 min   **B.** 3 h 45 min   **C.** 2 h 15 min   **D.** 2 h 45 min

25. The movie started at 4:45 P.M. and ended at 7:02 P.M. How long was the movie?   25. _____
   A. 2 h 17 min   **B.** 2 h 15 min   **C.** 1 h 17 min   **D.** 2 h 37 min

Chapter 6 Test, Form 2A

Round each number to the nearest half.

1. $\frac{3}{100}$

1. _____

2. $12\frac{80}{99}$

2. _____

3. $7\frac{1}{19}$

3. _____

4. $15\frac{7}{12}$

4. _____

5. Leonardo is going to hang curtains in a window that is $59\frac{1}{4}$ inches long. When he buys curtains, should he round $59\frac{1}{4}$ up or down to determine the proper curtain length?

5. _____

Estimate.

6. $13\frac{7}{9} - 9\frac{1}{4}$

6. _____

7. $\frac{24}{25} - \frac{4}{9}$

7. _____

8. $7\frac{31}{32} - \frac{5}{12}$

8. _____

9. $9 + 7\frac{1}{4}$

9. _____

Add or subtract. Write the answer in simplest form.

10. $\frac{2}{25} + \frac{3}{25}$

10. _____

11. $\frac{13}{16} - \frac{7}{16}$

11. _____

12. $\frac{5}{8} + \frac{1}{3}$

12. _____

13. $\frac{5}{14} - \frac{4}{21}$

13. _____

14. $8\frac{11}{12} - 3\frac{5}{12}$

14. _____

15. $9\frac{3}{7} + 5\frac{4}{9}$

15. _____

16. $12\frac{7}{8} - 4\frac{5}{9}$

16. _____

17. $15 - 3\frac{4}{9}$

17. _____

18. $7\frac{5}{12} - 3\frac{7}{9}$

18. _____

Mathematics: Applications and Connections, Course 1

Add or subtract. Write the answer in simplest form.

19. $8\frac{7}{12} - \frac{11}{15}$

19. _____

20. $22\frac{11}{18} - 9\frac{5}{27}$

20. _____

21. $\frac{2}{5} + \frac{1}{8} + \frac{3}{20}$

21. _____

22. $7\frac{7}{10} + 4\frac{3}{4}$

22. _____

23. Brenda is ordering a birthday cake for 47 people. Cakes are sold in 45 servings or 50 servings. Which should Brenda order?

23. _____

Solve each equation. Write the solution in simplest form.

24. $m = \frac{9}{16} + \frac{1}{4}$

24. _____

25. $r = \frac{7}{8} - \frac{2}{3}$

25. _____

26. $h = 10\frac{4}{5} + 2\frac{11}{15}$

26. _____

27. $a = 10\frac{2}{3} - 3\frac{3}{4}$

27. _____

28. In a picture frame, the glass and picture are a total of $\frac{1}{2}$ inch thick. If the glass is $\frac{5}{16}$ inch thick, how thick is the picture?

28. _____

29. A movie starts at 11:55 A.M. and ends at 2:25 P.M. How long is the movie?

29. _____

Add or subtract.

30.   5 h 48 min 21 s
    $+$ 2 h 28 min 15 s

30. _____

31.   5 h 23 min 15 s
    $-$ 3 h 49 min 21 s

31. _____

32. Lucas baby-sits after school. He makes $4 per hour. He worked 3 hours 15 minutes on Monday, 3 hours 15 minutes on Tuesday, and 3 hours 30 minutes on Wednesday. How much money did he make?

32. _____

33. Samantha had soccer practice for 2 hours 20 minutes on Friday. Practice ended at 5:00 P.M. When did practice start?

33. _____

Chapter 6 Test, Form 2B

Round each number to the nearest half.

1. $\frac{5}{11}$

1. _____

2. $\frac{19}{20}$

2. _____

3. $3\frac{1}{16}$

3. _____

4. $12\frac{1}{6}$

4. _____

5. Jermaine is buying a lava lamp that he will store in a bookcase with shelves that are $11\frac{3}{4}$ inches apart. When looking for the lamp, should he round up or round down to determine its proper height?

5. _____

Estimate.

6. $7\frac{1}{10} - 4\frac{19}{20}$

6. _____

7. $\frac{24}{25} - \frac{1}{9}$

7. _____

8. $\frac{17}{18} + \frac{9}{10}$

8. _____

9. $3\frac{3}{4} + 2\frac{1}{5}$

9. _____

Add or subtract. Write the answer in simplest form.

10. $\frac{5}{14} + \frac{3}{14}$

10. _____

11. $\frac{7}{10} - \frac{2}{10}$

11. _____

12. $\frac{1}{10} + \frac{2}{3}$

12. _____

13. $\frac{5}{6} - \frac{2}{15}$

13. _____

14. $7\frac{9}{16} - 3\frac{5}{16}$

14. _____

15. $5\frac{4}{5} + \frac{7}{8}$

15. _____

16. $6\frac{3}{16} + 6\frac{3}{16}$

16. _____

17. $12 - 3\frac{1}{15}$

17. _____

18. $18\frac{2}{5} - 14\frac{11}{20}$

18. _____

Add or subtract. Write the answer in simplest form.

19. $5\frac{3}{5} - 2\frac{5}{6}$

19. _____

20. $10\frac{15}{32} - 3\frac{1}{4}$

20. _____

21. $3\frac{1}{2} + 2\frac{3}{10} + 1\frac{1}{5}$

21. _____

22. $5\frac{3}{4} + 2\frac{5}{6}$

22. _____

23. Monica is going to buy a shirt for $15.99. Should she take $15 or $20 with her?

23. _____

Solve each equation. Write the solution in simplest form.

24. $x = \frac{11}{24} + \frac{5}{24}$

24. _____

25. $a = \frac{9}{14} - \frac{5}{14}$

25. _____

26. $m = 9\frac{3}{5} + 6\frac{1}{10}$

26. _____

27. $y = 9\frac{2}{3} - 3\frac{3}{4}$

27. _____

28. A recipe calls for $\frac{1}{2}$ cup of pecans, $\frac{3}{8}$ cup of almonds, and $\frac{1}{4}$ cup of raisins. How many total cups of pecans, almonds, and raisins are in the recipe?

28. _____

29. A train is scheduled to leave at 6:40 A.M. and arrive at 9:10 A.M. that same day. How long is the scheduled trip?

29. _____

Add or subtract.

30.　　4 h 39 min 22 s
　　+ 2 h 50 min 19 s

30. _____

31.　　13 h 25 min
　　− 11 h 50 min

31. _____

32.　　3 h 18 min
　　− 1 h 50 min

32. _____

33. Nicholas and Sarah watched two movies. One lasted 2 hours and 17 minutes, and the other lasted 3 hours and 21 minutes. How long were they watching the movies?

33. _____

Round each number to the nearest half.

1. $\frac{7}{12}$

1. _____

2. $5\frac{10}{11}$

2. _____

3. $\frac{15}{32}$

3. _____

4. $1\frac{1}{10}$

4. _____

5. Carlos is going to hang curtains in a window that is $38\frac{1}{2}$ inches long. When he buys curtains, should he round $38\frac{1}{2}$ up or down to determine the proper curtain length?

5. _____

Estimate.

6. $6\frac{15}{16} - 1\frac{1}{8}$

6. _____

7. $\frac{24}{25} + \frac{7}{8}$

7. _____

8. $\frac{17}{18} + 3\frac{9}{10}$

8. _____

9. $3\frac{1}{3} - 1\frac{1}{5}$

9. _____

Add or subtract. Write the answer in simplest form.

10. $\frac{5}{14} + \frac{2}{14}$

10. _____

11. $\frac{1}{8} + \frac{4}{8}$

11. _____

12. $\frac{1}{2} + \frac{3}{8}$

12. _____

13. $\frac{2}{3} - \frac{1}{2}$

13. _____

14. $4\frac{3}{4} - 2\frac{1}{4}$

14. _____

15. $3\frac{9}{10} + 1\frac{5}{10}$

15. _____

16. $7\frac{1}{10} + 4\frac{3}{10}$

16. _____

17. $6 - 3\frac{1}{3}$

17. _____

18. $4\frac{1}{6} - 2\frac{1}{2}$

18. _____

Mathematics: Applications and Connections, Course 1

Add or subtract. Write the answer in simplest form.

19. $3\frac{1}{6} - 1\frac{3}{4}$

19. _____

20. $6\frac{11}{12} - 2\frac{1}{6}$

20. _____

21. $\frac{3}{8} + \frac{5}{24} + \frac{1}{3}$

21. _____

22. $9\frac{2}{3} + 2\frac{1}{6}$

22. _____

23. Renee needs $\frac{3}{4}$ cup of sour cream for a recipe. Sour cream is sold in $\frac{1}{2}$ cup and 1 cup containers. Which container should Renee choose?

23. _____

Solve each equation. Write the solution in simplest form.

24. $m = \frac{19}{20} - \frac{9}{20}$

24. _____

25. $y = \frac{5}{18} + \frac{7}{18}$

25. _____

26. $a = 5\frac{3}{8} + 3\frac{1}{8}$

26. _____

27. $b = 7\frac{1}{3} - 5\frac{2}{3}$

27. _____

28. A sheet of glass is $\frac{1}{16}$ inch thick. The glass sits on a piece of wood that is $\frac{5}{8}$ inch thick. What is the total thickness of the glass and wood?

28. _____

29. A movie starts at 7:40 P.M. and ends at 9:20 P.M. How long is the movie?

29. _____

Add or subtract.

30.   3 h 45 min
     + 2 h 20 min

30. _____

31.   1 h 5 min 3 s
     + 2 h 22 min 7 s

31. _____

32.   2 h 15 min
     − 1 h 12 min

32. _____

33. Caroline watched TV from 7:30 P.M. until 10:00 P.M. How long did she watch TV?

33. _____

Mathematics: Applications and Connections, Course 1

Chapter 6 Performance Assessment

Instructions: *Demonstrate your knowledge by giving a clear, concise solution to each problem. Be sure to include all relevant drawings and justify your answers. You may show your solutions in more than one way or investigate beyond the requirements of the problems.*

1. Jennifer is making grape jelly. She adds $\frac{1}{2}$ cup of water and $3\frac{3}{4}$ cups of sugar to 4 cups of crushed grapes.

   a. Tell how to estimate the sum or difference of mixed numbers.

   b. Estimate the total amount of ingredients in the jelly.

   c. Tell why you must find a common denominator before adding fractions.

   d. Find the total ingredients of Jennifer's jelly. Show the steps.

   e. Give three meanings of subtraction and an example of each.

   f. If Jennifer plans to make a total of 12 cups of ingredients, how many more cups of ingredients will she need? Show your work.

2. The Indianapolis 500 auto race is called the greatest spectacle in racing. The slowest winning time for the race was 6 hours 42 minutes 8 seconds in the first race in 1911. The fastest winning time was 1 hour 42 minutes 53 seconds in 1976.

   a. What is the difference between the winning times in 1911 and 1976? Explain each step.

   b. Suppose the fastest winning time for the race were 2 hours 41 minutes 18 seconds. What would be the difference between the fastest and slowest times for the race?

   c. Give several reasons such a race may be stopped early.

   d. If the race starts at 11:00 A.M. and the winner crosses the finish line at 2:38 P.M., what is the winning time for the race? Explain your reasoning.

Chapter 6 Mid-Chapter Test

(Lessons 6-1 through 6-4)

Round each number to the nearest half.

1. $8\frac{7}{9}$

2. $7\frac{5}{12}$

3. $\frac{1}{31}$

4. $\frac{9}{11}$

5. If you are estimating that it will take $1\frac{3}{4}$ hours to do your homework, should you leave 2 hours or $1\frac{1}{2}$ hours free?

Estimate.

6. $6\frac{1}{4} + \frac{7}{15}$

7. $1 - \frac{6}{7}$

8. $2\frac{3}{5} + 3\frac{1}{5}$

9. $7\frac{3}{4} - \frac{9}{10}$

10. Rob wants to buy a frame for a picture that is $8\frac{1}{4}$ inches wide. Should he choose the 8-inch frame or the 9-inch frame?

Add or subtract. Write the answer in simplest form.

11. $\frac{9}{16} - \frac{5}{16}$

12. $\frac{2}{11} + \frac{3}{11}$

13. $\frac{7}{13} - \frac{7}{13}$

14. $\frac{9}{10} + \frac{3}{10}$

15. $\frac{5}{6} + \frac{3}{10}$

16. $\frac{4}{25} + \frac{1}{5}$

17. $\frac{4}{15} - \frac{1}{30}$

18. $\frac{9}{16} + \frac{3}{4}$

Solve each equation.

19. $x = \frac{7}{8} + \frac{1}{24}$

20. $a = \frac{11}{16} - \frac{1}{8}$

1. _____

2. _____

3. _____

4. _____

5. _____

6. _____

7. _____

8. _____

9. _____

10. _____

11. _____

12. _____

13. _____

14. _____

15. _____

16. _____

17. _____

18. _____

19. _____

20. _____

Chapter 6 Quiz A

(Lessons 6-1 and 6-2)

Round each number to the nearest half.

1. $2\frac{9}{10}$

2. $3\frac{9}{19}$

3. $\frac{1}{8}$

4. $15\frac{2}{7}$

5. $\frac{14}{27}$

Estimate.

6. $7\frac{1}{12} + 8\frac{17}{20}$

7. $9\frac{15}{16} - 3\frac{8}{9}$

8. $\frac{9}{10} + \frac{15}{16}$

9. $3\frac{6}{11} - \frac{19}{20}$

10. $14\frac{3}{11} + 6\frac{1}{12}$

1. _____
2. _____
3. _____
4. _____
5. _____
6. _____
7. _____
8. _____
9. _____
10. _____

- -

Chapter 6 Quiz B

(Lessons 6-3 and 6-4)

Add or subtract. Write the answer in simplest form.

1. $\frac{6}{25} + \frac{9}{25}$

2. $\frac{7}{32} - \frac{3}{32}$

3. $\frac{75}{83} - \frac{38}{83}$

4. $\frac{8}{9} - \frac{2}{3}$

5. $\frac{11}{15} - \frac{3}{10}$

6. $\frac{11}{32} + \frac{7}{24}$

Solve each equation.

7. $x = \frac{5}{12} + \frac{1}{12}$

8. $m = \frac{6}{7} - \frac{1}{7}$

9. $a = \frac{7}{12} - \frac{1}{9}$

10. $b = \frac{3}{4} + \frac{5}{12}$

1. _____
2. _____
3. _____
4. _____
5. _____
6. _____
7. _____
8. _____
9. _____
10. _____

Mathematics: Applications and Connections, Course 1

Chapter 6 Quiz C

(Lessons 6-5 and 6-6)

Add or subtract. Write the answer in simplest form.

1. $4\frac{3}{16} - 2\frac{1}{8}$ 2. $7\frac{9}{10} + 3\frac{1}{4}$

3. $5\frac{4}{7} - 1\frac{1}{5}$ 4. $2\frac{1}{2} + 7\frac{1}{2}$

5. $6\frac{1}{10} - 4\frac{3}{10}$ 6. $4\frac{1}{2} + 2\frac{1}{4}$

7. $8\frac{1}{8} - 2\frac{1}{4}$ 8. $7\frac{3}{5} - 1\frac{7}{8}$

9. $24\frac{1}{9} - 19\frac{2}{3}$ 10. $25\frac{1}{4} - 15\frac{3}{4}$

1. _____

2. _____

3. _____

4. _____

5. _____

6. _____

7. _____

8. _____

9. _____

10. _____

Chapter 6 Quiz D

(Lesson 6-7)

Add or subtract. Rename if necessary.

1.   12 min 38 s
     + 40 min 50 s

2.   9 h
     − 2 h 24 min 10 s

3. Find the elapsed time from 9:50 A.M. to 11:05 A.M.

4. Geraldo clocked in at work at 4:27 P.M. He clocked out at 10:09 P.M. How long did he work?

5. Kaya jogged a mile in 12 minutes 43 seconds. Courtney jogged a mile in 10 minutes 56 seconds. What was the difference in their times?

1. _____

2. _____

3. _____

4. _____

5. _____

                   Mathematics: Applications and Connections, Course 1

Chapter 6 Standardized Test Practice

1. If you mixed $\frac{3}{8}$ quart of red paint and $\frac{3}{8}$ quart of blue paint to make purple paint, how much paint would you have in all?

   A. $\frac{3}{8}$ quart **B.** $\frac{3}{4}$ quart **C.** $\frac{6}{16}$ quart **D.** none of these

   1._____

2. Luther's family drove across the U.S. on vacation. After driving $21\frac{1}{2}$ days, they called home to say they would arrive in another $1\frac{3}{4}$ days. Estimate the length of their trip.

   A. $23\frac{1}{2}$ days **B.** 22 days **C.** 25 days **D.** none of these

   2._____

3. The Weatherspoons spend $\frac{1}{3}$ of their budget on housing costs and $\frac{2}{5}$ of their budget on food and clothing. How much of their budget is spent on these items?

   A. $\frac{3}{8}$ **B.** $\frac{11}{15}$ **C.** $\frac{1}{2}$ **D.** none of these

   3._____

4. The first *Sputnik* took 96 minutes 12 seconds to go around Earth. If it passed over Paris at 10:28 A.M., what time did it pass over Paris again?

   A. 11:54 and 12 s **B.** 11:04 and 12 s
   C. 12:04 and 12 s **D.** none of these

   4._____

5. Lamont bought pens in packages of 5. Ricardo bought pens in packages of 6. Both boys purchased the same total number of pens. What was the fewest number of pens each boy could have bought?

   A. 30 **B.** 11 **C.** 15 **D.** none of these

   5._____

6. Write the fractions in order from least to greatest: $6\frac{5}{6}, 6\frac{1}{2}, 6\frac{1}{3}, 6\frac{1}{4}, 6\frac{11}{12}$.

   A. $6\frac{1}{4}, 6\frac{1}{3}, 6\frac{1}{2}, 6\frac{5}{6}, 6\frac{11}{12}$ **B.** $6\frac{1}{3}, 6\frac{1}{4}, 6\frac{1}{2}, 6\frac{11}{12}, 6\frac{5}{6}$
   C. $6\frac{11}{12}, 6\frac{5}{6}, 6\frac{1}{4}, 6\frac{1}{3}, 6\frac{1}{2}$ **D.** none of these

   6._____

7. When a number can be divided by a second number with no remainder, then the first number is __?__ the second number.

   A. comparable to **B.** a power of
   C. divisible by **D.** the LCM of

   7._____

8. The Schmidts' yard is 17 meters wide and 46 meters long. How much fencing do they need to go around the yard?

   A. 782 m² **B.** 126 m **C.** 63 m **D.** 126 m²

   8._____

9. Adrianne mailed a package for $4.30. If it cost $0.86 per kilogram, how much did the package weigh?

   A. 7 kg **B.** 4 kg **C.** 6 kg **D.** 5 kg

   9._____

10. What is the perimeter of a box with $\ell = 32.78$ centimeters and $w = 24.81$ centimeters if perimeter is $\ell + \ell + w + w$?

    A. 57.59 cm **B.** 115.18 cm **C.** 115 cm **D.** 114.18 cm

    10._____

11. Michael and his father were planning to measure their backyard in order to build a fence. What units would be most reasonable to use?

    A. kilometers   **B.** meters   **C.** centimeters   **D.** millimeters

    11. _____

12. Eric bought 4 cans of tomato paste. Each can cost $0.43. He gave the cashier $2. How much change did he receive?

    A. $0.28   **B.** $1.72   **C.** $1.57   **D.** $0.38

    12. _____

13. Marissa's bowling team had the following scores: 147, 198, 132, 161, 164, and 164. Choose the best interval to form a scale for a frequency table showing the bowling scores.

    A. 1   **B.** 10   **C.** 100   **D.** 200

    13. _____

14. What is the range of the bowling scores in Question 13?

    A. 132   **B.** 198   **C.** 66   **D.** 164

    14. _____

15. Which of the following is *not* one of the steps in the four-step plan for problem solving?

    A. Explore   **B.** Plan   **C.** Guess   **D.** Solve

    15. _____

16. Evaluate x^3 if $x = 10$.

    A. 1,000   **B.** 30   **C.** 10,000   **D.** 100

    16. _____

17. Abdul must order the batting averages of four baseball players. The averages are 3.9, 3.005, 3.0009, 3.55. Which is the correct order from least to greatest?

    A. 3.005, 3.0009, 3.55, 3.9   **B.** 3.0009, 3.005, 3.55, 3.9

    C. 3.0009, 3.005, 3.9, 3.55   **D.** 3.9, 3.55, 3.005, 3.0009

    17. _____

18. An urn holds 5 liters. How much of the urn would 2,800 milliliters of coffee fill?

    A. almost fills the urn   **B.** fills to overflow

    C. fills more than halfway   **D.** barely covers the bottom

    18. _____

19. What are the prime numbers between 1 and 15?

    A. 2, 3, 5, 7, 11, 15   **B.** 2, 3, 5, 9, 11

    C. 2, 3, 5, 11, 15   **D.** 2, 3, 5, 7, 11, 13

    19. _____

20. Tori had $10\frac{1}{6}$ pounds of clay to use in a sculpture. She used $3\frac{5}{12}$ pounds. How much clay was left?

    A. $6\frac{3}{4}$ lbs   **B.** $7\frac{1}{4}$ lbs   **C.** $5\frac{3}{4}$ lbs   **D.** $7\frac{2}{3}$ lbs

    20. _____

Cumulative Review, Chapters 1–6

Estimate. (Lessons 4-1 and 6-2)

1. 48.9×62.5

2. $3\frac{11}{12} + 5\frac{1}{10}$

Evaluate. (Lessons 1-4 and 1-6)

3. $8 \times 10 + 6 \div 2$

4. x^4 if $x = 8$

Order from least to greatest. (Lessons 3-3 and 5-8)

5. $0.08, 0.003, 0.23, 0.0009$

6. $\frac{9}{10}, \frac{3}{25}, \frac{7}{50}, \frac{13}{20}$

Divide. (Lessons 4-6 and 4-7)

7. $3.8\overline{)1.71}$

8. $0.57\overline{)17.442}$

Write as a decimal. (Lessons 3-1 and 5-10)

9. $\frac{13}{10,000}$

10. $\frac{7}{8}$

11. Find the area of a rectangle with a length of 12.5 meters and a width of 6.5 meters. (Lesson 4-4)

12. Which measure of central tendency best describes the data 5, 79, 81, 83? (Lesson 2-8)

13. Change 6.2 liters to milliliters. (Lesson 4-9)

14. State whether 420 is divisible by 2, 3, 5, 6, 9, or 10. (Lesson 5-1)

15. Find the GCF of 40 and 60. (Lesson 5-3)

16. Express 0.85 as a fraction in simplest form. (Lesson 5-9)

Add or subtract. Write the answer in simplest form. (Lessons 6-3, 6-4, 6-5, and 6-6)

17. $\frac{7}{25} + \frac{8}{25}$

18. $\frac{9}{15} + \frac{1}{30}$

19. $9\frac{9}{10} + 5\frac{3}{4}$

20. $6\frac{3}{16} - 4\frac{5}{12}$

1. _____
2. _____
3. _____
4. _____
5. _____
6. _____
7. _____
8. _____
9. _____
10. _____
11. _____
12. _____
13. _____
14. _____
15. _____
16. _____
17. _____
18. _____
19. _____
20. _____

Chapter 6 Answer Key

Form 1A

Page 141

1. C
2. B
3. D
4. A
5. C
6. B
7. A
8. D
9. C
10. A
11. B
12. D
13. C

Page 142

14. A
15. B
16. C
17. B
18. D
19. C
20. C
21. B
22. C
23. C
24. A
25. A

Form 1B

Page 143

1. C
2. A
3. C
4. A
5. C
6. A
7. B
8. B
9. A
10. D
11. A
12. D
13. D

Page 144

14. A
15. B
16. A
17. B
18. B
19. D
20. A
21. C
22. B
23. C
24. C
25. C

Mathematics: Applications and Connections, Course 1

Chapter 6 Answer Key

Form 1C

Page 145	Page 146
1. **A**	14. **A**
2. **C**	15. **C**
3. **B**	16. **D**
4. **C**	17. **C**
5. **C**	18. **B**
6. **C**	19. **A**
7. **D**	20. **B**
8. **B**	21. **D**
9. **A**	22. **B**
10. **B**	23. **C**
11. **C**	24. **D**
12. **D**	25. **A**
13. **A**	

Mathematics: Applications and Connections, Course 1

Chapter 6 Answer Key

Form 2A

Page 147	Page 148
1. 0	19. $7\frac{17}{20}$
2. 13	20. $13\frac{23}{54}$
3. 7	21. $\frac{27}{40}$
4. $15\frac{1}{2}$	22. $12\frac{9}{20}$
5. up	23. 50 servings
6. $14 - 9 = 5$	24. $\frac{13}{16}$
7. $1 - \frac{1}{2} = \frac{1}{2}$	25. $\frac{5}{24}$
8. $8 - \frac{1}{2} = 7\frac{1}{2}$	26. $13\frac{8}{15}$
9. $9 + 7 = 16$	27. $6\frac{11}{12}$
	28. $\frac{3}{16}$
10. $\frac{1}{5}$	29. 2 h 30 min
11. $\frac{3}{8}$	
12. $\frac{23}{24}$	30. 8 h 16 min 36 s
13. $\frac{1}{6}$	
14. $5\frac{1}{2}$	31. 1 h 33 min 54 s
15. $14\frac{55}{63}$	32. $40
16. $8\frac{23}{72}$	
17. $11\frac{5}{9}$	
18. $3\frac{23}{36}$	33. 2:40 P.M.

Mathematics: Applications and Connections, Course 1

Chapter 6 Answer Key

Form 2B

Page 149

1. $\dfrac{1}{2}$

2. 1

3. 3

4. 12

5. down

6. $7 - 5 = 2$

7. $1 - 0 = 1$

8. $1 + 1 = 2$

9. $4 + 2 = 6$

10. $\dfrac{4}{7}$

11. $\dfrac{1}{2}$

12. $\dfrac{23}{30}$

13. $\dfrac{7}{10}$

14. $4\dfrac{1}{4}$

15. $6\dfrac{27}{40}$

16. $12\dfrac{3}{8}$

17. $8\dfrac{14}{15}$

18. $3\dfrac{17}{20}$

Page 150

19. $2\dfrac{23}{30}$

20. $7\dfrac{7}{32}$

21. 7

22. $8\dfrac{7}{12}$

23. $20

24. $\dfrac{2}{3}$

25. $\dfrac{2}{7}$

26. $15\dfrac{7}{10}$

27. $5\dfrac{11}{12}$

28. $1\dfrac{1}{8}$ cups

29. 2 h 30 min

30. 7 h 29 min 41 s

31. 1 h 35 min

32. 1 h 28 min

33. 5 h 38 min

Mathematics: Applications and Connections, Course 1

Chapter 6 Answer Key

Form 2C

Page 151	Page 152
1. $\frac{1}{2}$	19. $1\frac{5}{12}$
2. 6	20. $4\frac{3}{4}$
3. $\frac{1}{2}$	21. $\frac{11}{12}$
4. 1	22. $11\frac{5}{6}$
5. up	23. 1 cup
6. $7 - 1 = 6$	24. $\frac{1}{2}$
7. $1 + 1 = 2$	25. $\frac{2}{3}$
8. $1 + 4 = 5$	26. $8\frac{1}{2}$
9. $3 - 1 = 2$	27. $1\frac{2}{3}$
	28. $\frac{11}{16}$ in.
10. $\frac{1}{2}$	
11. $\frac{5}{8}$	29. 1 h 40 min
12. $\frac{7}{8}$	
13. $\frac{1}{6}$	30. 6 h 5 min
14. $2\frac{1}{2}$	
15. $5\frac{2}{5}$	31. 3 h 27 min 10 s
16. $11\frac{2}{5}$	32. 1 h 3 min
17. $2\frac{2}{3}$	
18. $1\frac{2}{3}$	33. 2 h 30 min

Mathematics: Applications and Connections, Course 1

Chapter 6 Scoring Guide

Level	Specific Criteria
3 Superior	• Shows thorough understanding of the concepts *estimating and finding sums and differences of fractions and mixed numbers* and *adding and subtracting measures of time*. • Uses appropriate strategies to solve problems. • Computations are correct. • Written explanations are exemplary. • Goes beyond requirements of some or all problems.
2 Satisfactory, with Minor Flaws	• Shows understanding of the concepts *estimating and finding sums and differences of fractions and mixed numbers* and *adding and subtracting measures of time*. • Uses appropriate strategies to solve problems. • Computations are mostly correct. • Written explanations are effective. • Satisfies all requirements of problems.
1 Nearly Satisfactory, with Serious Flaws	• Shows understanding of most of the concepts *estimating and finding sums and differences of fractions and mixed numbers* and *adding and subtracting measures of time*. • May not use appropriate strategies to solve problems. • Computations are mostly correct. • Written explanations are satisfactory. • Satisfies most requirements of problems.
0 Unsatisfactory	• Shows little or no understanding of the concepts *estimating and finding sums and differences of fractions and mixed numbers* and *adding and subtracting measures of time*. • May not use appropriate strategies to solve problems. • Computations are incorrect. • Written explanations are not satisfactory. • Does not satisfy requirements of problems.

Chapter 6 Answer Key

1. a. To estimate the sum or difference of mixed numbers, round each number to the nearest whole number. Then add or subtract.

b. $4 + 1 + 4 = 9$ cups

c. You must have a common name (denominator) to name the sum.

d. $4 + \frac{1}{2} + 3\frac{3}{4} = 4 + \frac{2}{4} + 3\frac{3}{4} = 7\frac{5}{4} = 8\frac{1}{4}$ cups

e. The three meanings of subtraction are:

1. To take away part of a set.

Example: John ate $\frac{1}{4}$ of a pie. How much is left?

2. To find a missing addend.

Example: How much must be added to $2\frac{1}{2}$ to get $3\frac{1}{4}$?

3. To compare the size of two sets.

Example: How much more is $2\frac{1}{2}$ than $1\frac{3}{4}$?

f.
$$\begin{array}{r} 12 \quad \rightarrow \quad 11\frac{4}{4} \\ -8\frac{1}{4} \quad \rightarrow \quad -8\frac{1}{4} \\ \hline 3\frac{3}{4} \end{array}$$

Jennifer will need $3\frac{3}{4}$ cups more ingredients.

2. a.
$$\begin{array}{r} 6\text{ h }42\text{ min }8\text{ s} \\ -1\text{ h }42\text{ min }53\text{ s} \\ \hline 4\text{ h }59\text{ min }15\text{ s} \end{array}$$

Rename 42 min 8 s as 41 min 68 s.
$$\begin{array}{r} 6\text{ h }41\text{ min }68\text{ s} \\ -1\text{ h }42\text{ min }53\text{ s} \\ \hline 15\text{ s} \end{array}$$

Rename 6 h 41 min as 5 h 101 min.
$$\begin{array}{r} 5\text{ h }101\text{ min }68\text{ s} \\ -1\text{ h }\quad42\text{ min }53\text{ s} \\ \hline 4\text{ h }\quad59\text{ min }15\text{ s} \end{array}$$

b.
$$\begin{array}{r} 6\text{ h }42\text{ min }8\text{ s} \\ -2\text{ h }41\text{ min }18\text{s} \\ \hline 4\text{ h }\quad\quad50\text{ s} \end{array}$$

c. The race may be stopped for rain or for a very severe pile-up of cars.

d. One hour to noon and 2 h 38 min more is 3 h 38 min.

1. 9

2. $7\frac{1}{2}$

3. 0

4. 1

5. 2 hours

6. $6 + \frac{1}{2} = 6\frac{1}{2}$

7. $1 - 1 = 0$

8. $2\frac{1}{2} + 3 = 5\frac{1}{2}$

9. $8 - 1 = 7$

10. 9-inch

11. $\frac{1}{4}$

12. $\frac{5}{11}$

13. 0

14. $1\frac{1}{5}$

15. $1\frac{2}{15}$

16. $\frac{9}{25}$

17. $\frac{7}{30}$

18. $1\frac{5}{16}$

19. $\frac{11}{12}$

20. $\frac{9}{16}$

Chapter 6 Answer Key

Quiz A, Page 155

1. 3
2. $3\frac{1}{2}$
3. 0
4. 15
5. $\frac{1}{2}$
6. $7 + 9 = 16$
7. $10 - 4 = 6$
8. $1 + 1 = 2$
9. $3\frac{1}{2} - 1 = 2\frac{1}{2}$
10. $14 + 6 = 20$

Quiz B, Page 155

1. $\frac{3}{5}$
2. $\frac{1}{8}$
3. $\frac{37}{83}$
4. $\frac{2}{9}$
5. $\frac{13}{30}$
6. $\frac{61}{96}$
7. $\frac{1}{2}$
8. $\frac{5}{7}$
9. $\frac{17}{36}$
10. $1\frac{1}{6}$

Quiz C, Page 156

1. $2\frac{1}{16}$
2. $11\frac{3}{20}$
3. $4\frac{13}{35}$
4. 10
5. $1\frac{4}{5}$
6. $6\frac{3}{4}$
7. $5\frac{7}{8}$
8. $5\frac{29}{40}$
9. $4\frac{4}{9}$
10. $9\frac{1}{2}$

Quiz D, Page 156

1. 53 min 28 s
2. 6 h 35 min 50 s
3. 1 h 15 min
4. 5 h 42 min
5. 1 min 47 s

Mathematics: Applications and Connections, Course 1

Chapter 6 Answer Key

Standardized Test Practice		Cumulative Review
Page 157	Page 158	Page 159

Page 157

1. B

2. A

3. B

4. C

5. A

6. A

7. C

8. B

9. D

10. B

Page 158

11. B

12. A

13. B

14. C

15. C

16. A

17. B

18. C

19. D

20. A

Page 159

1. $50 \times 60 = 3{,}000$

2. $4 + 5 = 9$

3. 83

4. 4,096

5. 0.0009, 0.003, 0.08, 0.23

6. $\dfrac{3}{25}, \dfrac{7}{50}, \dfrac{13}{20}, \dfrac{9}{10}$

7. 0.45

8. 30.6

9. 0.0013

10. 0.875

11. 81.25 m^2

12. median

13. 6,200 mL

14. 2, 3, 5, 6, 10

15. 20

16. $\dfrac{17}{20}$

17. $\dfrac{3}{5}$

18. $\dfrac{19}{30}$

19. $15\dfrac{13}{20}$

20. $1\dfrac{37}{48}$

Mathematics: Applications and Connections, Course 1

Name_____ Date _____

Chapter 7 Test, Form 1A

1. Estimate $\frac{1}{6} \times 37$.
   A. 5   B. 6   C. 7   D. 8

   1. _____

2. Estimate $\frac{18}{19} \times \frac{3}{5}$.
   A. 0   B. $\frac{18}{19}$ C. $\frac{3}{5}$ D. 1

   2. _____

3. Estimate $12\frac{5}{8} \times 3\frac{1}{3}$.
   A. 39   B. 36   C. 48   D. 40

   3. _____

4. Find $\frac{11}{24} \times \frac{8}{15}$. Write in simplest form.
   A. $\frac{11}{45}$ B. $4\frac{1}{11}$ C. $1\frac{27}{165}$ D. $\frac{19}{39}$

   4. _____

5. Solve $24 \times \frac{5}{6} = n$. Write the solution in simplest form.
   A. $\frac{5}{6}$ B. $\frac{5}{144}$ C. $28\frac{4}{5}$ D. 20

   5. _____

6. A yard of material sells for $12. How much will $\frac{3}{4}$ yard cost?
   A. $12.75   B. $9
   C. $3   D. None of these

   6. _____

7. Find $4\frac{4}{5} \times 3\frac{1}{3}$. Write in simplest form.
   A. $12\frac{4}{5}$ B. $4\frac{1}{4}$
   C. 16   D. None of these

   7. _____

8. Solve $4\frac{3}{8} \times 1\frac{1}{2} = x$. Write the solution in simplest form.
   A. $6\frac{9}{16}$ B. $3\frac{4}{5}$ C. $2\frac{3}{8}$ D. $4\frac{3}{16}$

   8. _____

9. Find the area of a room that is $15\frac{1}{2}$ feet long by $10\frac{1}{2}$ feet wide.
   A. 52 ft²   B. 26 ft²   C. $150\frac{1}{4}$ ft²   D. $162\frac{3}{4}$ ft²

   9. _____

10. Find the circumference of a circle with a radius of 6.7 feet.
    A. 42.076 ft   B. 420.76 ft   C. 21.038 ft   D. 210.38 ft

    10. _____

11. Find the circumference of the circle.
    A. 169. 56 cm   B. 16.956 cm
    C. 847.8 cm   D. 8.478 cm

    5.4 cm

    11. _____

12. Find the circumference of a circle with a diameter of $8\frac{1}{4}$ inches.
    A. $25\frac{1}{28}$ in.   B. $8\frac{1}{4}$ in.   C. $25\frac{13}{14}$ in.   D. 25.37 in.

    12. _____

13. Find $28 \div \frac{2}{7}$. Write in simplest form.
    A. 98   B. 8   C. $\frac{56}{7}$ D. $\frac{1}{98}$

    13. _____

Mathematics: Applications and Connections, Course 1

14. Solve $\frac{5}{16} \div \frac{10}{11} = y$. Write the solution in simplest form. 14. _____

   A. $2\frac{10}{11}$ **B.** $\frac{25}{88}$ **C.** $3\frac{13}{25}$ **D.** $\frac{11}{32}$

15. Evaluate $a \div b$ if $a = \frac{7}{21}$ and $b = 2$. 15. _____

   A. $10\frac{1}{2}$ **B.** $\frac{1}{6}$ **C.** $2\frac{8}{21}$ **D.** $\frac{21}{50}$

16. Find $4\frac{11}{12} \div 3$. Write in simplest form. 16. _____

   A. $14\frac{3}{4}$ **B.** $\frac{36}{59}$ **C.** $\frac{12}{177}$ **D.** $1\frac{23}{36}$

17. Solve $5\frac{5}{24} \div 3\frac{1}{8} = m$. Write the solution in simplest form. 17. _____

   A. $\frac{5}{3}$ **B.** $15\frac{1}{2}$ **C.** $1\frac{2}{3}$ **D.** $\frac{3}{5}$

18. Divide $6\frac{2}{3}$ by $4\frac{1}{2}$. 18. _____

   A. 30   **B.** $\frac{1}{30}$ **C.** $\frac{27}{40}$ **D.** $1\frac{13}{27}$

19. Complete: 20 c = _?_ gal. 19. _____

   A. $1\frac{1}{4}$ **B.** $2\frac{1}{2}$ **C.** 5   **D.** 10

20. Complete: $3\frac{1}{2}$ qt = _?_ c. 20. _____

   A. 7   **B.** 14   **C.** $1\frac{3}{4}$ **D.** 28

21. Find the next number in the sequence 1, 8, 15, 22, ... 21. _____

   A. 27   **B.** 26   **C.** 29   **D.** 28

22. Find the next number in the sequence 34, $30\frac{1}{2}$, 27, $23\frac{1}{2}$, ... 22. _____

   A. 20   **B.** 27   **C.** 13   **D.** 16

23. Find the next number in the sequence 3, 18, 108, 648, ... 23. _____

   A. 2,888   **B.** 1,188   **C.** 788   **D.** 3,888

24. Kwasi is baking cakes that require 6 cups of sour cream. He buys 24. _____
   4 pints of sour cream. How many cups will he have left over?

   A. 6   **B.** 4   **C.** 2   **D.** 5

25. Mitch is practicing for a piano recital. He practices 30 minutes on the first 25. _____
   day, 40 minutes on the second, 50 minutes on the third, and 60 minutes on
   the fourth. If he continues this pattern, how many minutes will he have
   practiced in all at the end of 7 days?

   A. 90 minutes   **B.** 80 minutes
   C. 420 minutes   **D.** 330 minutes

Chapter 7 Test, Form 1B

1. Estimate $\frac{1}{3} \times 17$.
   A. 8   B. 60   C. 5   D. 6

   1. _____

2. Estimate $\frac{9}{10} \times \frac{5}{16}$.
   A. $\frac{9}{10}$ B. $\frac{5}{16}$ C. 0   D. 1

   2. _____

3. Estimate $5\frac{7}{8} \times 3\frac{1}{6}$.
   A. 15   B. 20   C. 18   D. 24

   3. _____

4. Find $\frac{15}{16} \times \frac{8}{21}$. Write in simplest form.
   A. $\frac{23}{37}$ B. $\frac{2}{3}$ C. $\frac{5}{14}$ D. $\frac{120}{336}$

   4. _____

5. Solve $18 \times \frac{5}{6} = n$. Write the solution in simplest form.
   A. 15   B. $\frac{5}{108}$ C. $\frac{5}{6}$ D. $21\frac{3}{5}$

   5. _____

6. A foot of metal pipe sells for $9. How much will $\frac{2}{3}$ foot cost?
   A. $\$\frac{2}{27}$ B. $13.50   C. $3   D. $6

   6. _____

7. Find $7\frac{1}{7} \times 4\frac{1}{5}$. Write in simplest form.
   A. $28\frac{2}{35}$ B. 30   C. $\frac{1}{30}$ D. $\frac{71}{12}$

   7. _____

8. Solve $2\frac{3}{16} \times 1\frac{3}{5} = x$. Write the solution in simplest form.
   A. $3\frac{1}{2}$ B. $2\frac{9}{80}$ C. $2\frac{1}{21}$ D. $1\frac{47}{128}$

   8. _____

9. Find the area of a room that is $5\frac{1}{2}$ yards long by $3\frac{1}{3}$ yards wide.
   A. $8\frac{5}{6}$ yd²   B. $18\frac{1}{3}$ yd²   C. $15\frac{1}{6}$ yd²   D. $3\frac{1}{2}$ yd²

   9. _____

10. Find the circumference of a circle with a radius of 18 feet. Use 3.14 for π.
    A. 113.04 ft   B. 56.52 ft   C. 36 ft   D. 9 ft

    10. _____

11. Find the circumference of the circle.
    A. 40.82 m   B. 163.28 m
    C. 8,164 m   D. 81.64 m

    26 m

    11. _____

12. Find the circumference of a circle with a diameter of $24\frac{1}{5}$ inches.
    A. $77\frac{3}{35}$ in.   B. $152\frac{4}{35}$ in.   C. $76\frac{2}{35}$ in.   D. $75\frac{5}{35}$ in.

    12. _____

13. Find $18 \div \frac{1}{3}$. Write in simplest form.
    A. $\frac{1}{54}$ B. 54   C. 6   D. $\frac{1}{6}$

    13. _____

14. Solve $\frac{2}{3} \div \frac{3}{5} = x$. Write the solution in simplest form.
    A. $1\frac{1}{9}$ B. $2\frac{1}{2}$ C. $\frac{9}{10}$ D. $\frac{2}{5}$

    14. _____

15. Evaluate $a \div b$ if $a = \frac{5}{18}$ and $b = 3$.

    A. $\frac{5}{21}$ **B.** $\frac{5}{54}$ **C.** $10\frac{4}{5}$ **D.** $\frac{5}{6}$

15. _____

16. Find $3\frac{5}{16} \div 2$. Write in simplest form.

    A. $6\frac{5}{8}$ **B.** $\frac{8}{53}$ **C.** $1\frac{21}{32}$ **D.** $\frac{32}{53}$

16. _____

17. Solve $2\frac{3}{16} \div 1\frac{3}{4} = m$. Write the solution in simplest form.

    A. $\frac{64}{245}$ **B.** $3\frac{53}{64}$ **C.** $\frac{4}{5}$ **D.** $1\frac{1}{4}$

17. _____

18. Divide $5\frac{1}{4}$ by $1\frac{1}{6}$.

    A. $\frac{2}{9}$ **B.** $\frac{87}{24}$ **C.** $4\frac{1}{2}$ **D.** $5\frac{1}{24}$

18. _____

19. Complete: 5 T = _?_ lb.

    A. 5,000   **B.** 10,000   **C.** 80   **D.** 1,000

19. _____

20. Complete: 80 oz = _?_ lb.

    A. 5   **B.** 1,280   **C.** 8   **D.** $6\frac{2}{3}$

20. _____

21. Find the next number in the sequence 200, 100, 50, 25, ...

    A. 10   **B.** 20   **C.** 12.5   **D.** 12

21. _____

22. Find the next number in the sequence 640, 565, 490, 415, ...

    A. 365   **B.** 75   **C.** 340   **D.** 400

22. _____

23. Find the next number in the sequence $\frac{1}{5}, \frac{1}{15}, \frac{1}{45}, \frac{1}{135}, \cdots$

    A. $\frac{1}{405}$ **B.** $\frac{1}{270}$ **C.** $\frac{1}{180}$ **D.** 405

23. _____

24. Keisha needs 12 gallons of water for a science project. The largest container she can find is a quart milk carton. How many times will she need to fill the quart carton to get 12 gallons?

    A. 3   **B.** 48   **C.** 24   **D.** 6

24. _____

25. Rashaan was measuring the speed of a dropped ball for science class. At 1 second, the speed was 32.16 ft/s. At 2 seconds, it was 64.32 ft/s. At 3 seconds, it was 96.48 ft/s. What will it be after 7 seconds?

    A. 192.96 ft/s   **B.** 32.16 ft/s

    C. 225.12 ft/s   **D.** 160.8 ft/s

25. _____

                  Mathematics: Applications and Connections, Course 1

Chapter 7 Test, Form 1C

1. Estimate $\frac{1}{4} \times 19$.   1. _____
   A. 8   B. 5   C. 10   D. 20

2. Estimate $\frac{8}{9} \times \frac{3}{8}$.   2. _____
   A. $\frac{8}{9}$ B. $\frac{3}{8}$ C. 0   D. 1

3. Estimate $6\frac{1}{5} \times 4\frac{1}{3}$.   3. _____
   A. 24   B. 28   C. 35   D. 30

4. Find $\frac{1}{9} \times \frac{1}{6}$. Write in simplest form.   4. _____
   A. $\frac{1}{15}$ B. $\frac{2}{15}$ C. $\frac{2}{3}$ D. $\frac{1}{54}$

5. Solve $12 \times \frac{5}{6} = n$. Write the solution in simplest form.   5. _____
   A. $12\frac{5}{6}$ B. $2\frac{5}{6}$ C. 10   D. $\frac{5}{6}$

6. A yard of fencing sells for $12. How much will $\frac{1}{2}$ yard cost?   6. _____
   A. $6   B. $\frac{1}{24}$ C. $12.50   D. $8

7. Find $4\frac{1}{6} \times 12$. Write in simplest form.   7. _____
   A. $\frac{25}{72}$ B. $2\frac{22}{25}$ C. 50   D. $\frac{1}{50}$

8. Find $2\frac{1}{12} \times 1\frac{1}{5}$. Write in simplest form.   8. _____
   A. $2\frac{1}{2}$ B. $1\frac{14}{17}$ C. $1\frac{53}{72}$ D. $2\frac{1}{60}$

9. Find the area of a room that is $2\frac{1}{2}$ yards long by $3\frac{1}{3}$ yards wide.   9. _____
   A. $6\frac{1}{6}$ yd²   B. $8\frac{1}{3}$ yd²   C. $7\frac{1}{2}$ yd²   D. $9\frac{2}{3}$ yd²

10. Find the circumference of a circle with a radius of 11 feet. Use 3.14 for π.   10. _____
    A. 34.54 ft   B. 22 ft   C. 62.80 ft   D. 69.08 ft

11. Find the circumference of the circle.   11. _____
    A. 14 mm   B. 21.98 mm
    C. 43.96 mm   D. 87.92 mm

    (14 mm)

12. Find the circumference of a circle with a diameter of 5.3 meters.   12. _____
    A. 16.642 m   B. 166.42 m   C. 33.284 m   D. 1.6642 m

173   *Mathematics: Applications and Connections, Course 1*

13. Find $8 \div \frac{1}{4}$. Write in simplest form. **13.** _____
    A. 2   B. 32   C. $\frac{1}{32}$ D. $\frac{1}{12}$

14. Solve $\frac{1}{4} \div \frac{1}{6}$. Write in simplest form. **14.** _____
    A. $\frac{1}{24}$ B. $\frac{6}{4}$ C. $\frac{3}{2}$ D. $1\frac{1}{2}$

15. Evaluate $a \div b$ if $a = \frac{2}{11}$ and $b = 5$. **15.** _____
    A. $27\frac{1}{2}$ B. $1\frac{1}{10}$ C. $\frac{2}{55}$ D. $\frac{10}{11}$

16. Find $4\frac{7}{9} \div 3$. Write in simplest form. **16.** _____
    A. $12\frac{7}{9}$ B. $1\frac{16}{27}$ C. $\frac{3}{43}$ D. $\frac{27}{43}$

17. Solve $2\frac{5}{8} \div 1\frac{1}{2} = x$. Write the solution in simplest form. **17.** _____
    A. $\frac{16}{63}$ B. $3\frac{5}{16}$ C. $2\frac{5}{16}$ D. $1\frac{3}{4}$

18. Divide $3\frac{3}{5}$ by $4\frac{1}{2}$. **18.** _____
    A. $\frac{4}{5}$ B. $1\frac{1}{4}$ C. $16\frac{1}{5}$ D. $\frac{5}{81}$

19. Complete: 9 c = _?_ fl oz. **19.** _____
    A. 72   B. 144   C. 18   D. 36

20. Complete: 14,000 lb = _?_ T. **20.** _____
    A. 14   B. 7   C. 1,400   D. 140

21. Find the next number in the sequence 10, 30, 90, 270, ... **21.** _____
    A. 810   B. 450   C. 330   D. 300

22. Find the next number in the sequence 6, $7\frac{1}{2}$, 9, $10\frac{1}{2}$, ... **22.** _____
    A. $12\frac{1}{2}$ B. $13\frac{1}{2}$ C. 14   D. 12

23. Find the next number in the sequence 16, 24, 32, 40, ... **23.** _____
    A. 80   B. 48   C. 64   D. 56

24. Candace needs 8 gallons of water for a science project. The largest **24.** _____
    container she can find is a quart milk carton. How many times will she
    need to fill the quart carton to get 8 gallons?
    A. 16   B. 4   C. 32   D. 2

25. Jerard saves $5 the first week, $8 the second, $11 the third, $14 the fourth, **25.** _____
    and $17 the fifth. If this pattern continues, how much will he save during
    the sixth week?
    A. $24   B. $23   C. $3   D. $20

                   *Mathematics: Applications
and Connections, Course 1*

Chapter 7 Test, Form 2A

Estimate.

1. $\frac{2}{7} \times 29$

2. $\frac{7}{10} \times \frac{15}{16}$

3. $3\frac{4}{5} \times 9\frac{7}{8}$

4. $\frac{6}{11} \times 2\frac{3}{13}$

1. _____

2. _____

3. _____

4. _____

Find each product. Write in simplest form.

5. $\frac{2}{5} \times \frac{3}{10}$

6. $42 \times \frac{5}{6}$

7. $7\frac{1}{2} \times 1\frac{3}{10}$

8. $11\frac{2}{3} \times 1\frac{5}{14}$

5. _____

6. _____

7. _____

8. _____

Find the circumference of each circle.

9. The diameter is 18.8 meters.

10.

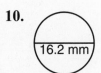
16.2 mm

11. The radius is $18\frac{1}{3}$ feet.

9. _____

10. _____

11. _____

Find each quotient. Write in simplest form.

12. $\frac{9}{25} \div \frac{3}{5}$

13. $\frac{15}{16} \div 5$

14. $\frac{19}{20} \div \frac{5}{8}$

15. $6\frac{1}{4} \div 1\frac{7}{8}$

16. $11\frac{1}{2} \div 1\frac{1}{9}$

17. $4\frac{5}{7} \div 2\frac{1}{5}$

12. _____

13. _____

14. _____

15. _____

16. _____

17. _____

Mathematics: Applications and Connections, Course 1

Find the next two numbers in each sequence.

18. 250, 50, 10, 2, . . .

18. _____

19. 21, $24\frac{1}{2}$, 28, $31\frac{1}{2}$, . . .

19. _____

20. 30, 15, $7\frac{1}{2}$, $3\frac{3}{4}$, . . .

20. _____

21. 4, 10, 25, $62\frac{1}{2}$, . . .

21. _____

Solve each equation. Write the solution in simplest form.

22. $x = 27 \div 1\frac{1}{2}$

22. _____

23. $a = \frac{5}{7} \div \frac{3}{14}$

23. _____

24. $y = 18 \div 3\frac{3}{5}$

24. _____

25. $b = \frac{6}{11} \div \frac{10}{33}$

25. _____

26. $n = 6\frac{4}{5} \times 2\frac{5}{6}$

26. _____

27. $m = 4\frac{1}{4} \times 3\frac{1}{4}$

27. _____

Complete.

28. $4\frac{1}{2}$ T = _?_ lb

28. _____

29. 9 gal = _?_ c

29. _____

30. 144 oz = _?_ lb

30. _____

31. $2\frac{1}{2}$ qt = _?_ c

31. _____

32. A certain type of fencing sells for $9 a yard. How much will $10\frac{2}{3}$ yards of fencing cost?

32. _____

33. Darnell is practicing basketball. On Monday he practices 30 minutes, on Tuesday he practices 45 minutes, and on Wednesday he practices 60 minutes. If he continues this pattern, how many minutes will he practice in all from Monday through Saturday?

33. _____

Name_____ **Date**_____

Chapter 7 Test, Form 2B

Estimate.

1. $\frac{1}{6} \times 29$

2. $\frac{11}{12} \times \frac{3}{8}$

3. $5\frac{7}{8} \times 3\frac{1}{6}$

4. $\frac{9}{10} \times 6\frac{1}{6}$

1. _____

2. _____

3. _____

4. _____

Find each product. Write in simplest form.

5. $\frac{3}{7} \times \frac{1}{4}$

6. $28 \times \frac{3}{7}$

7. $1\frac{11}{16} \times \frac{4}{5}$

8. $\frac{7}{10} \times 1\frac{9}{14}$

5. _____

6. _____

7. _____

8. _____

Find the circumference of each circle.

9. The radius is $4\frac{1}{2}$ inches.

9. _____

10.

0.5 m

10. _____

11. The diameter is 8 meters.

11. _____

Find each quotient. Write in simplest form.

12. $\frac{15}{32} \div \frac{5}{8}$

13. $\frac{9}{50} \div 18$

14. $\frac{21}{40} \div \frac{7}{20}$

15. $2\frac{2}{9} \div 5$

16. $8\frac{1}{10} \div 1\frac{4}{5}$

17. $2\frac{1}{12} \div 1\frac{7}{8}$

12. _____

13. _____

14. _____

15. _____

16. _____

17. _____

Mathematics: Applications and Connections, Course 1

Find the next two numbers in each sequence.

18. $15, 17\frac{1}{2}, 20, 22\frac{1}{2}, \ldots$ 18. _____

19. $729, 243, 81, 27, \ldots$ 19. _____

20. $2\frac{1}{2}, 12\frac{1}{2}, 62\frac{1}{2}, 312\frac{1}{2}, \ldots$ 20. _____

21. $112, 56, 28, 14, \ldots$ 21. _____

Solve each equation. Write the solution in simplest form.

22. $y = 12 \div 1\frac{1}{3}$ 22. _____

23. $\frac{3}{5} \div \frac{7}{15} = a$ 23. _____

24. $z = 11 \div 1\frac{3}{8}$ 24. _____

25. $\frac{6}{7} \div \frac{9}{14} = c$ 25. _____

26. $3\frac{2}{3} \times 2\frac{1}{5} = n$ 26. _____

27. $4\frac{1}{5} \times 1\frac{1}{7} = m$ 27. _____

Complete.

28. $80 \text{ oz} = \underline{\ ?\ } \text{ lb}$ 28. _____

29. $9 \text{ T} = \underline{\ ?\ } \text{ lb}$ 29. _____

30. $40 \text{ c} = \underline{\ ?\ } \text{ gal}$ 30. _____

31. $64 \text{ fl oz} = \underline{\ ?\ } \text{ qt}$ 31. _____

32. Eight bricks are laid end to end along the edge of a flower bed.   32. _____
    Each brick is $8\frac{1}{2}$ inches long. How long is the row of bricks?

33. Constance is writing a diary in which she plans to write   33. _____
    15 minutes the first day, 20 minutes the second, 25 minutes the
    third, and 30 minutes the fourth. If she continues the pattern,
    how many minutes will she write on the tenth day?

Chapter 7 Test, Form 2C

Estimate.

1. $\frac{1}{5} \times 29$

2. $\frac{9}{10} \times \frac{3}{5}$

3. $4\frac{7}{8} \times 3\frac{1}{6}$

4. $1\frac{1}{8} \times 3\frac{4}{5}$

1. _____

2. _____

3. _____

4. _____

Find each product. Write in simplest form.

5. $\frac{5}{18} \times \frac{3}{10}$

6. $24 \times \frac{3}{8}$

7. $5\frac{1}{3} \times \frac{3}{8}$

8. $3\frac{3}{8} \times 1\frac{1}{3}$

5. _____

6. _____

7. _____

8. _____

Find the circumference of each circle.

9. The diameter is 6.5 feet.

9. _____

10.

(5.6 mm)

10. _____

11. The radius is 14 meters.

11. _____

Find each quotient. Write in simplest form.

12. $\frac{8}{25} \div \frac{4}{5}$

13. $\frac{14}{19} \div 7$

14. $\frac{17}{21} \div \frac{3}{7}$

15. $3\frac{1}{2} \div 2\frac{1}{4}$

16. $1\frac{3}{8} \div 1\frac{3}{4}$

17. $2\frac{4}{7} \div 9$

12. _____

13. _____

14. _____

15. _____

16. _____

17. _____

Mathematics: Applications and Connections, Course 1

Find the next two numbers in each sequence.

18. 320, 160, 80, 40, . . .

18. _____

19. $27, 28\frac{1}{2}, 30, 31\frac{1}{2}, \ldots$

19. _____

20. $14, 17\frac{1}{2}, 21, 24\frac{1}{2}, \ldots$

20. _____

21. $999, 333, 111, \frac{111}{3}, \ldots$

21. _____

Solve each equation. Write the solution in simplest form.

22. $z = 10 \div 1\frac{1}{4}$

22. _____

23. $a = \frac{3}{7} \div \frac{1}{2}$

23. _____

24. $w = 9 \div 2\frac{1}{4}$

24. _____

25. $d = \frac{1}{8} \div \frac{5}{12}$

25. _____

26. $3\frac{1}{7} \times 5\frac{1}{4} = j$

26. _____

27. $5\frac{1}{4} \times 2\frac{6}{7} = m$

27. _____

Complete.

28. 2 qt = _?_ c

28. _____

29. 3 lb = _?_ oz

29. _____

30. 10,000 lb = _?_ T

30. _____

31. $7\frac{1}{2}$ T = _?_ lb

31. _____

32. A recipe for cookies calls for $\frac{3}{4}$ cup of milk. Dwayne plans to make only half a recipe. How much milk should he use?

32. _____

33. A certain bacteria doubles each hour. The first hour there are 2. The second hour there are 4. The third hour there are 8. How many will there be the sixth hour?

33. _____

Mathematics: Applications and Connections, Course 1

Chapter 7 Performance Assessment

Instructions: *Demonstrate your knowledge by giving a clear, concise solution to each problem. Be sure to include all relevant drawings and justify your answers. You may show your solutions in more than one way or investigate beyond the requirements of the problems.*

1. Corky the cat weighs $14\frac{1}{2}$ pounds. Drummer the dog weighs $3\frac{1}{5}$ times more.

   a. Estimate Drummer's weight.

   b. Find Drummer's weight by multiplying fractions. Show each step.

   c. How close is your estimate to the actual answer?

   d. Write a word problem that uses multiplication of mixed numbers. Solve and give the meaning of the answer. Show and explain your work.

2. The average weight of a pumpkin at the Circleville Pumpkin Show is $21\frac{1}{3}$ pounds. There are $938\frac{2}{3}$ total pounds of pumpkins.

   a. How many pumpkins are at the show? Write each step.

   b. If there is a pumpkin-pie-eating contest, how many whole pumpkin pies will they need if 25 people participate and each one eats $\frac{7}{8}$ of a pie in 2 minutes?

3. A ball is dropped from 16 feet. The height of each bounce of the ball is then 8 feet, 4 feet, 2 feet, and so on.

   a. Tell how to find how high the fourth bounce will be. Find the height of the fourth bounce.

   b. How high will the sixth bounce be? Explain your reasoning.

   c. Chris is participating in the high jump. He has cleared 24 inches, $24\frac{1}{2}$ inches, 25 inches, $25\frac{1}{2}$ inches, and 26 inches. What do you think the next height he will attempt to jump will be? Explain your reasoning.

   d. Tell how the sequence of ball bounces differs from the sequence of heights to be jumped.

   e. If the ball has a diameter of 5 inches, what is the circumference of the ball? Tell in your own words what the answer means.

4. An average blue whale weighs 200,000 pounds. What is this weight in ounces? in tons?

Chapter 7 Mid-Chapter Test

(Lessons 7-1 through 7-4)

Estimate each product.

1. $\frac{7}{8} \times \frac{4}{7}$

2. $3\frac{12}{13} \times 2\frac{8}{9}$

3. $4\frac{1}{3} \times \frac{10}{11}$

4. $\frac{24}{25} \times 12\frac{1}{17}$

Find each product. Write in simplest form.

5. $\frac{7}{12} \times \frac{3}{4}$

6. $\frac{1}{8} \times \frac{8}{9}$

7. $\frac{21}{25} \times \frac{5}{7}$

8. $1\frac{4}{9} \times \frac{3}{16}$

9. $5\frac{3}{4} \times 2\frac{2}{3}$

10. $7\frac{1}{8} \times 5\frac{1}{3}$

Solve each equation. Write the solution in simplest form.

11. $a = \frac{5}{8} \times \frac{16}{25}$

12. $\frac{1}{4} \times \frac{5}{6} = b$

13. $c = \frac{7}{9} \times \frac{3}{4}$

14. $3\frac{1}{2} \times 2\frac{5}{7} = d$

15. $f = 9\frac{1}{4} \times 12\frac{2}{5}$

16. $6\frac{3}{5} \times 5\frac{7}{11} = g$

Find the circumference of each circle.

17.

$6\frac{1}{7}$ yd

18. $r = 2\frac{7}{8}$ ft

19.

4.7 in.

20. $d = 9$ m

1. _____

2. _____

3. _____

4. _____

5. _____

6. _____

7. _____

8. _____

9. _____

10. _____

11. _____

12. _____

13. _____

14. _____

15. _____

16. _____

17. _____

18. _____

19. _____

20. _____

Mathematics: Applications and Connections, Course 1

Name_____ Date _____

Chapter 7 Quiz A

Estimate.

1. $\frac{2}{9} \times 37$

2. $\frac{3}{10} \times \frac{19}{20}$

3. $4\frac{1}{6} \times 8\frac{1}{10}$

Find each product. Write in simplest form.

4. $\frac{5}{6} \times \frac{8}{9}$

5. $\frac{7}{10} \times \frac{5}{21}$

6. $18 \times \frac{2}{9}$

Solve each equation. Write the solution in simplest form.

7. $\frac{2}{7} \times \frac{3}{5} = r$

8. $s = \frac{24}{35} \times \frac{7}{8}$

9. $t = 12 \times \frac{17}{24}$

10. A television network sells 34 minutes of a television program to advertisers. A company purchases $\frac{7}{13}$ of the total ad time. How many minutes of ad time did the company buy?

1. _____

2. _____

3. _____

4. _____

5. _____

6. _____

7. _____

8. _____

9. _____

10. _____

Name_____ Date _____

Chapter 7 Quiz B

Find each product. Write in simplest form.

1. $3\frac{3}{4} \times 20$

2. $1\frac{3}{5} \times 3\frac{1}{3}$

3. $4\frac{2}{7} \times 2\frac{1}{10}$

Solve each equation. Write the solution in simplest form.

4. $m = 7\frac{1}{12} \times 1\frac{3}{5}$

5. $2\frac{7}{8} \times 1\frac{4}{9} = n$

Find the circumference of each circle.

6.

18 ft

7.

1.7 m

8. The radius is $6\frac{4}{5}$ inches.

9. $r = 3.21$ cm

10. $d = 4\frac{1}{6}$ yd

1. _____

2. _____

3. _____

4. _____

5. _____

6. _____

7. _____

8. _____

9. _____

10. _____

Mathematics: Applications and Connections, Course 1

Chapter 7 Quiz C

Find each quotient. Write in simplest form.

1. $\frac{7}{16} \div \frac{3}{5}$

2. $42 \div \frac{6}{7}$

3. $\frac{7}{30} \div \frac{7}{10}$

4. $5\frac{3}{5} \div 2\frac{1}{10}$

5. $50 \div 1\frac{7}{8}$

6. $3\frac{5}{9} \div 4\frac{4}{5}$

Solve each equation. Write the solution in simplest form.

7. $a = \frac{7}{8} \div \frac{1}{2}$

8. $32 \div \frac{8}{9} = b$

9. $c = 1\frac{1}{7} \div 2\frac{3}{5}$

10. $3\frac{2}{3} \div 2\frac{1}{5} = d$

1. _____

2. _____

3. _____

4. _____

5. _____

6. _____

7. _____

8. _____

9. _____

10. _____

Chapter 7 Quiz D

Complete.

1. 128 oz = _?_ lb

2. 6 gal = _?_ c

3. 112 pt = _?_ gal

4. 25 T = _?_ lb

5. 32 qt = _?_ c

6. 64,000 oz = _?_ T

Find the next two numbers in each sequence.

7. 60, 72, 84, 96, . . .

8. $10, \frac{20}{3}, \frac{40}{9}, \frac{80}{27}, \ldots$

9. George is building a pyramid with cubes. The first layer has 100 cubes, the second has 81, the third has 64, and the fourth has 49. If he continues the pattern, how many cubes are needed for the seventh layer?

10. Matt and Caitlin are serving 1-cup glasses of juice at a school dance. If they buy 6 quarts of juice, how many glasses can they serve?

1. _____

2. _____

3. _____

4. _____

5. _____

6. _____

7. _____

8. _____

9. _____

10. _____

Chapter 7 Standardized Test Practice

1. Juliana would like $\frac{1}{4}$ of the money in the miscellaneous fund to be budgeted for outdoor lighting. If the fund has $595, about how much will be budgeted for outdoor lighting?
   A. $500   **B.** $100   **C.** $175   **D.** $150

   1. _____

2. The diameter of Earth is 7,927 miles. What is the circumference of Earth, rounded to the nearest ten?
   A. 49,780 miles   **B.** 24,910 miles
   C. 24,890 miles   **D.** 25,000 miles

   2. _____

3. How many times must you run around a $\frac{1}{4}$-mile track to run $2\frac{1}{2}$ miles?
   A. 12   **B.** $2\frac{1}{2}$ **C.** 8   **D.** 10

   3. _____

4. An elephant weighing 4.7 tons weighs about how many more pounds than a 2.8-ton rhinoceros?
   A. 3,800 lb   **B.** 4,200 lb   **C.** 6,000 lb   **D.** 1,900 lb

   4. _____

5. Fatima is reading about the metric system and discovers that 1 meter is equivalent to 39.37 inches. If Fatima is 1.31 meters tall, how many inches tall is she to the nearest hundredth?
   A. 51.57 in.   **B.** 40.68 in.   **C.** 30.05 in.   **D.** 51.575 in.

   5. _____

6. Logan is working at the grocery store unloading trucks. One truck has sacks of potatoes on it. What unit would the sacks be measured in?
   A. milligram   **B.** gram   **C.** kilogram   **D.** liter

   6. _____

7. Tom and Trish went out to eat. Tom's dinner was $9.95. Trish's dinner was $7.95. They each had a soft drink for $0.99. They wanted to leave a tip of about $4. What was a reasonable total amount for them to pay?
   A. $20   **B.** $26   **C.** $22   **D.** $24

   7. _____

8. 1 nautical mile equals 1.852 kilometers. Write the decimal in words.
   A. one thousand eight hundred fifty-two
   B. one point eight-five-two thousandths
   C. one and eight hundred fifty-two thousandths
   D. one and eight hundred and fifty-two thousands

   8. _____

9. Mrs. Klaus purchased 4 chairs that cost $59 each. She gave the cashier five $50 bills. How much change did she receive?
   A. $250   **B.** $236   **C.** $14   **D.** $9

   9. _____

10. Mr. Carter has a class of 27 students. He wants to separate the class into groups of 3. Which expression would help him solve this problem?
    A. $27 \div x = 3$
    B. $x \div 27 = 3$
    C. $x \div 3 = 27$
    D. none of these

10. _____

11. Use the bar graph to find how many more points were scored by Sims than by Juarez.

Points Scored

A. 4   B. 5   C. 18   D. 13

11. _____

12. Cameron has to make a stem-and-leaf plot of the data in the graph in Question 11. What stems would he use?
    A. 1
    B. 3, 4, 6, 8
    C. 0, 1, 2
    D. none of these

12. _____

13. The average depth of the Atlantic Ocean is 12,254 feet. Rounded to the nearest yard, how many yards is this?
    A. 1,021 yd
    B. 4,085 yd
    C. 340 yd
    D. none of these

13. _____

14. The Statue of Liberty in New York harbor is about 110 feet tall. Its right arm is 42 feet long. If a 55-inch tall statue were built to the same proportion, how long would its arm be?
    A. 144 in.   B. 84 in.   C. 21 in.   D. 27 in.

14. _____

15. The condor has an average wingspan of 9 feet. The Kalong fruit bat has an average wingspan of $5\frac{7}{12}$ feet. What is the difference in wingspans?
    A. $4\frac{7}{12}$ ft   B. $3\frac{7}{12}$ ft   C. $4\frac{5}{12}$ ft   D. $3\frac{5}{12}$ ft

15. _____

16. Captain James Gallagher flew the first non-stop flight around the world in $3\frac{11}{12}$ days. Dick Rutan and Jeana Yeager flew the first non-stop, non-refueled flight around the world in 9 days. How much longer did the Rutan and Yeager flight take than the Gallagher flight?
    A. $6\frac{1}{12}$ days
    B. $5\frac{1}{12}$ days
    C. $12\frac{11}{12}$ days
    D. none of these

16. _____

Mathematics: Applications and Connections, Course 1

Cumulative Review, Chapters 1–7

Estimate. (Lessons 1-3, 4-1, 6-2, and 7-1)

1. $3{,}510 \div 7$
2. 68.3×2.73

3. $\frac{9}{10} + \frac{11}{12}$
4. $7\frac{7}{8} \times 4\frac{1}{12}$

Solve each equation. Simplify if necessary. (Lessons 4-3, 1-6, 6-5, and 3-6)

5. $a = 3.4 \times 3.4$
6. $h = 3^3$

7. $m = \frac{15}{16} - \frac{1}{16}$
8. $x = 30 - 2.37$

Express each fraction as a decimal. (Lessons 3-1 and 5-10)

9. $\frac{99}{10{,}000}$
10. $\frac{4}{9}$

Order from least to greatest. (Lessons 3-3 and 5-8)

11. $3.9, 3.005, 3.0009, 3.55$

12. $\frac{1}{8}, \frac{2}{3}, \frac{11}{24}, \frac{5}{16}$

13. Elsa made the following bowling scores: 108, 120, 108, 141, 130. What is the median of her bowling scores? (Lesson 2-7)

14. What is the area of a room with a length of 18 feet and a width of 13 feet? (Lesson 4-4)

15. Evaluate 16^4. (Lesson 1-6)

16. What is the GCF of 32 and 40? (Lesson 5-3)

17. What is the LCM of 16 and 40? (Lesson 5-7)

Complete. (Lessons 4-9 and 7-7)

18. $1.4\,\text{L} = \underline{\ ?\ }\,\text{mL}$

19. $20{,}000\,\text{lb} = \underline{\ ?\ }\,\text{T}$

Perform the indicated operation. Write the answer in simplest form. (Lessons 6-4, 7-2, 7-5, 7-6, and 7-3)

20. $\frac{1}{12} + \frac{3}{4}$
21. $9\frac{1}{3} - 3\frac{3}{8}$

22. $\frac{9}{10} \times \frac{5}{8}$
23. $\frac{6}{11} \div \frac{3}{4}$

24. $20 \div 3\frac{1}{3}$
25. $2\frac{1}{6} \times 3\frac{3}{8}$

1. _____
2. _____
3. _____
4. _____
5. _____
6. _____
7. _____
8. _____
9. _____
10. _____
11. _____
12. _____
13. _____
14. _____
15. _____
16. _____
17. _____
18. _____
19. _____
20. _____
21. _____
22. _____
23. _____
24. _____
25. _____

Chapter 7 Answer Key

Form 1A

Page 169

1. B
2. C
3. A
4. A
5. D
6. B
7. C
8. A
9. D
10. A
11. B
12. C
13. A

Page 170

14. D
15. B
16. D
17. C
18. D
19. A
20. B
21. C
22. A
23. D
24. C
25. C

Form 1B

Page 171

1. D
2. B
3. C
4. C
5. A
6. D
7. B
8. A
9. B
10. A
11. D
12. C
13. B
14. A

Page 172

15. B
16. C
17. D
18. C
19. B
20. A
21. C
22. C
23. A
24. B
25. C

Mathematics: Applications and Connections, Course 1

Chapter 7 Answer Key

Form 1C

Page 173

1. ___B___
2. ___B___
3. ___A___
4. ___D___
5. ___C___
6. ___A___
7. ___C___
8. ___A___
9. ___B___
10. ___D___
11. ___C___
12. ___A___

Page 174

13. ___B___
14. ___D___
15. ___C___
16. ___B___
17. ___D___
18. ___A___
19. ___A___
20. ___B___
21. ___A___
22. ___D___
23. ___B___
24. ___C___
25. ___D___

Mathematics: Applications and Connections, Course 1

Chapter 7 Answer Key

Form 2A

Page 175

1. $\dfrac{2}{7} \times 28 = 8$

2. $\dfrac{7}{10} \times 28 = \dfrac{7}{10}$

3. $4 \times 10 = 40$

4. $\dfrac{1}{2} \times 2 = 1$

5. $\dfrac{3}{25}$

6. 35

7. $9\dfrac{3}{4}$

8. $15\dfrac{5}{6}$

9. 59.062 m

10. 50.868 mm

11. $115\dfrac{5}{21} \text{ ft}$

12. $\dfrac{3}{5}$

13. $\dfrac{3}{16}$

14. $1\dfrac{13}{25}$

15. $3\dfrac{1}{3}$

16. $10\dfrac{7}{20}$

17. $2\dfrac{1}{7}$

Page 176

18. $\dfrac{2}{5}, \dfrac{2}{25}$

19. $35, 38\dfrac{1}{2}$

20. $1\dfrac{7}{8}, \dfrac{15}{16}$

21. $156\dfrac{1}{4}, 390\dfrac{5}{8}$

22. 18

23. $3\dfrac{1}{3}$

24. 5

25. $1\dfrac{4}{5}$

26. $19\dfrac{4}{15}$

27. $13\dfrac{13}{16}$

28. $9,000$

29. 144

30. 9

31. 10

32. $\$96$

33. 405

Mathematics: Applications and Connections, Course 1

Chapter 7 Answer Key

Form 2B

Page 177

1. $\dfrac{1}{6} \times 30 = 5$

2. $1 \times \dfrac{3}{8} = \dfrac{3}{8}$

3. $6 \times 3 = 18$

4. $1 \times 6 = 6$

5. $\dfrac{3}{28}$

6. 12

7. $1\dfrac{7}{20}$

8. $1\dfrac{3}{20}$

9. 28.27 in.

10. 3.14 m

11. 25.12 m

12. $\dfrac{3}{4}$

13. $\dfrac{1}{100}$

14. $1\dfrac{1}{2}$

15. $\dfrac{4}{9}$

16. $4\dfrac{1}{2}$

17. $1\dfrac{1}{9}$

Page 178

18. $25,\ 27\dfrac{1}{2}$

19. $9,\ 3$

20. $1,562\dfrac{1}{2},\ 7,812\dfrac{1}{2}$

21. $7,\ 3\dfrac{1}{2}$

22. 9

23. $1\dfrac{2}{7}$

24. 8

25. $1\dfrac{1}{3}$

26. $8\dfrac{1}{15}$

27. $4\dfrac{4}{5}$

28. 5

29. $18,000$

30. 2.5

31. 2

32. 68 inches

33. 60

Mathematics: Applications and Connections, Course 1

Chapter 7 Answer Key

Form 2C

<table>
<tr><td colspan="2">Page 179</td><td colspan="2">Page 180</td></tr>
<tr><td>1.</td><td>$\frac{1}{5} \times 30 = 6$</td><td>18.</td><td>20, 10</td></tr>
<tr><td>2.</td><td>$1 \times \frac{3}{5} = \frac{3}{5}$</td><td>19.</td><td>$33, 34\frac{1}{2}$</td></tr>
<tr><td>3.</td><td>$5 \times 3 = 15$</td><td>20.</td><td>$27, 30\frac{1}{2}$</td></tr>
<tr><td>4.</td><td>$1 \times 4 = 4$</td><td>21.</td><td>$\frac{111}{9}, \frac{111}{27}$</td></tr>
<tr><td>5.</td><td>$\frac{1}{12}$</td><td></td><td></td></tr>
<tr><td>6.</td><td>9</td><td>22.</td><td>8</td></tr>
<tr><td>7.</td><td>2</td><td>23.</td><td>$\frac{6}{7}$</td></tr>
<tr><td>8.</td><td>$4\frac{1}{2}$</td><td>24.</td><td>4</td></tr>
<tr><td></td><td></td><td>25.</td><td>$\frac{3}{10}$</td></tr>
<tr><td>9.</td><td>20.42 ft</td><td>26.</td><td>$16\frac{1}{2}$</td></tr>
<tr><td>10.</td><td>17.584 mm</td><td>27.</td><td>15</td></tr>
<tr><td>11.</td><td>87.92 m</td><td>28.</td><td>8</td></tr>
<tr><td></td><td></td><td>29.</td><td>48</td></tr>
<tr><td>12.</td><td>$\frac{2}{5}$</td><td>30.</td><td>5</td></tr>
<tr><td>13.</td><td>$\frac{2}{19}$</td><td>31.</td><td>15,000</td></tr>
<tr><td>14.</td><td>$1\frac{8}{9}$</td><td></td><td></td></tr>
<tr><td>15.</td><td>$1\frac{5}{9}$</td><td>32.</td><td>$\frac{3}{8}$ c</td></tr>
<tr><td>16.</td><td>$\frac{11}{14}$</td><td>33.</td><td>64</td></tr>
<tr><td>17.</td><td>$\frac{2}{7}$</td><td></td><td></td></tr>
</table>

Mathematics: Applications and Connections, Course 1

Chapter 7 Scoring Guide

Level	Specific Criteria
3 Superior	• Shows thorough understanding of the concepts *estimating products, multiplying and dividing fractions and mixed numbers, finding circumference of a circle, changing customary units,* and *evaluating sequences.* • Uses appropriate strategies to solve problems. • Computations are correct. • Word problem concerning *multiplication of mixed numbers* is appropriate and makes sense. • Written explanations are exemplary. • Goes beyond requirements of some or all problems.
2 Satisfactory, with Minor Flaws	• Shows understanding of the concepts *estimating products, multiplying and dividing fractions and mixed numbers, finding circumference of a circle, changing customary units,* and *evaluating sequences.* • Uses appropriate strategies to solve problems. • Computations are mostly correct. • Word problem concerning *multiplication of mixed numbers* is appropriate and makes sense. • Written explanations are effective. • Satisfies all requirements of problems.
1 Nearly Satisfactory, with Serious Flaws	• Shows understanding of most of the concepts *estimating products, multiplying and dividing fractions and mixed numbers, finding circumference of a circle, changing customary units,* and *evaluating sequences.* • May not use appropriate strategies to solve problems. • Computations are mostly correct. • Word problem concerning *multiplication of mixed numbers* is mostly appropriate and sensible. • Written explanations are satisfactory. • Satisfies most requirements of problems.
0 Unsatisfactory	• Shows little or no understanding of the concepts *estimating products, multiplying and dividing fractions and mixed numbers, finding circumference of a circle, changing customary units,* and *evaluating sequences.* • May not use appropriate strategies to solve problems. • Computations are incorrect. • Word problem concerning *multiplication of mixed numbers* is not appropriate and sensible. • Written explanations are not satisfactory. • Does not satisfy requirements of problems.

Chapter 7 Answer Key

Performance Assessment Sample Answers
Page 181

1. a. about 45 pounds

b. $14\frac{1}{2} \times 3\frac{1}{5} = \frac{29}{2} \times \frac{16}{5} = \frac{29}{1} \times \frac{8}{5} = \frac{232}{5} = 46\frac{4}{10} = 46\frac{2}{5}$ lb

c. The estimate was $1\frac{2}{5}$ pounds less.

d. Find the area of a flower bed that is $5\frac{1}{2}$ yd long and $1\frac{1}{2}$ yd wide. The area of the flower bed is $5\frac{1}{2} \times 1\frac{1}{2}$. Change $5\frac{1}{2}$ and $1\frac{1}{2}$ to improper fractions and multiply.

$\frac{11}{2} \times \frac{3}{2} = \frac{33}{4}$

$\frac{33}{4}$ is $8\frac{1}{4}$, so the area is $8\frac{1}{4}$ yd².

2. a. 44 pumpkins

$938\frac{2}{3} \div 21\frac{1}{3} = \frac{2816}{3} \div \frac{64}{3} = \frac{2816}{3} \times \frac{3}{64} =$

$\frac{2816}{1} \times \frac{1}{64} = \frac{2816}{64} = 44$ pumpkins

b. 22 pies

3. a. Multiply $\frac{1}{2}$ by the height of the third bounce. $\frac{1}{2} \times 2 = 1$ ft

b. The sixth bounce will be $\frac{1}{2}$ the height of the fifth bounce. $\frac{1}{2} \times \frac{1}{2}$ ft $= \frac{1}{4}$ ft

c. The next height will be $26\frac{1}{2}$ in. because the height is increasing $\frac{1}{2}$ in. each time.

d. In the first example, you multiply the last bounce by $\frac{1}{2}$ ft to find the height of the next bounce. In the second example, you add $\frac{1}{2}$ in. to the last height to find the next height to be jumped.

e. $c = \pi d \approx 3.14 \times 5$
The distance around the ball is about 15.7 inches.

4. 200,000 pounds = 3,200,000 ounces = 100 tons

Mid-Chapter Test
Page 182

1. $\frac{4}{7}$

2. 12

3. $4\frac{1}{3}$

4. $12\frac{1}{17}$

5. $\frac{7}{16}$

6. $\frac{1}{9}$

7. $\frac{3}{5}$

8. $\frac{13}{48}$

9. $15\frac{1}{3}$

10. 38

11. $\frac{2}{5}$

12. $\frac{5}{24}$

13. $\frac{7}{12}$

14. $9\frac{1}{2}$

15. $114\frac{7}{10}$

16. $37\frac{1}{5}$

17. $19\frac{15}{49}$ yd

18. $18\frac{1}{14}$ ft

19. 29.516 in.

20. 28.26 m

Mathematics: Applications and Connections, Course 1

Chapter 7 Answer Key

Quiz A, Page 183

1. $\frac{2}{9} \times 36 = 8$
2. $\frac{3}{10} \times 1 = \frac{3}{10}$
3. $4 \times 8 = 32$
4. $\frac{20}{27}$
5. $\frac{1}{6}$
6. 4
7. $\frac{6}{35}$
8. $\frac{3}{5}$
9. $8\frac{1}{2}$
10. $18\frac{4}{13}$ min

Quiz C, Page 184

1. $\frac{35}{48}$
2. 49
3. $\frac{1}{3}$
4. $2\frac{2}{3}$
5. $26\frac{2}{3}$
6. $\frac{20}{27}$
7. $1\frac{3}{4}$
8. 36
9. $\frac{40}{91}$
10. $1\frac{2}{3}$

Quiz B, Page 183

1. 75
2. $5\frac{1}{3}$
3. 9
4. $11\frac{1}{3}$
5. $4\frac{11}{72}$
6. 56.52 ft
7. 10.676 m
8. $42\frac{26}{35}$ in.
9. 20.1588 cm
10. $13\frac{2}{21}$ yd

Quiz D, Page 184

1. 8
2. 96
3. 14
4. $50,000$
5. 128
6. 2
7. $108,120$
8. $\frac{160}{81}, \frac{320}{243}$
9. 16 cubes
10. 24 glasses

Mathematics: Applications and Connections, Course 1

Chapter 7 Answer Key

Page 185

1. $\underline{\quad D \quad}$

2. $\underline{\quad C \quad}$

3. $\underline{\quad D \quad}$

4. $\underline{\quad A \quad}$

5. $\underline{\quad A \quad}$

6. $\underline{\quad C \quad}$

7. $\underline{\quad D \quad}$

8. $\underline{\quad C \quad}$

9. $\underline{\quad C \quad}$

Page 186

10. $\underline{\quad A \quad}$

11. $\underline{\quad B \quad}$

12. $\underline{\quad A \quad}$

13. $\underline{\quad B \quad}$

14. $\underline{\quad C \quad}$

15. $\underline{\quad D \quad}$

16. $\underline{\quad B \quad}$

Cumulative Review
Page 187

1. $3,500 \div 7 = 500$

2. $70 \times 3 = 210$

3. $1 + 1 = 2$

4. $8 \times 4 = 32$

5. 11.56

6. 27

7. $\frac{7}{8}$

8. 27.63

9. 0.0099

10. $0.4\overline{4}$

11. $3.0009, 3.005$ $3.55, 3.9$

12. $\frac{1}{8}, \frac{5}{16}, \frac{11}{24}, \frac{2}{3}$

13. 120

14. 234 ft^2

15. $65,536$

16. 8

17. 80

18. $1,400 \text{ mL}$

19. 10 T

20. $\frac{5}{6}$

21. $5\frac{23}{24}$

22. $\frac{9}{16}$

23. $\frac{8}{11}$

24. 6

25. $7\frac{5}{16}$

Chapter 8 Test, Form 1A

1. Express *84 out of 126 people* as a fraction in simplest form.   1. _____
   A. $\frac{3}{2}$ B. $\frac{42}{63}$ C. $\frac{14}{21}$ D. $\frac{2}{3}$

2. A car travels 350 kilometers in 5 hours. Express the rate in kilometers per   2. _____
   hour.
   A. 70 kilometers   B. 70 kilometers per hour
   C. $\frac{5}{350}$ kilometers per hour   D. none of these

3. Which of the following does *not* express the ratio of 3 to 5?   3. _____
   A. 3:5   B. $\frac{3}{5}$ C. 3 to 5   D. $\frac{5}{3}$

4. Which pair of ratios forms a proportion?   4. _____
   A. $\frac{9}{16}, \frac{17}{32}$ B. $\frac{50}{100}, \frac{3}{6}$ C. $\frac{7}{50}, \frac{6}{25}$ D. $\frac{9}{75}, \frac{17}{150}$

5. Solve the proportion $\frac{28}{y} = \frac{4}{7}$.   5. _____
   A. 16   B. 50   C. 49   D. none of these

6. Solve the proportion $\frac{18}{27} = \frac{x}{18}$.   6. _____
   A. 12   B. 324   C. $\frac{2}{3}$ D. none of these

7. 27 out of 60 people prefer a certain brand of soap. At that rate, how many   7. _____
   out of 100 people would that be?
   A. $\frac{9}{20}$ B. 222   C. 45   D. 47

8. A rectangular pigpen is completely surrounded by a fence with posts that   8. _____
   are 5 feet apart. The pen is 20 feet long and 10 feet wide. A post is at each
   corner. What is the total number of posts?
   A. 12 posts   B. 30 posts   C. 16 posts   D. none of these

9. What is the actual length of the car shown   9. _____
   in the scale drawing?
   A. 16 ft   B. 18 ft
   C. 20 ft   D. none of these

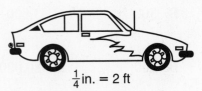
$\frac{1}{4}$ in. = 2 ft

10. According to the scale drawing, what is the actual height of the car?   10. _____
    A. 4 ft   B. 5 ft   C. 7 ft   D. none of these

11. Express 154% as a fraction in simplest form.   11. _____
    A. $\frac{100}{154}$ B. $\frac{50}{77}$ C. $1\frac{27}{50}$ D. $\frac{27}{50}$

12. Express $\frac{17}{20}$ as a percent.   12. _____
    A. 85%   B. 17%   C. 34%   D. 95%

13. Express the shaded portion of the square as a percent.

   A. $\frac{37}{100}$%   **B.** 3.7%

   C. 63%   **D.** 37%

13. _____

14. What percent of the rectangle is shaded?

14. _____

   A. 6%   **B.** 40%   **C.** 60%   **D.** $\frac{6}{15}$

15. Express 1.35 as a percent.

   A. 0.0135%   **B.** 13.5%   **C.** 135%   **D.** 0.135%

15. _____

16. Express 141% as a decimal.

   A. 14.1   **B.** 1.41   **C.** 0.141   **D.** 141

16. _____

17. Express 0.5% as a decimal.

   A. 0.5   **B.** 0.05   **C.** 0.005   **D.** 50

17. _____

18. Express 1.8 as a percent.

   A. 1.8%   **B.** 18%   **C.** 0.18%   **D.** 180%

18. _____

19. Express 0.054 as a percent.

   A. 5.4%   **B.** 54%   **C.** 540%   **D.** 0.54%

19. _____

20. Estimate 30% of 242.

   A. 8   **B.** 80   **C.** 90   **D.** 600

20. _____

21. Estimate 49% of 59,800.

   A. 30   **B.** 300   **C.** 3,000   **D.** 30,000

21. _____

22. Estimate 21% of 38,051.

   A. 8,000   **B.** 800   **C.** 80,000   **D.** 80

22. _____

23. Find 12% of 84.

   A. 1,008   **B.** 7   **C.** 10.08   **D.** 100.8

23. _____

24. Alicia's savings account pays 2.25% interest. If she has $400 in her savings account for a year, how much interest did she earn?

   A. $900   **B.** $9   **C.** $90   **D.** $0.90

24. _____

25. Find 137% of 600.

   A. 822   **B.** 82   **C.** 222   **D.** none of these

25. _____

Chapter 8 Test, Form 1B

1. Express *64 cars out of 80 cars* as a fraction in simplest form.
   A. $\frac{64}{80}$ **B.** $\frac{80}{64}$ **C.** $\frac{32}{40}$ **D.** $\frac{4}{5}$

1. _____

2. A car travels 180 miles on 10 gallons of gasoline. Express the rate in miles per gallon.
   A. 18 miles
   C. $\frac{10}{180}$ miles per gallon
   B. 18 miles per gallon
   D. none of these

2. _____

3. Which of the following does *not* express the ratio of 3 to 4?
   A. $\frac{4}{3}$ **B.** 3 to 4   **C.** 3:4   **D.** $\frac{3}{4}$

3. _____

4. Which pair of ratios forms a proportion?
   A. $\frac{14}{20}, \frac{21}{30}$ **B.** $\frac{3}{100}, \frac{6}{49}$ **C.** $\frac{6}{8}, \frac{3}{5}$ **D.** $\frac{18}{20}, \frac{8}{9}$

4. _____

5. Solve the proportion $\frac{m}{80} = \frac{15}{20}$.
   A. 6   **B.** 60   **C.** 1,200   **D.** none of these

5. _____

6. Solve the proportion $\frac{18}{54} = \frac{10}{x}$.
   A. 30   **B.** 3   **C.** 540   **D.** none of these

6. _____

7. 18 out of 40 people prefer a certain type of shampoo. At that rate, how many out of 100 people would that be?
   A. 9   **B.** 720   **C.** 45   **D.** none of these

7. _____

8. Martha has a piece of ribbon that is 100 inches long. She plans to cut the ribbon into 5 equal pieces. How many cuts does she need to make?
   A. 20   **B.** 5   **C.** 4   **D.** none of these

8. _____

9. What is the actual length of the living room shown in the scale drawing?
   A. 20 ft   **B.** 16 ft
   C. 12 ft   **D.** none of these

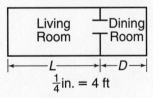

9. _____

10. According to the scale drawing, what is the actual length of the dining room? (Refer to the side labeled *D*.)
    A. 8 ft   **B.** 9 ft   **C.** 10 ft   **D.** none of these

10. _____

11. Express 72% as a fraction in simplest form.
    A. $\frac{72}{100}$ **B.** $\frac{8}{25}$ **C.** $\frac{36}{50}$ **D.** $\frac{18}{25}$

11. _____

12. Express $\frac{17}{25}$ as a percent.
    A. 17%   **B.** 34%   **C.** 50%   **D.** 68%

12. _____

Mathematics: Applications and Connections, Course 1

13. Express the shaded portion of the square as a percent.   13. _____
    A. 3%   B. 30%
    C. 70%   D. none of these

14. What percent of the rectangle is shaded?   14. _____

    A. 20%   B. 40%   C. 2%   D. none of these

15. Express 0.98 as a percent.   15. _____
    A. 9.8%   B. 98%   C. 0.98%   D. 980%

16. Express 0.04 as a percent.   16. _____
    A. 40%   B. 0.04%   C. 0.4%   D. 4%

17. Express 0.9% as a decimal.   17. _____
    A. 0.09   B. 0.009   C. 9   D. 90

18. Express 2.4 as a percent.   18. _____
    A. 2.4%   B. 24%   C. 0.024%   D. 240%

19. Express 3.8% as a decimal.   19. _____
    A. 0.038   B. 380   C. 0.38   D. 38

20. Estimate 25% of 1,589.   20. _____
    A. 40   B. 400   C. 4,000   D. 60,000

21. Estimate 48% of 160.   21. _____
    A. 80   B. 8   C. 10,000   D. 1,000

22. Estimate 25% of 1,211.   22. _____
    A. 30   B. 300   C. 3,000   D. 36,000

23. Find 15% of 30.   23. _____
    A. 45   B. 450   C. 2   D. 4.5

24. On a test, Jordan answered 98% of the questions correctly. If there were   24. _____
    50 questions on the test, how many questions did he answer correctly?
    A. 40   B. 98   C. 49   D. none of these

25. Find 125% of 400.   25. _____
    A. 4   B. 50   C. 500   D. none of these

Name_____ Date _____

Chapter 8 Test, Form 1C

1. Express *20 out of 35 people* as a fraction in simplest form.   1. _____
   A. $\frac{20}{35}$ **B.** $\frac{35}{20}$ **C.** $\frac{8}{14}$ **D.** $\frac{4}{7}$

2. Josie walked 6 miles in 2 hours. Express the rate in miles per hour.   2. _____
   A. 3 miles   **B.** 3 miles per hour
   C. $\frac{2}{6}$ miles per hour   **D.** none of these

3. Which of the following does *not* express the ratio of 1 to 2?   3. _____
   A. $\frac{2}{1}$ **B.** 1 to 2   **C.** 1:2   **D.** $\frac{1}{2}$

4. Which pair of ratios forms a proportion?   4. _____
   A. $\frac{1}{3}, \frac{5}{10}$ **B.** $\frac{1}{2}, \frac{5}{10}$ **C.** $\frac{1}{4}, \frac{2}{7}$ **D.** $\frac{3}{5}, \frac{5}{7}$

5. Solve the proportion $\frac{m}{32} = \frac{6}{8}$.   5. _____
   A. 192   **B.** 48   **C.** 24   **D.** 27

6. Solve the proportion $\frac{2}{3} = \frac{y}{21}$.   6. _____
   A. 6   **B.** 42   **C.** 63   **D.** 14

7. 5 out of 10 people prefer a certain type of juice. At that rate, how many   7. _____
   out of 100 people would that be?
   A. 500   **B.** 50   **C.** 15   **D.** none of these

8. Emily has a piece of paper she needs to fold into three parts. How many   8. _____
   folds does she need to make?
   A. 2   **B.** 1   **C.** 3   **D.** none of these

9. What is the actual length of the living room   9. _____
   shown in the scale drawing?
   A. 8 ft   **B.** 16 ft
   C. 24 ft   **D.** 1 in.

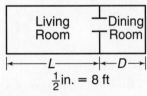

10. According to the scale drawing, what is the actual length of the dining   10. _____
   room? (Refer to the side labeled *D*.)
   A. 8 ft   **B.** $\frac{1}{2}$ in.   **C.** 16 ft   **D.** 4 ft

11. Express 60% as a fraction in simplest form.   11. _____
   A. $\frac{60}{100}$ **B.** $\frac{30}{50}$ **C.** $\frac{15}{25}$ **D.** $\frac{3}{5}$

12. Express $\frac{18}{50}$ as a percent.   12. _____
   A. 18%   **B.** 50%   **C.** 36%   **D.** none of these

13. Express the shaded portion of the square as a percent.
    A. 10%   **B.** 20%
    C. 2%   **D.** 80%

13. _____

14. What percent of the rectangle is shaded?

    A. 6%   **B.** 60%   **C.** 50%   **D.** none of these

14. _____

15. Express 0.86 as a percent.
    A. 8.6%   **B.** 860%   **C.** 0.86%   **D.** 86%

15. _____

16. Express 0.02 as a percent.
    A. 0.2%   **B.** 2%   **C.** 20%   **D.** 0.02%

16. _____

17. Express 15% as a decimal.
    A. 0.015   **B.** 150   **C.** 0.15   **D.** 15

17. _____

18. Express 0.09 as a percent.
    A. 9%   **B.** 0.9%   **C.** 90%   **D.** 0.09%

18. _____

19. Express 2% as a decimal.
    A. 20   **B.** 2   **C.** 0.02   **D.** 0.2

19. _____

20. Estimate 25% of 395.
    A. 10   **B.** 100   **C.** 1,000   **D.** 1,600

20. _____

21. Estimate 48% of 60.
    A. 3,000   **B.** 300   **C.** 3   **D.** 30

21. _____

22. Estimate 19% of 201.
    A. 4   **B.** 40   **C.** 400   **D.** 4,000

22. _____

23. Find 10% of 25.
    A. 2.5   **B.** 25   **C.** 250   **D.** 0.25

23. _____

24. Mrs. Saunders made $600 last week, and she put 15% of that amount into savings. How much did she save?
    A. $40   **B.** $90   **C.** $400   **D.** $900

24. _____

25. Find 150% of 12.
    A. 1,800   **B.** 180   **C.** 18   **D.** 1.8

25. _____

Mathematics: Applications and Connections, Course 1

Name_____ Date _____

Chapter 8 Test, Form 2A

Write each ratio as a fraction in simplest form.

1. 35 shots made out of 55 attempted

1. _____

2. 60 fish to 440 frogs

2. _____

Express each ratio as a rate.

3. 162 heartbeats in 60 seconds

3. _____

4. 135 push-ups in 6 minutes

4. _____

5. 84 feet in 12 seconds

5. _____

Solve each proportion.

6. $\frac{25}{50} = \frac{6}{x}$

6. _____

7. $\frac{60}{y} = \frac{80}{120}$

7. _____

8. $\frac{z}{14} = \frac{48}{168}$

8. _____

9. $\frac{74}{100} = \frac{a}{150}$

9. _____

10. $\frac{54}{b} = \frac{72}{124}$

10. _____

11. A scale drawing of a swimming pool is shown below. The scale is $\frac{1}{8}$ in. = 4 ft. What is the actual length of the pool?

11. _____

12. On a map, the scale is 1 cm = 10 km. If the map distance between Princeton and Bellville is 4.6 centimeters, what is the actual distance between the two towns?

12. _____

13. On a map, the scale is 1 in. = 20 mi. If the distance on the map between two cities is $3\frac{1}{2}$ inches, what is the actual distance?

13. _____

Express each fraction as a percent.

14. $\frac{16}{25}$

14. _____

15. $\frac{19}{50}$

15. _____

16. $\frac{23}{100}$

16. _____

Mathematics: Applications and Connections, Course 1

Express each percent as a fraction in simplest form and as a decimal.

17. 95%

17. _____

18. 6%

18. _____

19. 0.8%

19. _____

Express each decimal as a percent.

20. 0.029

20. _____

21. 0.89

21. _____

22. 2.3

22. _____

Estimate each percent.

23. 32% of 19

23. _____

24. 10.3% of 181

24. _____

25. 51% of 606

25. _____

26. 32% of 152

26. _____

27. 76% of 123

27. _____

Find the percent of each number.

28. 35% of 105

28. _____

29. 6% of 300

29. _____

30. 47% of 237

30. _____

31. 80% of 320

31. _____

32. 96% of 85

32. _____

Solve by drawing a diagram.

33. The Garcias are building a patio by using square patio stones that are 2 feet by 2 feet. If the patio is going to be 10 feet by 16 feet, how many stones are needed?

33. _____

Mathematics: Applications and Connections, Course 1

Name_____ Date _____

Chapter 8 Test, Form 2B

Write each ratio as a fraction in simplest form.

1. 16 blue-eyed people out of 50 people

1. _____

2. $25 out of every $500 collected

2. _____

Express each ratio as a rate.

3. 424 kilometers in 8 hours

3. _____

4. $60 for 12 months

4. _____

5. 40 feet in 5 seconds

5. _____

Solve each proportion.

6. $\frac{10}{15} = \frac{18}{x}$

6. _____

7. $\frac{18}{m} = \frac{27}{30}$

7. _____

8. $\frac{40}{100} = \frac{y}{20}$

8. _____

9. $\frac{c}{25} = \frac{16}{200}$

9. _____

10. $\frac{62}{d} = \frac{93}{168}$

10. _____

11. The scale drawing of a window is shown at the right. The scale is $\frac{1}{4}$ in. = 2 ft. What is the actual width labeled w?

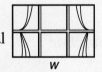

11. _____

12. On a map, the scale is 1 cm = 20 km. If the map distance between Ironton and Bedford is 1.6 centimeters, what is the actual distance?

12. _____

13. On a map, the scale is 1 in. = 10 mi. If the distance on the map between two cities is 4 inches, what is the actual distance?

13. _____

Express each fraction as a percent.

14. $\frac{28}{50}$

14. _____

15. $\frac{17}{20}$

15. _____

16. $\frac{4}{5}$

16. _____

Mathematics: Applications and Connections, Course 1

Express each percent as a fraction in simplest form and as a decimal.

17. 82%

17. _____

18. 6%

18. _____

19. 3.4%

19. _____

Express each decimal as a percent.

20. 0.77

20. _____

21. 0.046

21. _____

22. 4.7

22. _____

Estimate each percent.

23. 48% of 61

23. _____

24. 74% of 21

24. _____

25. 19% of 203

25. _____

26. 32% of 62

26. _____

27. 52% of 143

27. _____

Find the percent of each number.

28. 30% of 80

28. _____

29. 51% of 63

29. _____

30. 3% of 500

30. _____

31. 20% of 160

31. _____

32. 60% of 240

32. _____

Solve by drawing a diagram.

33. Ricardo has a piece of lumber that is 105 inches long. He wants to cut it into 15-inch pieces. How many cuts does he need to make?

33. _____

Mathematics: Applications and Connections, Course 1

Name _____ **Date** _____

Chapter 8 Test, Form 2C

Write each ratio as a fraction in simplest form.

1. 18 shots made out of 40 attempted

1. _____

2. 2 winners out of 50 players

2. _____

Express each ratio as a rate.

3. 240 miles on 8 gallons of gasoline

3. _____

4. 180 students for 6 classes

4. _____

5. 16 feet in 2 seconds

5. _____

Solve each proportion.

6. $\frac{n}{3} = \frac{5}{15}$

6. _____

7. $\frac{5}{10} = \frac{h}{14}$

7. _____

8. $\frac{10}{12} = \frac{15}{m}$

8. _____

9. $\frac{7}{f} = \frac{14}{16}$

9. _____

10. $\frac{g}{24} = \frac{15}{36}$

10. _____

11. The scale drawing of a poster is shown at the right. The scale is $\frac{1}{2}$ in. = 1 ft. What is the actual width labeled w?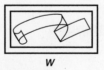

11. _____

12. On a map, the scale is 1 cm = 10 km. If the map distance between Montgomery and Indian Hill is 2 centimeters, what is the actual distance?

12. _____

13. On a map, the scale is 1 in. = 5 mi. If the distance on the map between two cities is 2 inches, what is the actual distance?

13. _____

Express each fraction as a percent.

14. $\frac{1}{2}$

14. _____

15. $\frac{3}{10}$

15. _____

16. $\frac{42}{100}$

16. _____

Mathematics: Applications and Connections, Course 1

Express each percent as a fraction in simplest form and as a decimal.

17. 75%

17. _____

18. 12%

18. _____

19. 10%

19. _____

Express each decimal as a percent.

20. 0.84

20. _____

21. 0.62

21. _____

22. 0.07

22. _____

Estimate each percent.

23. 10% of 203

23. _____

24. 25% of 406

24. _____

25. 50% of 248

25. _____

26. 30% of 59

26. _____

27. 75% of 119

27. _____

Find the percent of each number.

28. 15% of 140

28. _____

29. 64% of 25

29. _____

30. 75% of 20

30. _____

31. 40% of 120

31. _____

32. 25% of 800

32. _____

Solve by drawing a diagram.

33. Sabrina and her father are building a kennel for their dog. They need to put posts every 2 feet. If the kennel is 6 feet by 4 feet, how many posts do they need? (*Hint:* Don't forget the corner posts.)

33. _____

Mathematics: Applications and Connections, Course 1

Chapter 8 Performance Assessment

Instructions: *Demonstrate your knowledge by giving a clear, concise solution to each problem. Be sure to include all relevant drawings and justify your answers. You may show your solutions in more than one way or investigate beyond the requirements of the problems.*

1. a. Tell in your own words the meaning of *ratio*.

b. Give an example of a ratio. Write the ratio in four ways.

c. Tell in your own words the meaning of *rate*. Give two examples of rates.

d. Tell in your own words the meaning of *proportion*.

e. Write a word problem that uses proportions. Include a scale drawing.

f. Solve the word problem in part e. Explain each step.

2. Matthew is in charge of marking merchandise down for the back-to-school sale. Clothing is to be marked down 30%. School supplies are to be on sale for $\frac{1}{4}$ off, and sporting goods prices will be reduced 20%.

a. Tell how to express a percent as a fraction and as a decimal.

b. Find the sale price of a $35 basketball in two ways.

c. Estimate the sale price of a jacket regularly priced $40. Explain your reasoning.

d. Find the sale price of the jacket in part c.

e. Tell how to express a fraction as a percent.

f. Express $\frac{1}{4}$ as a percent. Show your work.

g. On which item would a customer save more money, the $35 basketball or a $32 book for school? Explain your reasoning.

Chapter 8 Mid-Chapter Test

(Lessons 8-1 through 8-4)

1. Write the ratio in three different ways: 7 out of 23 M & M's are brown.

1. _____

Express each ratio as a fraction in simplest form.

2. 22 games won out of 44 games played

2. _____

3. 15 sheep out of 55 animals

3. _____

Express each ratio as a rate.

4. 360 miles in 6 hours   5. 4 tapes for $23.96

4. _____

Use cross products to determine whether each pair of ratios forms a proportion.

5. _____

6. $\frac{9}{20}, \frac{18}{42}$ 7. $\frac{5}{10}, \frac{4}{8}$

6. _____

Solve each proportion.

7. _____

8. $\frac{2}{20} = \frac{6}{w}$ 9. $\frac{6}{c} = \frac{18}{30}$

8. _____

10. $\frac{y}{36} = \frac{6}{8}$

9. _____

10. _____

11. Leslie is setting up a singles tennis tournament. She wants each player to play every other player one time. If 4 players enter, how many games will Leslie need to set up?

11. _____

Scale drawings were made of four famous structures. The scale for each drawing is 1 cm = 30 m. The given measurement is the size of the drawing to the nearest centimeter. Find the actual height of each structure.

12. Statue of Liberty, New York City, 3 cm

12. _____

13. Washington Monument, Washington, D.C., 5 cm

13. _____

14. Gateway Arch, St. Louis, Missouri, 6 cm

14. _____

15. _____

If you were to make a scale drawing for the following structures with a scale of 1 in. = 50 ft, what would be the measurement of the drawing?

16. _____

15. a skyscraper 500 ft tall   16. a space shuttle 125 ft long

17. _____

Express each percent as a fraction in simplest form.

18. _____

17. 56%   18. 143%

19. _____

Express each fraction as a percent.

19. $\frac{2}{5}$ 20. $\frac{9}{50}$

20. _____

Chapter 8 Quiz A

(Lessons 8-1 and 8-2)

Express each ratio as a fraction in simplest form.

1. 45 people out of 60

2. 12 red marbles out of 28 marbles

Express each ratio as a rate.

3. 178 feet in 2 seconds

4. 12 muffins for $3

5. 24 cans of soft drink for $4.99

Solve each proportion.

6. $\frac{18}{m} = \frac{50}{100}$ 7. $\frac{27}{36} = \frac{x}{16}$ 8. $\frac{45}{60} = \frac{60}{y}$

9. Use cross products to determine if $\frac{5}{19}$ and $\frac{15}{56}$ form a proportion.

10. Use cross products to determine if $\frac{7}{12}$ and $\frac{14}{24}$ form a proportion.

1. _____

2. _____

3. _____

4. _____

5. _____

6. _____

7. _____

8. _____

9. _____

10. _____

Chapter 8 Quiz B

(Lessons 8-3 and 8-4)

Solve by drawing a diagram.

1. The Hys choose mirror squares that are 16 inches by 16 inches to cover a wall that is 8 feet tall and 4 feet wide. How many mirror squares are needed?

2. The distance between two cities on a map is $3\frac{3}{4}$ inches. The scale reads "1 in. = 24 mi." What is the actual distance between the cities?

Express each fraction as a percent.

3. $\frac{23}{25}$ 4. $\frac{13}{20}$

5. $\frac{7}{8}$ 6. $\frac{7}{20}$

Express each percent as a fraction.

7. 95%   8. 15%

9. 24%   10. 58%

1. _____

2. _____

3. _____

4. _____

5. _____

6. _____

7. _____

8. _____

9. _____

10. _____

Mathematics: Applications and Connections, Course 1

Chapter 8 Quiz C

(Lessons 8-5 and 8-6)

Express each decimal as a percent.

1. 0.86

2. 2.7

3. 0.78

Express each percent as a decimal.

4. 7%

5. 31.5%

6. 120%

Estimate each percent.

7. 25% of 789

8. 32% of 118

9. 64% of 147

10. 47% of 489

1. _____

2. _____

3. _____

4. _____

5. _____

6. _____

7. _____

8. _____

9. _____

10. _____

Chapter 8 Quiz D

(Lesson 8-7)

Find the percent of each number.

1. 70% of 210   2. 39% of 432

3. 10% of 80   4. 7% of 22

5. 73% of 200   6. 40% of 120

7. 1% of 410   8. 50% of 150

9. The sales tax in Chicago is 8%. How much is the sales tax on a $45 jogging suit?

10. A $10.80 scarf is on sale for 85% of its original price. What is the sale price?

1. _____

2. _____

3. _____

4. _____

5. _____

6. _____

7. _____

8. _____

9. _____

10. _____

Mathematics: Applications and Connections, Course 1

Chapter 8 Standardized Test Practice

1. An average camel can drink 114 liters in 10 minutes. Express this ratio as a rate.
   A. 114 liters
   B. 11.4 liters per minute
   C. 10 minutes per liter
   D. none of these

   1. _____

2. Alex used a proportion to convert between feet and inches. He knows that 1 foot = 12 inches. He is 56 inches tall. Solve the proportion $\frac{12}{1} = \frac{56}{x}$ to determine Alex's height in feet.
   A. 5 ft 6 in.
   B. 5.6 ft
   C. $4\frac{2}{3}$ ft
   D. $4\frac{1}{3}$ ft

   2. _____

3. Oxygen makes up 65% of the chemical elements in the human body. Express this percent as a decimal.
   A. $\frac{65}{100}$
   B. 65.0
   C. 0.65
   D. 6.5

   3. _____

4. Five of the first 25 presidents were born in March. What percent of the first 25 presidents were born in March?
   A. 20%
   B. $\frac{1}{5}$
   C. $\frac{5}{25}$
   D. 25%

   4. _____

5. In music, putting a flag on the stem of a note halves the value of the note. If you start with a quarter note and add a flag, what note results?
   A. half note
   B. quarter note
   C. eighth note
   D. sixteenth note

   5. _____

6. Josiah is making dip for a party. The recipe calls for $\frac{1}{2}$ teaspoon of lemon juice. He wants to make $2\frac{1}{2}$ times the recipe. How much lemon juice does Josiah need?
   A. $1\frac{1}{4}$ tsp
   B. $2\frac{1}{4}$ tsp
   C. $\frac{1}{4}$ tsp
   D. none of these

   6. _____

7. Mrs. Smith is ordering pizzas for her class as a reward. She has decided that she needs $4\frac{1}{4}$ pizzas to feed her class. How many pizzas should she order?
   A. 4
   B. $4\frac{1}{2}$
   C. 5
   D. none of these

   7. _____

8. If $\frac{2}{9}$ of the marbles in a bag are red and $\frac{5}{9}$ of the marbles are white, what portion of the marbles are neither red nor white?
   A. $\frac{7}{9}$
   B. $\frac{1}{3}$
   C. 2
   D. $\frac{2}{9}$

   8. _____

9. Eight presidents out of 41 were born in Virginia. Express this ratio as a decimal rounded to the nearest thousandth.
   A. $\frac{8}{41}$
   B. 0.195
   C. 5.125
   D. 19.5

   9. _____

10. Joy wanted to bundle by weight the newspapers collected for recycling by each of the three classes in the sixth grade. The classes collected 22 pounds, 55 pounds, and 44 pounds. Joy used the greatest common factor of these numbers for the weight of each newspaper bundle. That way no class would have unbundled newspapers left over. How many pounds did each bundle weigh?

    A. 11 lb   **B.** 5 lb   **C.** 7 lb   **D.** none of these

10. _____

11. An average mountain lion weighs 77 kilograms. What is this weight in grams?

    A. 0.077 g   **B.** 77 g   **C.** 77,000 g   **D.** 7,700 g

11. _____

12. Solve $3 \times 12{,}541 = a$ using the distributive property.

    A. 4,180   **B.** 37,623   **C.** 3,762   **D.** none of these

12. _____

13. The cubit is an old unit of length. The Roman cubit is 0.444 meter. The Greek cubit is 0.463 meter. The Assyrian cubit is 0.469 meter. The Egyptian short cubit is 0.450 meter. Put these decimals in order from least to greatest.

    A. 0.444, 0.450, 0.463, 0.469   **B.** 0.469, 0.463, 0.450, 0.444

    C. 0.450, 0.469, 0.463, 0.444   **D.** none of these

13. _____

14. One square meter is equivalent to 1.196 square yards. Round the square yards to the nearest hundredth.

    A. 2.0   **B.** 1.20   **C.** 1.0   **D.** none of these

14. _____

15. Mrs. Overbeck's math class had the following scores on a test: 75, 90, 85, 90, 80, 52, 95, 83, 90. What is the best measure of central tendency to describe this data?

    A. range   **B.** mode   **C.** mean   **D.** median

15. _____

16. Susie started taking piano lessons. The first week she practiced 2 hours, the second week she practiced $2\frac{1}{2}$ hours, the third week she practiced 3 hours, and the fourth week she practiced $3\frac{1}{2}$ hours. If she continues this pattern, how many hours will she practice the sixth week?

    A. 4 hours   **B.** $4\frac{1}{2}$ hours   **C.** 5 hours   **D.** $5\frac{1}{2}$ hours

16. _____

Name_____ Date _____

Cumulative Review, Chapters 1–8

Estimate. (Lessons 7-1 and 8-6)

1. $8\frac{7}{8} \times 10\frac{5}{6}$ 2. 32% of 152

Solve each equation. (Lessons 4-3 and 4-7)

3. $3.12 \times 1.8 = m$ 4. $x = 73.44 \div 3.6$

5. Find the LCM of 50 and 80. (Lesson 5-7)

Order from greatest to least. (Lessons 3-3 and 5-8)

6. 1.008, 1.7, 1.09   7. $\frac{5}{16}, \frac{17}{48}, \frac{5}{24}$

Complete. (Lessons 4-9 and 7-7)

8. 8,500 mg = _?_ g   9. 12 gal = _?_ c

10. Subtract 3 h 52 min from 7 h 12 min. (Lesson 6-7)

Perform the indicated operation. Write answers in simplest form. (Lessons 6-4, 6-5, 7-2, and 7-6)

11. $\frac{7}{20} + \frac{1}{30}$ 12. $3\frac{1}{5} - 1\frac{9}{10}$

13. $\frac{1}{18} \times \frac{3}{4}$ 14. $5\frac{1}{3} \div 2\frac{1}{4}$

15. A stadium has 15,000 seats. If 12,892 people attend a game in the stadium, how many seats are left? Solve using the four-step plan. (Lesson 1-1)

16. List the stems for a stem-and-leaf plot for this set of data: 88, 93, 74, 68, 97, 82. (Lesson 2-6)

17. Solve the proportion $\frac{26}{40} = \frac{39}{x}$. (Lesson 8-2)

Express each percent as a fraction in simplest form and as a decimal. (Lessons 8-4 and 8-5)

18. 38%   19. 5.4%

20. Find 40% of 800. (Lesson 8-7)

1. _____

2. _____

3. _____

4. _____

5. _____

6. _____

7. _____

8. _____

9. _____

10. _____

11. _____

12. _____

13. _____

14. _____

15. _____

16. _____

17. _____

18. _____

19. _____

20. _____

Mathematics: Applications and Connections, Course 1

Chapter 8 Answer Key

Form 1A

Page 197

1. D
2. B
3. D
4. B
5. C
6. A
7. C
8. A
9. A
10. B
11. C
12. A

Page 198

13. D
14. B
15. C
16. B
17. C
18. D
19. A
20. B
21. D
22. A
23. C
24. B
25. A

Form 1B

Page 199

1. D
2. B
3. A
4. A
5. B
6. A
7. C
8. C
9. B
10. A
11. D
12. D

Page 200

13. B
14. B
15. B
16. D
17. B
18. D
19. A
20. B
21. A
22. B
23. D
24. C
25. C

Mathematics: Applications and Connections, Course 1

Chapter 8 Answer Key

Form 1C

Page 201

1. D
2. B
3. A
4. B
5. C
6. D
7. B
8. A
9. B
10. A
11. D
12. C

Page 202

13. B
14. B
15. D
16. B
17. C
18. A
19. C
20. B
21. D
22. B
23. A
24. B
25. C

Mathematics: Applications and Connections, Course 1

Chapter 8 Answer Key

Form 2A

Page 203

1. $\dfrac{7}{11}$

2. $\dfrac{3}{22}$

3. 2.7 beats per s

4. 22.5 push-ups per min

5. 7 ft per s

6. 12

7. 90

8. 4

9. 111

10. 93

11. 52 ft

12. 46 km

13. 70 miles

14. 64%

15. 38%

16. 23%

Page 204

17. $\dfrac{19}{20}$, 0.95

18. $\dfrac{3}{50}$, 0.06

19. $\dfrac{1}{125}$, 0.008

20. 2.9%

21. 89%

22. 230%

23. $\dfrac{1}{3}$ of 18 = 6

24. $\dfrac{1}{10}$ of 180 = 18

25. $\dfrac{1}{2}$ of 600 = 300

26. $\dfrac{1}{3}$ of 150 = 50

27. $\dfrac{3}{4}$ of 120 = 90

28. 36.75

29. 18

30. 111.39

31. 256

32. 81.6

33. 40

Mathematics: Applications and Connections, Course 1

Chapter 8 Answer Key

Form 2B

Page 205

1. $\dfrac{8}{25}$

2. $\dfrac{1}{20}$

3. 53 km/h

4. $5/month

5. 8 ft per s

6. 27

7. 20

8. 8

9. 2

10. 112

11. 7 ft

12. 32 km

13. 40 miles

14. 56%

15. 85%

16. 80%

Page 206

17. $\dfrac{41}{50}$, 0.82

18. $\dfrac{3}{50}$, 0.06

19. $\dfrac{17}{500}$, 0.034

20. 77%

21. 4.6%

22. 470%

23. $\dfrac{1}{2}$ of 60 = 30

24. $\dfrac{3}{4}$ of 20 = 15

25. $\dfrac{1}{5}$ of 200 = 40

26. $\dfrac{1}{3}$ of 60 = 20

27. $\dfrac{1}{2}$ of 140 = 70

28. 24

29. 32.13

30. 15

31. 32

32. 144

33. 6

Mathematics: Applications and Connections, Course 1

Chapter 8 Answer Key

Page 207

1. $\dfrac{9}{20}$

2. $\dfrac{1}{25}$

3. 30 mpg

4. 30 students per class

5. 8 ft per s

6. 1

7. 7

8. 18

9. 8

10. 10

11. 2 ft

12. 20 km

13. 10 miles

14. 50%

15. 30%

16. 42%

Page 208

17. $\dfrac{3}{4}$, 0.75

18. $\dfrac{3}{25}$, 0.12

19. $\dfrac{1}{10}$, 0.1

20. 84%

21. 62%

22. 7%

23. $\dfrac{1}{10}$ of 200 = 20

24. $\dfrac{1}{4}$ of 400 = 100

25. $\dfrac{1}{2}$ of 250 = 125

26. $\dfrac{1}{3}$ of 60 = 20

27. $\dfrac{3}{4}$ of 120 = 90

28. 21

29. 16

30. 15

31. 48

32. 200

33. 10

Mathematics: Applications and Connections, Course 1

Chapter 8 Scoring Guide

Level	Specific Criteria
3 Superior	• Shows thorough understanding of the concepts *ratio, rate, proportion, scale drawing,* and *expressing fractions and decimals as percents and vice versa.* • Uses appropriate strategies to solve problems. • Computations are correct. • Written explanations are exemplary. • Word problem concerning proportions is appropriate and makes sense. • Diagram is accurate and appropriate. • Goes beyond requirements of some or all problems.
2 Satisfactory, with Minor Flaws	• Shows understanding of the concepts *ratio, rate, proportion, scale drawing,* and *expressing fractions and decimals as percents and vice versa.* • Uses appropriate strategies to solve problems. • Computations are mostly correct. • Written explanations are effective. • Word problem concerning proportions is appropriate and makes sense. • Diagram is mostly accurate and appropriate. • Satisfies all requirements of problems.
1 Nearly Satisfactory, with Serious Flaws	• Shows understanding of most of the concepts *ratio, rate, proportion, scale drawing,* and *expressing fractions and decimals as percents and vice versa.* • May not use appropriate strategies to solve problems. • Computations are mostly correct. • Written explanations are satisfactory. • Word problem concerning proportions is mostly appropriate and sensible. • Diagram is somewhat accurate or appropriate. • Satisfies most requirements of problems.
0 Unsatisfactory	• Shows little or no understanding of the concepts *ratio, rate, proportion, scale drawing,* and *expressing fractions and decimals as percents and vice versa.* • May not use appropriate strategies to solve problems. • Computations are incorrect. • Written explanations are not satisfactory. • Word problem concerning proportions is not appropriate or sensible. • Diagram is not accurate or appropriate. • Does not satisfy requirements of problems.

Chapter 8 Answer Key

Performance Assessment Sample Answers
Page 209

1. a. A ratio is the comparison of two numbers by division.

b. 3 out of 4, 3:4, 3 to 4, $\frac{3}{4}$

c. If the quantities you are comparing have different units of measure, the ratio is called a rate. Sample Answers: 25 miles per hour, $12 per shirt

d. A proportion is a statement that two ratios are equivalent.

e. Brad needed to enlarge a 4 × 5 photo. If the enlargement is 8 inches wide, how long will it be?

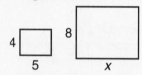

f. $\frac{4}{5} = \frac{8}{x}$ *Write the proportion.*
$4x = 40$ *Write the cross products.*
$x = 10$ *Solve for x.*
The picture will be 10 inches long.

2. a. To express a percent as a fraction, write it with a denominator of 100 and simplify.

To express a percent as a decimal, rewrite the percent as a fraction with a denominator of 100. Then express the fraction as a decimal, or move the decimal point two places to the left.

b. $20\% = \frac{1}{5} = 0.20$
$\frac{1}{5} \times \$35 = \$7$ $0.20 \times \$35 = \$7$
The sale price is $35 − $7 = $28.

c. $30\% \approx \frac{1}{3}$, $\$40 \approx 39$, $\frac{1}{3} \times \$39 = \$13$, $\$40 - \$13 = \$27$
The sale price of the jacket is about $27.

d. 30% of $40 = 0.30 × $40 = $12, $40 − $12 = $28

e. To express a fraction as a percent, write a proportion with the fraction equal to $\frac{n}{100}$. Then solve for n and write as $n\%$.

f. $\frac{1}{4} = \frac{n}{100}$; $4n = 100$; $n = 25$; $\frac{1}{4} = 25\%$

g. 20% of $35 = $7; $\frac{1}{4}$ of $32 = $8.
A customer would save more money on the book.

Mid-Chapter Test
Page 210

1. $\frac{7}{23}$; 7:23; **7 out of 23**

2. $\frac{1}{2}$

3. $\frac{3}{11}$

4. **60 mph**

5. **$5.99 per tape**

6. **no**

7. **yes**

8. **60**

9. **10**

10. **27**

11. **6 games**

12. **90 m**

13. **150 m**

14. **180 m**

15. **10 in.**

16. **2.5 in.**

17. $\frac{14}{25}$

18. $1\frac{43}{100}$

19. **40%**

20. **18%**

Mathematics: Applications and Connections, Course 1

Chapter 8 Answer Key

Quiz A, Page 211

1. $\dfrac{3}{4}$
2. $\dfrac{3}{7}$
3. 89 ft per s
4. $0.25 per muffin
5. $0.21 per can
6. 36
7. 12
8. 80
9. no
10. yes

Quiz B, Page 211

1. 18
2. 90 miles
3. 92%
4. 65%
5. 87.5%
6. 35%
7. $\dfrac{19}{20}$
8. $\dfrac{3}{20}$
9. $\dfrac{6}{25}$
10. $\dfrac{29}{50}$

Quiz C, Page 212

1. 86%
2. 270%
3. 78%
4. 0.07
5. 0.315
6. 1.2
7. $\dfrac{1}{4} \times 800 = 200$
8. $\dfrac{1}{3} \times 120 = 40$
9. $\dfrac{2}{3} \times 150 = 100$
10. $\dfrac{1}{2} \times 500 = 250$

Quiz D, Page 212

1. 147
2. 168.48
3. 8
4. 1.54
5. 146
6. 48
7. 4.1
8. 75
9. $3.60
10. $9.18

Mathematics: Applications and Connections, Course 1

Chapter 8 Answer Key

Standardized Test Practice

Page 213

1. B
2. C
3. C
4. A
5. C
6. A
7. C
8. D
9. B

Page 214

10. A
11. C
12. B
13. A
14. B
15. D
16. B

Cumulative Review
Page 215

1. $9 \times 11 = 99$
2. $\frac{1}{3} \times 150 = 50$
3. 5.616
4. 20.4
5. 400
6. 1.7, 1.09, 1.008
7. $\frac{17}{48}, \frac{5}{16}, \frac{5}{24}$
8. 8.5 g
9. 192 c
10. 3 h 20 min
11. $\frac{23}{60}$
12. $1\frac{3}{10}$
13. $\frac{1}{24}$
14. $2\frac{10}{27}$
15. 2,108
16. 6, 7, 8, 9
17. 60
18. $\frac{19}{50}$, 0.38
19. $\frac{27}{500}$, 0.054
20. 320

Mathematics: Applications and Connections, Course 1

Chapter 9 Test, Form 1A

1. Classify the angle shown at the right.
   A. acute
   B. right
   C. obtuse
   D. none of these

   1. _____

2. Classify an angle that measures 90.5°.
   A. acute   B. right   C. obtuse   D. none of these

   2. _____

3. Use a protractor to measure ∠GHI.
   A. 155°   B. 20°
   C. 152°   D. 25°

   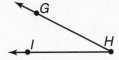

   3. _____

4. Complete: The measure of ∠PQR is __?__ 85°.
   A. greater than
   B. less than
   C. about equal to

   4. _____

5. Complete: The measure of ∠RST is __?__ 91°.
   A. greater than
   B. less than
   C. about equal to

   5. _____

6. Estimate which angle has a measure closest to 125°.
   A.   B.

   C.   D.

   6. _____

7. What is the name of the angle at the right?
   A. ∠ELT   B. ∠LTE
   C. ∠LET   D. ∠ETL

   7. _____

8. Which figure shows an angle of 46° that is bisected?
   A.   B.   C.   D.

   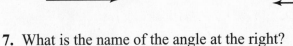

   8. _____

9. Name the figure at the right.
   A. decagon   B. hexagon
   C. crown   D. pentagon

   9. _____

Mathematics: Applications and Connections, Course 1

Chapter 9 Test, Form 1A (continued)

10. Which figure is a parallelogram?

   A.   B.   C.   D.

   10. _____

11. How many sides does a decagon have?
   A. 8   B. 9   C. 10   D. 12

   11. _____

12. How many sides does an octagon have?
   A. 12   B. 6   C. 10   D. 8

   12. _____

13. Which dashed line is a line of symmetry?

   A.   B.   C.   D.

   13. _____

14. How many lines of symmetry does a regular pentagon have?
   A. 6   B. 5   C. 4   D. 3

   14. _____

15. The figure at the right shows __?__ .
   A. a reflection   B. a congruent line segment
   C. a bisector   D. similar figures

   15. _____

16. Describe the polygons at the right.
   A. congruent
   B. similar
   C. neither

   16. _____

17. Two figures that are congruent have the
   A. same shape and angles but different size.
   B. same area.
   C. same size and shape.
   D. same color.

   17. _____

18. The symbol ≅ means __?__ .
   A. is equal to   B. is similar to
   C. is congruent to   D. none of these

   18. _____

19. A hinged lid opens 130°. What type of angle is formed by the open lid?
   A. obtuse   B. acute   C. right   D. none of these

   19. _____

20. There are 40 students in art class. Of these, 18 students are painting pictures, 12 students are making sculptures, and 7 students are doing both. How many students in art class are neither painting pictures nor making sculptures?
   A. 10 students   B. 17 students   C. 30 students   D. 3 students

   20. _____

9

Chapter 9 Test, Form 1B

1. Classify the angle shown at the right.
   A. acute　　　　　　　　B. right
   C. obtuse　　　　　　　　D. none of these

1. _____

2. Classify an angle that measures 34°.
   A. acute　　B. right　　C. obtuse　　D. none of these

2. _____

3. Use a protractor to measure ∠LMN.
   A. 33°　　　　　　　　B. 147°
   C. 153°　　　　　　　　D. none of these

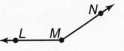

3. _____

4. Complete: The measure of ∠ABC is _?_ 20°.
   A. greater than
   B. less than
   C. about equal to

4. _____

5. Complete: The measure of ∠PQR is _?_ 130°.
   A. greater than
   B. less than
   C. about equal to

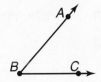

5. _____

6. Estimate which angle has a measure closest to 100°.
   A.　　　　　B.　　　　　C.　　　　　D.

6. _____

7. What is the name of the angle at the right?
   A. ∠TSV　　　　　　　　B. ∠TVS
   C. ∠SVT　　　　　　　　D. ∠STV

7. _____

8. Which figure shows a line segment that is bisected?
   A.　　　　　　　　　　B.

   C.　　　　　　　　　　D.

8. _____

9. Name the figure at the right.
   A. octagon　　　　　　　B. hexagon
   C. pentagon　　　　　　　D. quadrilateral

9. _____

Mathematics: Applications and Connections, Course 1

Chapter 9 Test, Form 1B (continued)

10. Which figure is an equilateral triangle?

A. **B.** **C.** **D.**

10. _____

11. How many sides does an octagon have?

A. 5 **B.** 6 **C.** 8 **D.** 10

11. _____

12. How many sides does a pentagon have?

A. 5 **B.** 6 **C.** 8 **D.** 10

12. _____

13. Which dashed line is a line of symmetry?

A. **B.** **C.** **D.**

13. _____

14. How many lines of symmetry does a rectangle have?

A. 1 **B.** 2 **C.** 0 **D.** 4

14. _____

15. The figure at the right shows __?__.

A. a reflection **B.** congruent line segments

C. a bisector **D.** obtuse angles

15. _____

16. Describe the polygons at the right.

A. congruent

B. similar

C. neither

16. _____

17. Describe the polygons at the right.

A. congruent

B. similar

C. neither

17. _____

18. The symbol ~ means __?__.

A. is equal to **B.** is congruent to

C. is similar to **D.** none of these

18. _____

19. One of the hills on a roller coaster makes a 50° angle with the ground. What type of angle is formed?

A. obtuse **B.** acute **C.** right **D.** none of these

19. _____

20. There are 95 teenagers at the mall. Of these, 42 teenagers go to the record store, 25 teenagers go to a clothing store, and 18 teenagers go to both stores. How many teenagers went only to the record store?

A. 24 **B.** 42 **C.** 17 **D.** 18

20. _____

Mathematics: Applications and Connections, Course 1

Chapter 9 Test, Form 1C

1. Classify the angle shown at the right.
   A. acute   B. right
   C. obtuse   D. none of these

   1. _____

2. Classify an angle that measures 90°.
   A. acute   B. right   C. obtuse   D. none of these

   2. _____

3. Use a protractor to measure ∠XYZ.
   A. 150°   B. 155°
   C. 25°   D. 30°

   3. _____

4. Complete: The measure of ∠DEF is __?__ 100°.
   A. greater than
   B. less than
   C. about equal to

   4. _____

5. Complete: The measure of ∠PQR is __?__ 15°.
   A. greater than
   B. less than
   C. about equal to

   5. _____

6. Estimate which angle has a measure closest to 170°.
   A.   B.

   C.   D.

   6. _____

7. What is the name of the angle at the right?
   A. ∠RPQ   B. ∠RQP
   C. ∠PRQ   D. ∠PQR

   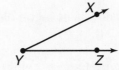

   7. _____

8. Which figure shows a line segment that is bisected?
   A.   B.

   C.   D.

   8. _____

9. Name the figure at the right.
   A. pentagon   B. quadrilateral
   C. hexagon   D. octagon

   9. _____

Mathematics: Applications and Connections, Course 1

10. Which figure is a rectangle? 10. _____
    A.

    B.

    C.

    D.

11. How many sides does a hexagon have? 11. _____
    A. 10   **B.** 8   **C.** 6   **D.** 5

12. How many sides does an isosceles triangle have? 12. _____
    A. 3   **B.** 6   **C.** 8   **D.** 4

13. Which dashed line is a line of symmetry? 13. _____
    A.

    B.

    C.

    D.

14. How many lines of symmetry does an equilateral triangle have? 14. _____
    A. 0   **B.** 1   **C.** 2   **D.** 3

15. The figure at the right shows __?__ . 15. _____
    A. a reflection   **B.** a line segment   A ↕ A
    C. a bisector   **D.** obtuse angles

16. Describe the polygons at the right. 16. _____
    A. congruent   **B.** similar   **C.** neither

17. Describe the polygons at the right. 17. _____
    A. congruent   **B.** similar   **C.** neither

18. The symbol ≅ means __?__ . 18. _____
    A. is equal to   **B.** is congruent to   **C.** is similar to   **D.** none of these

19. A handicap ramp is graded at 12°. What type of angle is formed by this 19. _____
    grade?
    A. acute   **B.** right   **C.** obtuse   **D.** none of these

20. A sixth-grade class has 60 students. Of these, 18 students are on the swim 20. _____
    team, 22 students are on the gymnastics team, and 7 students are on both
    teams. How many students are only on the swim team?
    A. 18   **B.** 11   **C.** 25   **D.** none of these

Mathematics: Applications and Connections, Course 1

Name_____ Date _____

Chapter 9 Test, Form 2A

Classify each angle as acute, right, or obtuse.

1. 60°

2.

3.

4. 96°

5. 174°

6. 2°

1. _____

2. _____

3. _____

4. _____

5. _____

6. _____

Tell whether each angle is greater than, less than, or about equal to the measurement given.

7.   190°

8.   22°

9.   92°

7. _____

8. _____

9. _____

10. Use a protractor to find the measure of ∠MNO.

10. _____

Draw an angle or segment with the given measurement. Then use a straightedge or compass to bisect each angle or segment.

11. 3.2 cm

12. 48°

13. What is the length of the bisected segment in Question 11?

11. _____

12. _____

13. _____

Mathematics: Applications and Connections, Course 1

Name each polygon.

14.

14. _____

15.

15. _____

Tell the number of lines of symmetry for each figure.

16. the polygon in Question 14

16. _____

17. the polygon in Question 15

17. _____

Tell whether each pair of figures is congruent, similar, or neither.

18.

18. _____

19.

19. _____

20. Name the polygons in Question 18.

20. _____

21. Name the polygons in Question 19.

21. _____

Tell the number of lines of symmetry for each figure.

22. the polygons in Question 18

22. _____

23. the polygons in Question 19

23. _____

24. What is the difference between complementary angles and supplementary angles?

24. _____

25. Of the 175 chorale members, 71 can sing alto parts, 58 can sing soprano, and 12 can sing both. How many chorale members can't sing alto or soprano?

25. _____

Name_____ Date _____

Chapter 9 Test, Form 2B

Classify each angle as acute, right, or obtuse.

1. 53°

1. _____

2.

2. _____

3.

3. _____

4. 120°

4. _____

5. 93°

5. _____

6. 3°

6. _____

Tell whether each angle is greater than, less than, or about equal to the measurement given.

7.   87°

7. _____

8.   45°

8. _____

9.   80°

9. _____

10. Use a protractor to find the measure of ∠RST.

10. _____

Draw an angle or segment with the given measurement. Then use a straightedge or compass to bisect each angle or segment.

11. 2.5 cm

11. _____

12. 32°

12. _____

13. What is the length of the bisected segment in Question 11?

13. _____

Mathematics: Applications and Connections, Course 1

Chapter 9 Test, Form 2B (continued)

Name each polygon.

14.

14. _____

15.

15. _____

Tell the number of lines of symmetry for each figure.

16. the polygon in Question 14

16. _____

17. the polygon in Question 15

17. _____

Tell whether each pair of figures is congruent, similar, or neither.

18.

18. _____

19.

19. _____

20. Name the polygons in Question 18.

20. _____

21. Name the polygons in Question 19.

21. _____

Tell the number of lines of symmetry for each figure.

22. the polygons in Question 18

22. _____

23. the polygons in Question 19

23. _____

24. If the sum of the measures of two angles is 180°, the angles are __?__.

24. _____

25. Of the 70 students in the music club, 18 play piano, 27 play a brass horn, and 4 play both. How many students play neither piano nor a brass horn?

25. _____

Mathematics: Applications and Connections, Course 1

Name_____ **Date** _____

Chapter 9 Test, Form 2C

Classify each angle as acute, right, or obtuse.

1. 42°

1. _____

2.

2. _____

3. ⌐→
   ↓

3. _____

4. 179°

4. _____

5. 90°

5. _____

6. 1°

6. _____

Tell whether each angle is greater than, less than, or about equal to the measurement given.

7.   90°

7. _____

8.   30°

8. _____

9.   89°

9. _____

10. Use a protractor to find the measure of ∠XYZ.

10. _____

Draw an angle or segment with the given measurement. Then use a straightedge or compass to bisect each angle or segment.

11. 3 cm

11. _____

12. 50°

12. _____

13. What is the length of the bisected segment in Question 11?

13. _____

Mathematics: Applications and Connections, Course 1

Name each polygon.

14.

14. _____

15.

15. _____

Tell the number of lines of symmetry for each figure.

16. the polygon in Question 14

16. _____

17. the polygon in Question 15

17. _____

Tell whether each pair of figures is congruent, similar, or neither.

18.

18. _____

19.

19. _____

20. Name the polygons in Question 18.

20. _____

21. Name the polygons in Question 19.

21. _____

Tell the number of lines of symmetry for each figure.

22. the polygons in Question 18

22. _____

23. the polygons in Question 19

23. _____

24. If the sum of the measures of two angles is 90°, the angles are __?__.

24. _____

25. Of the 20 students in the language club, 12 speak Spanish, 8 speak French, and 3 speak both. How many students speak neither French nor Spanish?

25. _____

Chapter 9 Performance Assessment

Instructions: Demonstrate your knowledge by giving a clear, concise solution to each problem. Be sure to include all relevant drawings and justify your answers. You may show your solutions in more than one way or investigate beyond the requirements of the problems.

1. Taylor planted a garden that looks like the figure.

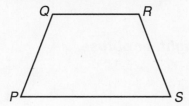

   a. Name the shape of the garden. Explain your reasoning.

   b. Name each of the angles as acute, obtuse, or right. Explain your reasoning and estimate the measures of each angle.

   c. She wishes to bury a pipe for a sprinkler along the bisector of ∠QPS. Use a compass and straightedge to bisect ∠QPS. Explain each step.

   d. If Taylor wants her garden to be symmetrical, where could she draw lines of symmetry in her garden?

   e. Taylor decides that she wants a smaller garden that is exactly like her large garden. Tell the term that describes that other garden and explain what parts must be the same.

 Name_____ Date_____

Chapter 9 Mid-Chapter Test
(Lessons 9-1 through 9-3)

Use a protractor to find the measure of each angle.

1. 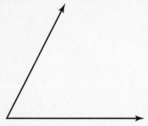   2.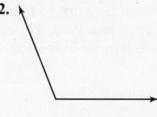

1. _____

2. _____

Classify each angle measure as acute, right, or obtuse.

3. 90°   4. 1°

3. _____

4. _____

5. 36°   6. 141°

5. _____

6. _____

Classify the following angle pairs as complementary, supplementary, or neither.

7. 38° and 52°   8. 116° and 65°

7. _____

8. _____

Use a protractor and straightedge to draw angles having the following measurements.

9. 42°   10. 139°

9. _____

10. _____

Estimate the measure of each angle shown.

11.   12.

11. _____

12. _____

Draw the angle or line segment for the given measurement. Then use a straightedge and compass to bisect each.

13. 2.4 cm   14. 36°

13. _____

14. _____

15. Of the 28 pets in the classroom, 8 are reptiles, 15 live in water, and 2 are reptiles that live in the water. How many of the pets are not reptiles and do not live in the water?

15. _____

16. In the sixth grade, there are 236 students. 128 sixth-graders are in chorus, 132 are in band, and 74 are in both. How many sixth-graders are not in chorus or band?

16. _____

Mathematics: Applications and Connections, Course 1

Chapter 9 Quiz A

Use a protractor to find the measure of each angle.

1.   2.

Classify each angle as acute, right, or obtuse.

3. the angle in Question 1   4. the angle in Question 2

5. 170°   6. 90°   7. 5°

Tell whether the measure of each angle is greater than, less than, or about equal to the measurement given.

8. 78°   9. 92°

10. Of 50 students, 18 are in the chorus, 14 are on the baseball team, and 5 are in both. How many students are neither in the chorus nor on the baseball team?

1. _____

2. _____

3. _____

4. _____

5. _____

6. _____

7. _____

8. _____

9. _____

10. _____

- -

Chapter 9 Quiz B

1. Draw a 28° angle. Then use a compass and straightedge to bisect it.

2. What are the measures of the resulting angles in Question 1?

3. Draw a line segment 2.8 centimeters long. Then use a compass and straightedge to bisect it.

4. What are the measures of the resulting line segments in Question 3?

5. What does bisect mean?

1. _____

2. _____

3. _____

4. _____

5. _____

Chapter 9 Quiz C

(Lessons 9-4 and 9-5)

Name each polygon.

1.

2.

1. _____

2. _____

Tell the number of lines of symmetry for each figure.

3. the polygon in Question 1

3. _____

4. the polygon in Question 2

4. _____

5. Draw all lines of symmetry in the figure at the right.

5. _____

Chapter 9 Quiz D

(Lesson 9-6)

1. What symbol means *is similar to*?

1. _____

2. What symbol means *is congruent to*?

2. _____

3. To be congruent, two figures must have the same _?_ and _?_.

3. _____

4. To be similar, two figures must have the same _?_ and _?_.

4. _____

5. Tell whether the pair of polygons is congruent, similar, or neither.

5. _____

Mathematics: Applications and Connections, Course 1

Name_____ Date _____

Chapter 9 Standardized Test Practice

1. Three road blinkers are turned on at the same time. One blinks every 6 seconds, another every 10 seconds, and the third every 12 seconds. How many times per hour do they blink at once?
   A. 72　　　**B.** 60　　　**C.** 30　　　**D.** 36

   1. _____

2. Dale bought a package of meat weighing 0.88 pound. Express this decimal as a fraction in lowest terms.
   A. $\frac{22}{25}$　　**B.** $\frac{88}{100}$　　**C.** $\frac{44}{50}$　　**D.** $\frac{11}{12}$

   2. _____

3. Therese took 10 karate lessons. She spent a total of $7\frac{1}{2}$ hours in instruction. How long was each lesson?
   A. $\frac{2}{3}$ hour　　**B.** $\frac{3}{4}$ hour　　**C.** $17\frac{1}{2}$ hours　　**D.** 1 hour

   3. _____

4. Madison rents an apartment for $725 a month. Each year the monthly rent is expected to increase $14.75. What will the monthly rent be at the end of six years?
   A. $815.30　　**B.** $798.75　　**C.** $813.50　　**D.** $828.25

   4. _____

5. A movie company made a large model of a domino. The actual width of a domino is 15 millimeters. If the scale is 1 m = 2.5 mm, what is the width of the model?
   A. 6 m　　**B.** 37.5 m　　**C.** 17.5 m　　**D.** 12.5 m

   5. _____

6. The local appliance center purchases their vacuum cleaners for $129. When they sell the vacuum cleaners, they mark the price up 43%. What is the final cost of a vacuum cleaner?
   A. $55.47　　**B.** $129　　**C.** $184.47　　**D.** $73.53

   6. _____

7. Elena found a cone from a Scotch pine that was $1\frac{1}{6}$ inches long and a cone from a white pine that was $4\frac{3}{8}$ inches long. Estimate how much longer the cone from the white pine is than the cone from the Scotch pine.
   A. 3 in.　　**B.** $4\frac{1}{4}$ in.　　**C.** 5 in.　　**D.** $3\frac{1}{2}$ in.

   7. _____

8. Jamie spent $\frac{3}{8}$ of her free time on Tuesday morning and $\frac{1}{6}$ of her free time on Tuesday afternoon at the pool. What fraction of her free time did Jamie spend at the pool on Tuesday?
   A. $\frac{5}{24}$　　**B.** $\frac{13}{24}$　　**C.** $\frac{4}{14}$　　**D.** none of these

   8. _____

9. Miranda has 27 CDs. She gave g CDs to her friend Charmaine. She has 21 CDs left. Which equation represents the situation?
   A. $g - 21 = 27$　　　　**B.** $27 + 21 = g$
   C. $27 - g = 21$　　　　**D.** none of these

   9. _____

Mathematics: Applications and Connections, Course 1

10. The owner of the Pachyderm Press Bookstore is reviewing her sales records for the past six months. She wants to make a graph to more easily compare her results. Which type of graph should she use?
    A. bar graph
    B. number line
    C. circle graph
    D. stem-and-leaf plot

10. _____

11. Jackie walked 3.8 kilometers on Monday, 2.1 kilometers on Tuesday, 3.4 kilometers on Wednesday, 2.8 kilometers on Thursday, and 3.4 kilometers on Friday. Estimate the total distance she walked that week.
    A. 13 km   **B.** 15 km   **C.** 17 km   **D.** none of these

11. _____

12. A class of 40 students went to a museum. The trip cost $294.40, which included bus rental of $156.40. How much was each student's museum ticket?
    A. $7.36   **B.** $3.45   **C.** $3.91   **D.** $5.00

12. _____

13. Macauley's dad bought a new lawn chair. Macauley decided to practice his math skills and measure the chair at each of the settings. He made a drawing of the most comfortable setting. Use a protractor to measure the angle.

    A. 19°   **B.** 109°   **C.** 161°   **D.** 172°

13. _____

14. Mandy and Jenny went to the art museum. They were looking at a modern sculpture similar to the figure at the right. How many lines of symmetry does the figure have?
    A. 0   **B.** 1   **C.** 2   **D.** 4

14. _____

15. Andre and Darrell were drawing two-dimensional figures, but they couldn't remember how many sides a parallelogram has. How many sides does a parallelogram have?
    A. 3   **B.** 4   **C.** 5   **D.** 6

15. _____

16. Tyree made a drawing of his dad's office and included a bird's eye view of two desks as shown. Tell whether the shapes are congruent, similar, or neither.

    A. congruent   **B.** similar   **C.** neither   **D.** both A & B

16. _____

Mathematics: Applications and Connections, Course 1

Name_____ Date _____

Cumulative Review, Chapters 1–9

Perform the indicated operation. (Lessons 3-6 and 4-1)
1. $1.98 + 36.1$ 2. 78×3.7

1. _____

2. _____

Estimate. (Lessons 6-2 and 7-1)

3. _____

3. $\frac{1}{10} + \frac{17}{20}$ 4. $9\frac{1}{6} \times 7\frac{9}{10}$

4. _____

Solve each equation. Write the solution in simplest form.
(Lessons 6-3, 6-4, 7-2, and 7-6)

5. _____

5. $\frac{1}{16} + \frac{7}{16} = m$ 6. $x = \frac{27}{32} - \frac{3}{8}$

6. _____

7. $a = \frac{7}{18} \times \frac{1}{3}$ 8. $q = 3\frac{1}{6} \div 1\frac{1}{4}$

7. _____

9. Solve the proportion $\frac{28}{32} = \frac{14}{y}$. (Lesson 8-2)

8. _____

9. _____

10. Express 0.6% as a decimal. (Lesson 8-5)

10. _____

11. Express 2.4 as a percent. (Lesson 8-5)

11. _____

12. What is/are the mode(s) of the following scores: 96, 83, 96, 80, 85, 80, 78? (Lesson 2-7)

12. _____

13. State whether 195 is divisible by 2, 3, 5, 6, 9, or 10. (Lesson 5-1)

13. _____

14. Write 0.95 as a fraction in simplest form. (Lesson 5-9)

14. _____

15. Evaluate xy if $x = 7$ and $y = 10$. (Lesson 1-5)

15. _____

16. Round $39.36 \div 74$ to the nearest tenth. (Lesson 4-5)

16. _____

17. How many pounds are in $9\frac{1}{2}$ tons? (Lesson 7-7)

17. _____

18. Classify a 120° angle as acute, right, or obtuse. (Lesson 9-1)

18. _____

19. Tell whether the dashed line in the figure is a line of symmetry. Write *yes* or *no*. (Lesson 9-5)

19. _____

20. Tell whether the pair of polygons is congruent, similar, or neither. (Lesson 9-6)

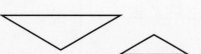

20. _____

Mathematics: Applications and Connections, Course 1

Chapter 9 Answer Key

Form 1A

Page 225

1. _____A_____
2. _____C_____
3. _____D_____
4. _____B_____
5. _____C_____
6. _____B_____
7. _____C_____
8. _____B_____
9. _____D_____

Page 226

10. _____A_____
11. _____C_____
12. _____D_____
13. _____A_____
14. _____B_____
15. _____A_____
16. _____B_____
17. _____C_____
18. _____C_____
19. _____A_____
20. _____B_____

Form 1B

Page 227

1. _____C_____
2. _____A_____
3. _____B_____
4. _____A_____
5. _____B_____
6. _____C_____
7. _____D_____
8. _____A_____
9. _____B_____

Page 228

10. _____A_____
11. _____C_____
12. _____A_____
13. _____C_____
14. _____B_____
15. _____A_____
16. _____B_____
17. _____A_____
18. _____C_____
19. _____B_____
20. _____A_____

Mathematics: Applications and Connections, Course 1

Chapter 9 Answer Key

Form 1C

Page 229	Page 230
1. A	10. D
2. B	
3. C	11. C
	12. A
4. B	13. B
5. A	
6. D	14. D
	15. A
	16. B
7. A	17. C
8. C	18. B
	19. A
9. B	20. B

Chapter 9 Answer Key

Form 2A

Page 231

1. acute

2. obtuse

3. right

4. obtuse

5. obtuse

6. acute

7. less than

8. greater than

9. about equal to

10. 110°

11.

12.

13. 1.6 cm

Page 232

14. quadrilateral

15. octagon

16. 0

17. 1

18. congruent

19. neither

20. octagons

21. pentagon, hexagon

22. 4

23. 5, 2

24. complementary angles' sum = 90°; supplementary angles' sum = 180°

25. 58

Mathematics: Applications and Connections, Course 1

Chapter 9 Answer Key

Form 2B

Page 233		Page 234	
1.	acute	14.	pentagon
2.	right	15.	hexagon
3.	obtuse		
4.	obtuse		
5.	obtuse		
6.	acute	16.	1
		17.	2
7.	about equal to		
8.	about equal to	18.	neither
9.	greater than	19.	similar
		20.	parallelogram and rectangle or quadrilaterals
10.	15°	21.	triangles
11.		22.	0, 2
		23.	1
12.		24.	supplementary
13.	1.25 cm	25.	29

Mathematics: Applications and Connections, Course 1

Chapter 9 Answer Key

Form 2C

Page 235

1. acute
2. acute
3. right
4. obtuse
5. right
6. acute

7. less than
8. greater than
9. about equal to
10. 130°

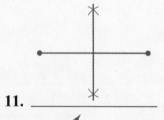

11. _____

12. _____
13. 1.5 cm

Page 236

14. pentagon
15. square

16. 1
17. 4

18. similar
19. neither
20. triangles
21. square, rectangle, or quadrilaterals

22. 0
23. 4, 2
24. complementary
25. 3

Mathematics: Applications and Connections, Course 1

Chapter 9 Scoring Guide

Level	Specific Criteria
3 Superior	• Shows thorough understanding of the concepts *classifying, drawing, and measuring angles, bisecting line segments and angles, naming two-dimensional figures, describing lines of symmetry,* and *determining similarity.* • Uses appropriate strategies to solve problems. • Computations are correct. • Written explanations are exemplary. • Diagram is accurate and appropriate. • Goes beyond requirements of some or all problems.
2 Satisfactory, with Minor Flaws	• Shows understanding of the concepts *classifying, drawing, and measuring angles, bisecting line segments and angles, naming two-dimensional figures, describing lines of symmetry,* and *determining similarity.* • Uses appropriate strategies to solve problems. • Computations are mostly correct. • Diagram is mostly accurate and appropriate. • Written explanations are effective. • Satisfies all requirements of problems.
1 Nearly Satisfactory, with Serious Flaws	• Shows understanding of most of the concepts *classifying, drawing, and measuring angles, bisecting line segments and angles, naming two-dimensional figures, describing lines of symmetry,* and *determining similarity.* • May not use appropriate strategies to solve problems. • Computations are mostly correct. • Diagram is mostly accurate and appropriate. • Written explanations are satisfactory. • Satisfies most requirements of problems.
0 Unsatisfactory	• Shows little or no understanding of the concepts *classifying, drawing, and measuring angles, bisecting line segments and angles, naming two-dimensional figures, describing lines of symmetry,* and *determining similarity.* • May not use appropriate strategies to solve problems. • Computations are incorrect. • Diagram is not accurate or appropriate. • Written explanations are not satisfactory. • Does not satisfy requirements of problems.

Chapter 9 Answer Key

1. **a.** The shape of the garden is a quadrilateral because it is a four-sided polygon.

   b. ∠Q and ∠R are obtuse because they are greater than 90°. They measure about 110°. ∠P and ∠S are acute because they are less than 90°. They measure about 70°.

   c.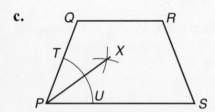

   1. Set the compass at a length less than the length of $\overline{PQ}$ and draw an arc TU as shown.

   2. Place the point of the compass at T and draw an arc as shown.

   3. With the same compass setting, place the point of the compass at U and draw an arc intersecting the arc from part 2 at X.

   4. Draw $\overline{PX}$.

   d. The line of symmetry would bisect $\overline{PS}$ and $\overline{QR}$.

   e. The second garden would be similar. The shape and angles would be the same, but the size would be different.

Mid-Chapter Test
Page 238

1. _____63°_____

2. _____115°_____

3. _____right_____

4. _____acute_____

5. _____acute_____

6. _____obtuse_____

7. __complementary__

8. _____neither_____

9. _____

10. _____

11. _____75°_____

12. _____125°_____

13. _____

14. _____

15. _____7_____

16. _____50_____

Chapter 9 Answer Key

Quiz A, Page 239

1. _____22°_____
2. _____126°_____

3. _____acute_____
4. _____obtuse_____
5. _____obtuse_____
6. _____right_____
7. _____acute_____
8. _greater than_
9. _about equal to_
10. _____23_____

Quiz B, Page 239

1.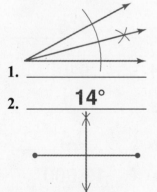
2. _____14°_____
3. _____
4. _____1.4 cm_____
5. _to separate into two congruent parts_

Quiz C, Page 240

1. _____decagon_____
2. _____octagon_____

3. _____5_____

4. _____1_____

5.

Quiz D, Page 240

1. _____~_____

2. _____≅_____

3. _size, shape_

4. _shape, angles_

5. _congruent_

Chapter 9 Answer Key

Standardized Test Practice

Page 241

1. B
2. A
3. B
4. C
5. A
6. C
7. D
8. B
9. C

Page 242

10. A
11. B
12. B
13. C
14. C
15. B
16. A

Cumulative Review

Page 243

1. 38.08
2. 288.6
3. $0 + 1 = 1$
4. $9 \times 8 = 72$
5. $\frac{1}{2}$
6. $\frac{15}{32}$
7. $\frac{7}{54}$
8. $2\frac{8}{15}$
9. 16
10. 0.006
11. 240%
12. 80, 96
13. 3, 5
14. $\frac{19}{20}$
15. 70
16. 0.5
17. 19,000
18. obtuse
19. no
20. similar

Mathematics: Applications and Connections, Course 1

Chapter 10 Test, Form 1A

1. Find the area of the parallelogram shown at the right.
   A. 9 square units
   B. 18 square units
   C. 19.35 square units
   D. 17.2 square units

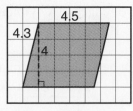

1. _____

2. Find the area of a parallelogram if the base is 34 feet and the height is 20 feet.
   A. 580 ft²   B. 108 ft²   C. 640 ft²   D. none of these

2. _____

3. Find the area of the parallelogram shown at the right.
   A. 17.92 in²
   B. 20.72 in²
   C. 17.92 in.
   D. none of these

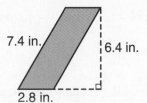

3. _____

4. Find the area of the triangle shown at the right.
   A. 290.25 mm²   B. 1,161 mm²
   C. 580.5 mm²   D. none of these

4. _____

5. What is the area of a triangle with a base of 127 feet and a height of 136 feet?
   A. 8,636 ft²   B. 17,272 ft²   C. 4,318 ft²   D. none of these

5. _____

6. Find the area of the triangle shown at the right.
   A. 844.48 m²   B. 422.24 m²
   C. 211.12 m²   D. none of these

6. _____

7. Find the area of the circle shown at the right.
   Use 3.14 for π.
   A. 10,597.5 in²   B. 94.2 in²
   C. 7,065 in²   D. none of these

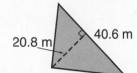

7. _____

8. Find the area of a circle with a diameter of 6.8 centimeters. Use 3.14 for π.
   A. 21.352 cm²   B. 3,629.84 cm²   C. 145.19 cm²   D. none of these

8. _____

9. State the number of vertices in a cone.
   A. 1   B. 2   C. 0   D. none of these

9. _____

10. Name the figure shown at the right.
    A. cone
    B. rectangular prism
    C. triangular pyramid
    D. sphere

10. _____

Mathematics: Applications and Connections, Course 1

11. State the number of edges in a cylinder.
    A. 1   **B.** 2   **C.** 0   **D.** none of these

    11. _____

12. Which pattern can be folded to form a box shaped like a square pyramid?
    A.   **B.**   **C.**   **D.**

    12. _____

13. How many different rectangular prisms can be formed by using exactly 24 cubes?
    A. 2   **B.** 6   **C.** 4   **D.** none of these

    13. _____

14. Find the volume of the rectangular prism shown at the right.
    A. 72 in³   **B.** 13,456 in³
    C. 13,824 in³   **D.** none of these

    24 in. 24 in. 24 in.

    14. _____

15. A cabinet is 30 inches long by 18 inches wide by 24 inches high. What is the volume of the cabinet?
    A. 72 in³   **B.** 1,692 in³   **C.** 3,384 in³   **D.** none of these

    15. _____

16. Find the volume of the rectangular prism described at the right.
    A. 1,850 ft³   **B.** 958.5 ft³
    C. 479.25 ft³   **D.** none of these

    length, 18.5 ft
    width, 12.5 ft
    height, 8 ft

    16. _____

17. Find the surface area of the rectangular prism shown at the right.
    A. 648 ft²   **B.** 972 ft²
    C. 324 ft²   **D.** none of these

    9 ft 6 ft 18 ft

    17. _____

18. Find the surface area of the rectangular prism described at the right.
    A. 72 cm²   **B.** 12,288 cm²   **C.** 1,664 cm²   **D.** none of these

    length, 32 cm
    width, 24 cm
    height, 16 cm

    18. _____

19. A silo has a diameter of 14 feet. What is the area of the base of the silo? Use 3.14 for π.
    A. 615.44 ft²   **B.** 153.86 ft²   **C.** 43.96 ft²   **D.** none of these

    19. _____

20. How much paper would it take to cover a box that is 42 inches by 38 inches by 27 inches if there is no overlap?
    A. 3,756 in²   **B.** 43,092 in²   **C.** 7,512 in²   **D.** none of these

    20. _____

Chapter 10 Test, Form 1B

1. Find the area of the parallelogram shown at the right.
   A. 18 square units
   B. 24 square units
   C. 30 square units
   D. 27 square units

   1. _____

2. Find the area of a parallelogram if the base is 18 centimeters and the height is 25 centimeters.
   A. 430 cm²   B. 86 cm²   C. 450 cm²   D. none of these

   2. _____

3. Find the area of the parallelogram shown at the right.
   A. 245 ft²   B. 196 ft²
   C. 69 ft²   D. none of these

   3. _____

4. Find the area of the triangle shown at the right.
   A. 49 cm²   B. 12.25 cm²
   C. 24.5 cm²   D. none of these

   4. _____

5. What is the area of a triangle with a base of 64 feet and a height of 36 feet?
   A. 1,152 ft²   B. 100 ft²   C. 2,304 ft²   D. none of these

   5. _____

6. Find the area of the triangle shown at the right.
   A. 20.6 in²   B. 50.84 in²
   C. 101.68 in²   D. none of these

   6. _____

7. Find the area of the circle shown at the right. Use 3.14 for π.
   A. 28.26 in²   B. 254.34 in²
   C. 2,289.06 in²   D. none of these

   7. _____

8. Find the area of a circle with a diameter of 4.2 centimeters. Use 3.14 for π.
   A. 13.188 cm²   B. 13.8474 cm²   C. 6.594 cm²   D. none of these

   8. _____

9. State the number of edges in a square pyramid.
   A. 4   B. 3   C. 5   D. none of these

   9. _____

10. Name the figure shown at the right.
    A. cone   B. rectangular prism
    C. square pyramid   D. sphere

    10. _____

11. State the number of faces in a rectangular prism.   11. _____
    A. 6   **B.** 12   **C.** 8   **D.** none of these

12. Which pattern can be folded to form a box shaped like a rectangular prism?   12. _____
    A.   **B.**   **C.**   **D.**

13. How many different rectangular prisms can be formed by using exactly   13. _____
    15 cubes?
    A. 1   **B.** 2   **C.** 3   **D.** none of these

14. Find the volume of the rectangular prism shown at the   14. _____
    right.
    A. 48 mm³   **B.** 1,536 mm³
    C. 4,096 mm³   **D.** none of these

    16 mm
    16 mm
    16 mm

15. A box is 26 inches long by 15 inches wide by 12 inches high. What is the   15. _____
    volume of the box?
    A. 53 in³   **B.** 4,680 in³   **C.** 1,764 in³   **D.** none of these

16. Find the volume of the rectangular prism described at   16. _____
    the right.

    length, 10.5 ft
    width, 8.5 ft
    height, 5 ft

    A. 223.125 ft³   **B.** 446 ft³   **C.** 89.25 ft³   **D.** none of these

17. Find the surface area of the rectangular prism shown   17. _____
    at the right.
    A. 26 m²   **B.** 576 m²
    C. 432 m²   **D.** none of these

    6 m
    8 m
    12 m

18. Find the surface area of the rectangular prism described   18. _____
    at the right.

    length, 17 in.
    width, 13 in.
    height, 8 in

    A. 922 in²   **B.** 461 in²   **C.** 1,768 in²   **D.** none of these

19. A circular tabletop has a radius of 30 inches. What is the area of the   19. _____
    tabletop? Use 3.14 for π.
    A. 94.2 in²   **B.** 2,826 in²   **C.** 188.4 in²   **D.** none of these

20. How much paper would it take to cover a box that is 32 centimeters by   20. _____
    20 centimeters by 10 centimeters if there is no overlap?
    A. 62 cm²   **B.** 6,400 cm²   **C.** 1,160 cm²   **D.** none of these

Chapter 10 Test, Form 1C

1. Find the area of the parallelogram shown at the right.
   A. 12 square units   **B.** 14.2 square units
   C. 6 square units   **D.** 12.3 square units

   1. _____

2. Find the area of a parallelogram if the base is 10 centimeters and the height is 10 centimeters.
   A. 50 cm²   **B.** 20 cm²   **C.** 100 cm²   **D.** none of these

   2. _____

3. Find the area of the parallelogram shown at the right.
   A. 12 ft²   **B.** 8 ft²
   C. 6 ft²   **D.** 9 ft²

   3. _____

4. Find the area of the triangle shown at the right.
   A. 31 m²   **B.** 198 m²
   C. 99 m²   **D.** none of these

   4. _____

5. What is the area of a triangle with a base of 12 millimeters and a height of 24 millimeters?
   A. 36 mm²   **B.** 72 mm²   **C.** 288 mm²   **D.** none of these

   5. _____

6. Find the area of the triangle shown at the right.
   A. 4.84 in²   **B.** 9.68 in²
   C. 6.6 in²   **D.** none of these

   6. _____

7. Find the area of the circle shown at the right. Use 3.14 for π.
   A. 4.14 in²   **B.** 3.14 in²
   C. 6.28 in²   **D.** none of these

   7. _____

8. Find the area of a circle with a diameter of 2.4 centimeters. Use 3.14 for π.
   A. 7.536 cm²   **B.** 18.0864 cm²   **C.** 4.5216 cm²   **D.** none of these

   8. _____

9. State the number of faces in a square pyramid.
   A. 4   **B.** 3   **C.** 5   **D.** none of these

   9. _____

10. Name the figure shown at the right.
    A. cone   **B.** sphere
    C. cylinder   **D.** pyramid

    10. _____

11. State the number of edges in a rectangular prism.
    A. 6   **B.** 12   **C.** 8   **D.** none of these

    11. _____

12. Which pattern can be folded to form a cylinder?   **12.** _____
   A.   **B.**   **C.**   **D.** none of these

13. How many different rectangular prisms can be formed by using exactly   **13.** _____
   9 cubes?
   A. 1   **B.** 2   **C.** 3   **D.** none of these

14. Find the volume of the rectangular prism shown at the right.   **14.** _____
   A. 12 ft³   **B.** 32 ft³
   C. 256 ft³   **D.** 64 ft³
   4 ft
   4 ft
   4 ft

15. A box is 14 inches long by 12 inches wide by 4 inches high. What is the   **15.** _____
   volume of the box?
   A. 30 in³   **B.** 336 in³   **C.** 672 in³   **D.** none of these

16. Find the volume of the rectangular prism described at   **16.** _____
   the right.
   A. 90 ft³   **B.** 14.5 ft³
   C. 129 ft³   **D.** none of these

   | length, 7.5 ft |
   | width, 3 ft |
   | height, 4 ft |

17. Find the surface area of the rectangular prism shown at   **17.** _____
   the right.
   A. 192 cm²   **B.** 208 cm²
   C. 18 cm²   **D.** none of these
   4 cm   6 cm
   8 cm

18. Find the surface area of the rectangular prism described   **18.** _____
   at the right.
   A. 480 m²   **B.** 392 m²
   C. 25 m²   **D.** none of these

   | length, 12 m |
   | width, 8 m |
   | height, 5 m |

19. A circular pool has a radius of 12 feet. What is the area of the pool?   **19.** _____
   Use 3.14 for π.
   A. 452.16 ft²   **B.** 75.36 ft²   **C.** 1,808.64 ft²   **D.** none of these

20. How much paper would it take to cover a box that is 20 inches by 16 inches   **20.** _____
   by 10 inches if there is no overlap?
   A. 1,360 in²   **B.** 680 in²   **C.** 3,200 in²   **D.** none of these

       Mathematics: Applications and Connections, Course 1

Chapter 10 Test, Form 2A

Find the area of each figure. Use 3.14 for π.

1.
   72 cm
   103 cm

   1. _____

2.
   51 m

   2. _____

3.
   18 in.
   37 in.

   3. _____

4. 13 mm 12 mm
   15 mm

   4. _____

5.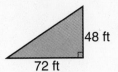
   122 m

   5. _____

6.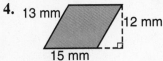
   48 ft
   72 ft

   6. _____

7. A seat of a circular stool has a diameter of 15 inches. What is the area of the seat? Use 3.14 for π.

   7. _____

Name each figure.

8.

9.

   8. _____

   9. _____

10. State the number of edges for the figure in Question 9.

   10. _____

Mathematics: Applications and Connections, Course 1

Find the surface area of each rectangular prism.

11.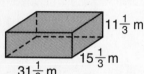

9 ft
27 ft
46 ft

11. _____

12.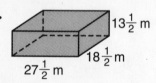

$11\frac{1}{3}$ m
$15\frac{1}{3}$ m
$31\frac{1}{3}$ m

12. _____

13. length, 97 mm; width, 82 mm; height, 31 mm

13. _____

14. length, 56 in.; width, 39 in.; height, 3 in.

14. _____

Find the volume of each rectangular prism.

15.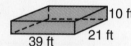

10 ft
21 ft
39 ft

15. _____

16.

$13\frac{1}{2}$ m
$18\frac{1}{2}$ m
$27\frac{1}{2}$ m

16. _____

17. length, 82 mm; width, 79 mm; height, 42 mm

17. _____

18. length, 60 in.; width, 47 in.; height, 4 in.

18. _____

19. A cube has a surface area of 384 square inches. Find the volume of the cube.

19. _____

20. How many different rectangular prisms can be formed by using exactly 36 cubes?

20. _____

Mathematics: Applications and Connections, Course 1

Chapter 10 Test, Form 2B

Find the area of each figure. Use 3.14 for π.

1.
   49 mm
   84 mm

   1. _____

2.
   20 m

   2. _____

3.
   14 cm
   24 cm

   3. _____

4.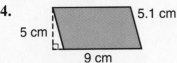
   5.1 cm
   5 cm
   9 cm

   4. _____

5.
   54 ft

   5. _____

6.
   5.8 cm
   12 cm

   6. _____

7. A circular tablecloth has a diameter of 50 inches. What is the area of the tablecloth? Use 3.14 for π.

   7. _____

Name each figure.

8.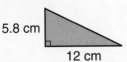

9.

   8. _____

   9. _____

10. State the number of edges for the figure in Question 9.

   10. _____

Mathematics: Applications and Connections, Course 1

Find the surface area of each rectangular prism.

11. 13 mm   51 mm   8 mm

11. _____

12. 4.5 ft   6 ft   15 ft

12. _____

13. length, 42 in.; width, 30 in.; height, 12 in.

13. _____

14. length, 33 cm; width, 24 cm; height, 8 cm

14. _____

Find the volume of each rectangular prism.

15. 13 mm   51 mm   8 mm

15. _____

16. 6 ft   8.5 ft   18 ft

16. _____

17. length, 36 in.; width, 22 in.; height, 17 in.

17. _____

18. length, 29 cm; width, 20 cm; height, 11 cm

18. _____

19. A rectangular aquarium is 20 inches long by 12 inches wide by 10 inches deep. What is the volume of the aquarium?

19. _____

20. How many different rectangular prisms can be formed by using exactly 12 cubes?

20. _____

Name_____ Date _____

Chapter 10 Test, Form 2C

Find the area of each figure. Use 3.14 for π.

1.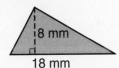
   18 cm
   28 cm

2.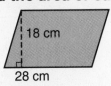
   22 in.

3.
   8 mm
   18 mm

4.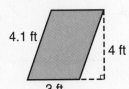
   4.1 ft
   4 ft
   3 ft

5.
   6 cm

6.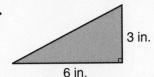
   3 in.
   6 in.

1. _____

2. _____

3. _____

4. _____

5. _____

6. _____

7. A circular window has a radius of 12 inches. What is the area of the window? Use 3.14 for π.

7. _____

Name each figure.

8.

9.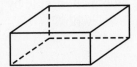

8. _____

9. _____

10. State the number of edges for the figure in Question 8.

10. _____

Mathematics: Applications and Connections, Course 1

Chapter 10 Test, Form 2C (continued)

Find the surface area of each rectangular prism.

11.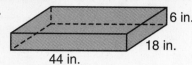
6 in.
18 in.
44 in.

11. _____

12.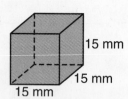
15 mm
15 mm
15 mm

12. _____

13. length, 14 cm; width, 11 cm; height, 8 cm

13. _____

14. length, 49 m; width, 40 m; height, 10 m

14. _____

Find the surface area of each rectangular prism.

15.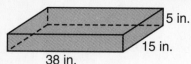
5 in.
15 in.
38 in.

15. _____

16.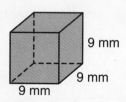
9 mm
9 mm
9 mm

16. _____

17. length, 19 cm; width, 16 cm; height, 11 cm

17. _____

18. length, 45 m; width, 35 m; height, 15 m

18. _____

19. A jewelry box is 12 inches long by 6 inches wide by 3 inches high. What is the volume of the jewelry box?

19. _____

20. How many different rectangular prisms can be formed by using exactly 10 cubes?

20. _____

Mathematics: Applications and Connections, Course 1

10

Chapter 10 Performance Assessment

Instructions: Demonstrate your knowledge by giving a clear, concise solution to each problem. Be sure to include all relevant drawings and to justify your answers. You may show your solutions in more than one way or investigate beyond the requirements of the problems.

1. Diana and her mother are making some flags of the states and territories for a report in social studies class. Diana needs to find the amount of material to buy.

   a. How many square inches of material will be needed to make the Alaska flag?

   b. How many square inches of blue material will be needed to make the rectangular Virginia flag? How many square inches of white material will be needed to make the circle in the middle? Assume no material will be wasted. Show your work. Use 3.14 for π.

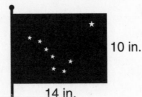

10 in.

14 in.

15 in.

10 in.

diameter of circle: 7 in.

   c. Tell in your own words how to find the area of a triangle.

   d. Find the amount of white material needed to make the triangular part of the American Samoa flag. Show your work.

9 in.

10 in.

20 in.

triangle height: 18 in.

   e. Tell in your own words how to find the area of a parallelogram.

   f. Find the area of the white parallelogram in the Arkansas flag. Show your work.

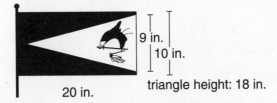

ARKANSAS

10 in.

15 in.

parallelogram: side 6 in.
height 5 in.

   g. Diana's mother made a Wyoming flag. How would you estimate the area of the buffalo in the center?

2. Write a word problem that involves finding the surface area and volume of a rectangular prism. Draw an illustration for your word problem.

Mathematics: Applications and Connections, Course 1

Chapter 10 Mid-Chapter Test

(Lessons 10-1 through 10-3)

Find the area of each figure. Use 3.14 for π.

1.
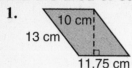
10 cm
13 cm
11.75 cm

2.
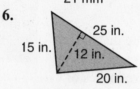
12 m
20 m
15 m

3.

8 ft 6 ft
23 ft

4.
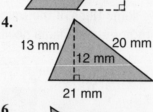
13 mm 20 mm
12 mm
21 mm

5.
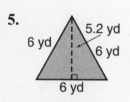
5.2 yd
6 yd 6 yd
6 yd

6.
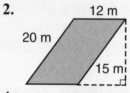
25 in.
15 in. 12 in.
20 in.

7.

15 cm

8.

14 m

9.

7 in.

10.
10 mi

1. _____
2. _____
3. _____
4. _____
5. _____
6. _____
7. _____
8. _____
9. _____
10. _____

11. Find the area of a parallelogram that is 18 yards wide and 5 yards high.

11. _____

12. Maureen buys a parallelogram-shaped rug to fit a hallway. The rug is 12 feet long and 9 feet wide. How much of the floor does the rug cover?

12. _____

13. Find the area of a triangle with a base of 50 centimeters and a height of 26 centimeters.

13. _____

14. The area of a triangle is 135 square inches. If the height is 15 inches, what is the length of the base?

14. _____

15. Big Ben is a famous clock in London. The face of Big Ben has a diameter of 29 feet. What is the area?

15. _____

16. A circular sprinkler spreads water up to 8 meters away. What area of the lawn gets watered?

16. _____

Mathematics: Applications and Connections, Course 1

Chapter 10 Quiz A

(Lessons 10-1 and 10-2)

Find the area of each figure.

1.
48 mm
75 mm

2.
33 cm
50 cm

3.
5.6 in.
3.8 in.

1. _____

2. _____

3. _____

4.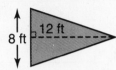
8 ft
12 ft

5.
8 ft
12 ft

6.
21 m
11 m

4. _____

5. _____

6. _____

7. a parallelogram with a base of 26 centimeters and a height of 13 centimeters

8. a parallelogram with a base of 32 millimeters and a height of 44 millimeters

9. a triangle with a base of 6 miles and a height of 5 miles

10. a triangle with a base of 10 centimeters and a height of 7 centimeters

7. _____

8. _____

9. _____

10. _____

Chapter 10 Quiz B

(Lesson 10-3)

Find the area of each figure. Use 3.14 for π.

1.
9 in.

2.
40 ft

1. _____

2. _____

3.
2.4 cm

4.
7 m

3. _____

4. _____

5. A circular rug has a diameter of 5 feet. How much of the floor is covered by the rug?

5. _____

Mathematics: Applications and Connections, Course 1

Chapter 10 Quiz C

Name each figure.

1.

1._____

2.

2._____

3. State the number of faces and edges in the figure for Question 1.

3._____

Find the volume of each rectangular prism.

4.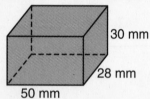
0.8 m
1.5 m
2.8 m

4._____

5. length, 80 mm
   width, 60 mm
   height, 25 mm

5._____

Chapter 10 Quiz D

Find the surface area of each rectangular prism.

1.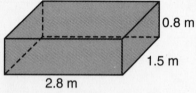
30 mm
28 mm
50 mm

2. length, 23 ft
   width, 14 ft
   height, 7 ft

1._____

2._____

3.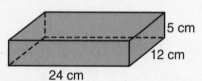
5 cm
12 cm
24 cm

4. length, $12\frac{1}{2}$ in.
   width, 6 in.
   height, $3\frac{3}{4}$ in.

3._____

4._____

5. How much sheet metal is needed to cover the trailer of a truck if the trailer is 30 feet by 7 feet by 8 feet?

5._____

Name_____ Date _____

Chapter 10 Standardized Test Practice

1. Kisha's dog is tied to a pole in the backyard. The length of the rope is 14 feet. If the dog can run in a full circle around the pole, how much area can Kisha's dog run on? (Use 3.14 for π.)
   A. 43.96 ft²   B. 153.86 ft²
   C. 615.44 ft²   D. none of these

1. _____

2. One lap around the track at the Indianapolis Motor Speedway is $2\frac{1}{2}$ miles. How far would you travel in 18 laps?
   A. $50\frac{1}{2}$ miles   B. 36 miles   C. $64\frac{1}{2}$ miles   D. 45 miles

2. _____

3. A rectangular prism has a length of 30 centimeters, a width of 22 centimeters, and a height of 10 centimeters. Find the surface area.
   A. 1,180 cm²   B. 2,360 cm²   C. 6,600 cm²   D. 6,600 cm³

3. _____

4. The flag for Trinidad and Tobago has a black stripe in the shape of a parallelogram running from top to bottom. If the base of the black parallelogram is 13 inches and the flag is 30 inches high, find the area of the black parallelogram.
   A. 195 in²   B. 360 in²   C. 390 in²   D. none of these

4. _____

5. A stone mason is tiling a floor with parallelogram-shaped tiles. If the smaller corner of the tile measures 37°, what is the measure of its supplementary angle?
   A. 90°   B. 53°   C. 143°   D. 133°

5. _____

6. If the sales tax is 5.5%, what is the sales tax on a car that costs $11,000?
   A. $6,050   B. $60.50   C. $605.00   D. $550.00

6. _____

7. On a square, the diagonals bisect the angles. What is the measure of an angle of a square after it has been bisected?
   A. 180°   B. 60°   C. 90°   D. 45°

7. _____

8. It cost Mr. Quinn $16.25 to buy lunch for his family. If each lunch cost $3.25, how many lunches did he buy?
   A. 5   B. 4   C. 6   D. none of these

8. _____

9. A person expends 5.2 Calories per minute walking, w, and 19.4 Calories per minute running, r. Evaluate $5.2w + 19.4r$ to find the number of Calories burned on a 40-minute hike with 35 minutes of walking and 5 minutes of running.
   A. 705 Calories   B. 279 Calories
   C. 305 Calories   D. none of these

9. _____

10. A circle graph shows people's preferences for different types of pets. Dog owners account for 40% of pet owners and snake owners for 10%. What part of the circle graph would represent these two groups?
    A. insufficient information   B. 50%
    C. 30%   D. none of these

10. _____

Mathematics: Applications and Connections, Course 1

11. If a public library collection expanded from 1.91 million volumes to 3.27 million volumes, about how many volumes were added to the collection?
    A. 2 million **B.** 4 million **C.** 5 million **D.** 1 million

    11. _____

12. If it cost $25.13 for 19.6 gallons of gasoline, how much was the gasoline per gallon rounded to the nearest cent?
    A. $1.28 **B.** $0.78 **C.** $1.30 **D.** $1.32

    12. _____

13. Express 204 as a product of prime numbers.
    A. $2^2 \times 51$ **B.** $4 \times 3 \times 17$ **C.** $2^2 \times 3 \times 17$ **D.** $2 \times 3 \times 17$

    13. _____

14. Carol is making picture frames in woodworking class. Each frame uses 3.8 feet of wood. If Carol wants to make 6 frames, estimate how much wood she needs.
    A. 18 feet **B.** 20 feet
    C. 24 feet **D.** none of these

    14. _____

15. What is the elapsed time from 7:55 A.M. to 10:10 A.M?
    A. 2 h 15 min **B.** 1 h 15 min
    C. 3 h 45 min **D.** none of these

    15. _____

16. Racetown holds a 15-km race every year. Last year, $\frac{1}{3}$ of the 300 runners were men. About how many runners were women?
    A. 100 **B.** 200 **C.** 300 **D.** 50

    16. _____

17. If the radius of a button is $\frac{3}{8}$ inch, what is the circumference of the button?
    A. $1\frac{5}{28}$ in. **B.** $2\frac{5}{14}$ in. **C.** $4\frac{5}{7}$ in. **D.** 1 in.

    17. _____

18. If 7 out of 10 students like pizza, how many students in a school of 832 like pizza?
    A. 522 **B.** 564 **C.** 582 **D.** 5,824

    18. _____

19. Sales tax is 5.75%. Would the tax on a $20 purchase be less than $2?
    A. yes **B.** no
    C. maybe **D.** cannot calculate

    19. _____

20. Carla scored 9 out of 10 correct on a test. Singi got 7 out of 8 correct on her test. How do their grades compare?
    A. the same **B.** Carla scored higher.
    C. Singi scored higher. **D.** cannot compare

    20. _____

Mathematics: Applications and Connections, Course 1

10 Cumulative Review, Chapters 1–10

Solve each equation. Write in simplest form. (Lessons 3-6, 4-3, and 6-3)

1. $m = 90 - 9.2$ 2. $3.5 \times 0.6 = y$ 3. $y + \frac{1}{16} = \frac{15}{16}$

4. The sum of a number and its double is 60. Find the number. (Lesson 1-7)

5. In the ordered pair (3, 7), the *x*-coordinate is __?__. (Lesson 2-9)

6. Find the prime factorization of 115. (Lesson 5-2)

Perform the indicated operation. Write in simplest form. (Lessons 6-4, 6-6, 7-2, 7-3, 7-5, and 7-6)

7. $\frac{5}{18} + \frac{1}{12}$ 8. $6\frac{1}{5} - 3\frac{7}{10}$ 9. $\frac{7}{16} \times \frac{8}{9}$

10. $4\frac{3}{5} \times 1\frac{1}{4}$ 11. $\frac{5}{32} \div 10$ 12. $6\frac{2}{3} \div 1\frac{2}{3}$

13. Name the figure at the right. (Lesson 9-4)

14. How many lines of symmetry does the figure at the right have? (Lesson 9-5)

15. Express $\frac{19}{25}$ as a percent. (Lesson 8-4)

16. Express 3.8% as a decimal. (Lesson 8-5)

17. Find the area of a circle with a diameter of 26 inches. Round to the nearest tenth. (Lesson 10-3)

Refer to the figure at the right. (Lessons 10-4, 10-5, and 10-6)

18. Find the number of edges in the rectangular prism.

11 in.
18 in.
16 in.

19. Find the surface area of the rectangular prism.

20. Find the volume of the rectangular prism.

1. _____
2. _____
3. _____
4. _____
5. _____
6. _____
7. _____
8. _____
9. _____
10. _____
11. _____
12. _____
13. _____
14. _____
15. _____
16. _____
17. _____
18. _____
19. _____
20. _____

Mathematics: Applications and Connections, Course 1

10 Chapter 10 Answer Key

Page 253

1. B

2. D

3. A

4. C

5. A

6. B

7. D

8. D

9. A

10. A

Page 254

11. B

12. C

13. B

14. C

15. D

16. A

17. A

18. D

19. B

20. C

Page 255

1. B

2. C

3. B

4. C

5. A

6. B

7. B

8. B

9. D

10. B

Page 256

11. A

12. B

13. B

14. C

15. B

16. D

17. C

18. A

19. B

20. D

Chapter 10 Answer Key

Form 1C

Page 257

1. _____ A _____

2. _____ C _____

3. _____ B _____

4. _____ C _____

5. _____ D _____

6. _____ A _____

7. _____ B _____

8. _____ C _____

9. _____ C _____

10. _____ C _____

11. _____ B _____

Page 258

12. _____ A _____

13. _____ B _____

14. _____ D _____

15. _____ C _____

16. _____ A _____

17. _____ B _____

18. _____ B _____

19. _____ A _____

20. _____ A _____

Mathematics: Applications and Connections, Course 1

Chapter 10 Answer Key

Form 2A

Page 259

1. $7{,}416 \text{ cm}^2$

2. $8{,}167.14 \text{ m}^2$

3. 333 in^2

4. 180 mm^2

5. $11{,}683.94 \text{ m}^2$

6. $1{,}728 \text{ ft}^2$

7. 176.625 in^2

8. cylinder

9. pentagonal pyramid

10. 10

Page 260

11. $3{,}798 \text{ ft}^2$

12. $2{,}018\frac{2}{3} \text{ m}^2$

13. $27{,}006 \text{ mm}^2$

14. $4{,}938 \text{ in}^2$

15. $8{,}190 \text{ ft}^3$

16. $6{,}868.125 \text{ m}^3$

17. $272{,}076 \text{ mm}^3$

18. $11{,}280 \text{ in}^3$

19. 512 in^3

20. 8

Mathematics: Applications and Connections, Course 1

Chapter 10 Answer Key

Form 2B

Page 261

1. **4,116 mm²**

2. **1,256 m²**

3. **168 cm²**

4. **45 cm²**

5. **2,289.06 ft²**

6. **34.8 cm²**

7. **1,962.5 in²**

8. **sphere**

9. **square pyramid**

10. **8**

Page 262

11. **2,350 mm²**

12. **369 ft²**

13. **4,248 in²**

14. **2,496 cm²**

15. **5,304 mm³**

16. **918 ft³**

17. **13,464 in³**

18. **6,380 cm³**

19. **2,400 in³**

20. **4**

Mathematics: Applications and Connections, Course 1

Chapter 10 Answer Key

Form 2C

Page 263

1. **504 cm²**

2. **379.94 in²**

3. **72 mm²**

4. **12 ft²**

5. **113.04 cm²**

6. **9 in²**

7. **452.16 in²**

8. **triangular pyramid**

9. **rectangular prism**

10. **6**

Page 264

11. **2,328 in²**

12. **1,350 mm²**

13. **708 cm²**

14. **5,700 m²**

15. **2,850 in³**

16. **729 mm³**

17. **3,344 cm³**

18. **23,625 m³**

19. **216 in³**

20. **2**

Mathematics: Applications and Connections, Course 1

Chapter 10 Scoring Guide

Level	Specific Criteria
3 Superior	• Shows thorough understanding of the concepts *areas of rectangles, parallelograms, triangles, and circles,* and *volume and surface area of rectangular prisms.* • Uses appropriate strategies to solve problems. • Computations are correct. • Word problem concerning *surface area and volume of rectangular prisms* is appropriate and makes sense. • Illustration is accurate and appropriate. • Written explanations are exemplary. • Goes beyond requirements of some or all problems.
2 Satisfactory, with Minor Flaws	• Shows understanding of the concepts *areas of rectangles, parallelograms, triangles, and circles,* and *volume and surface area of rectangular prisms.* • Uses appropriate strategies to solve problems. • Computations are mostly correct. • Word problem concerning *surface area and volume of rectangular prisms* is appropriate and makes sense. • Illustration is accurate and appropriate. • Written explanations are effective. • Satisfies all requirements of problems.
1 Nearly Satisfactory, with Serious Flaws	• Shows understanding of most of the concepts *areas of rectangles, parallelograms, triangles, and circles,* and *volume and surface area of rectangular prisms.* • May not use appropriate strategies to solve problems. • Computations are mostly correct. • Word problem concerning *surface area and volume of rectangular prisms* is appropriate and makes sense. • Illustration is accurate and appropriate. • Written explanations are satisfactory. • Satisfies most requirements of problems.
0 Unsatisfactory	• Shows little or no understanding of the concepts *areas of rectangles, parallelograms, triangles, and circles,* and *volume and surface area of rectangular prisms.* • May not use appropriate strategies to solve problems. • Computations are incorrect. • Word problem concerning *surface area and volume of rectangular prisms* is not appropriate and does not make sense. • Illustration is not accurate or appropriate. • Written explanations are not satisfactory. • Does not satisfy requirements of problems.

Chapter 10 Answer Key

Performance Assessment Sample Answers
Page 265

1. a. $14 \times 10 = 140$ in²

b. blue: $15 \times 10 = 150$ in²; white: $3.14 (3.5)^2 \approx 38.465$ in²

c. The area of a triangle is equal to half the product of its base (b) and height (h).

d. $\frac{1}{2}(9)(18) = 81$ in²

e. The area of a parallelogram equals the product of its base (b) and height (h).

f. $6 \times 5 = 30$ in²

g. Trace the buffalo on grid paper and count the number of squares within the outline. Then count the number of squares that touch the outline. Add the two numbers. Find the estimate by averaging this sum and the number of squares within the outline.

2. Sample answer: Cary is shipping a box that is 18 inches × 12 inches × 6 inches. How much paper does he need in order to wrap it with no overlaps? **792 in²** How much room does he have in the box for the materials he is shipping? **1,296 in³**

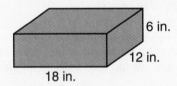

6 in.

12 in.

18 in.

Mid-Chapter Test
Page 266

1. ___117.5 cm²___

2. ___180 m²___

3. ___138 ft²___

4. ___126 mm²___

5. ___15.6 yd²___

6. ___150 in²___

7. ___176.625 cm²___

8. ___615.44 m²___

9. ___153.86 in²___

10. ___78.5 mi²___

11. ___90 yd²___

12. ___108 ft²___

13. ___650 cm²___

14. ___18 in.___

15. ___660.185 ft²___

16. ___200.96 m²___

Mathematics: Applications and Connections, Course 1

Chapter 10 Answer Key

Quiz A, Page 267

1. $3{,}600 \text{ mm}^2$
2. 825 cm^2
3. 21.28 in^2
4. 48 ft^2
5. 96 ft^2
6. 115.5 m^2
7. 338 cm^2
8. $1{,}408 \text{ mm}^2$
9. 15 mi^2
10. 35 cm^2

Quiz C, Page 268

1. square pyramid
2. rectangular prism
3. faces = 5 edges = 8
4. 3.36 m^3
5. $120{,}000 \text{ mm}^3$

Quiz B, Page 267

1. 254.34 in^2
2. $1{,}256 \text{ ft}^2$
3. 4.5216 cm^2
4. 153.86 m^2
5. 19.625 ft^2

Quiz D, Page 268

1. $7{,}480 \text{ mm}^2$
2. $1{,}162 \text{ ft}^2$
3. 936 cm^2
4. $288\frac{3}{4} \text{ in}^2$
5. $1{,}012 \text{ ft}^2$

Chapter 10 Answer Key

Standardized Test Practice		Cumulative Review

Page 269

1. C
2. D
3. B
4. C
5. C
6. C
7. D
8. A
9. B
10. B

Page 270

11. D
12. A
13. C
14. C
15. A
16. B
17. B
18. C
19. A
20. B

Page 271

1. 80.8
2. 2.1
3. $\frac{7}{8}$
4. 20
5. 3
6. $5 \cdot 23$
7. $\frac{13}{36}$
8. $2\frac{1}{2}$
9. $\frac{7}{18}$
10. $5\frac{3}{4}$
11. $\frac{1}{64}$
12. 4
13. pentagon
14. 1
15. 76%
16. 0.038
17. 530.9 in^2
18. 12
19. $1,324 \text{ in}^2$
20. $3,168 \text{ in}^3$

Mathematics: Applications and Connections, Course 1

Name_____ **Date**_____

Chapter 11 Test, Form 1A

1. Name the integer represented by R on the number line below.   1. _____

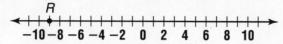

   A. -7 **B.** 7 **C.** -9 **D.** 9

2. Which situation is represented by -12?   2. _____
   A. back up 12 places   **B.** a rise of 12 feet
   C. a profit of $12   **D.** a stock increase of 12 points

3. Which integer is the least?   3. _____
   A. 0 **B.** -98 **C.** 25 **D.** -91

4. Which of the following is true?   4. _____
   A. $300 < -400$ **B.** $-25 > 10$
   C. $-100 < -99$ **D.** none of these

5. Order the following from least to greatest: $50, -60, -70$.   5. _____
   A. $-70, 50, -60$ **B.** $-60, -70, 50$
   C. $50, -60, -70$ **D.** $-70, -60, 50$

6. What sum is represented by the set of counters at the right?   6. _____
   A. 1 **B.** -1
   C. 6 **D.** -5

For Questions 7–12, use counters or a number line if necessary.

7. Find the sum: $-9 + (-12)$.   7. _____
   A. 3 **B.** -21 **C.** -3 **D.** 21

8. The high temperature yesterday was $-3°F$. Today the high temperature was 7 degrees higher. What was the high temperature today?   8. _____
   A. $10°F$ **B.** $-10°F$ **C.** $4°F$ **D.** none of these

9. Find the difference: $5 - (-6)$.   9. _____
   A. -11 **B.** -1 **C.** 1 **D.** 11

10. Find the difference: $-9 - (-7)$.   10. _____
   A. -16 **B.** -2 **C.** 2 **D.** 16

11. Find the product: $-8 \times (-13)$.   11. _____
   A. 104 **B.** -104 **C.** 21 **D.** -5

12. Which product is *not* equal to -30?   12. _____
   A. $-6(5)$ **B.** $30(-1)$ **C.** $-3(-10)$ **D.** $-2(15)$

Mathematics: Applications and Connections, Course 1

Chapter 11 Test, Form 1A (continued)

For Questions 13–15, use counters or patterns if necessary.

13. Which quotient equals −11?   13. _____
   A. −77 ÷ 7   **B.** −66 ÷ (−6)   **D.** −44 ÷ (−4)   **D.** −99 ÷ (−9)

14. Which quotient is *not* equal to −9?   14. _____
   A. 18 ÷ (−2)   **B.** −27 ÷ (−3)   **C.** −45 ÷ 5   **D.** −36 ÷ 4

15. Find the quotient: 54 ÷ (−9).   15. _____
   A. −7   **B.** 6   **C.** 45   **D.** −6

16. Kendratta has a present balance of $182 in her savings account. Since her   16. _____
   last bank statement, she had a withdrawal of $18, a deposit of $23,
   another withdrawal of $9, and another deposit of $36. How much money
   was in her account at the time of her last statement?
   A. $214   **B.** $168   **C.** $150   **D.** $224

Refer to the coordinate grid.

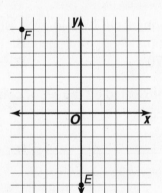

17. Name the ordered pair for point *E*.   17. _____
   A. (−6, 0)   **B.** (0, −6)
   C. (6, 0)   **D.** (0, 6)

18. Name the ordered pair for point *F*.   18. _____
   A. (7, −5)   **B.** (5, −7)
   C. (−7, 5)   **D.** (−5, 7)

Triangle GHI has vertices G(−1, 2), H(1, 2), and I(1, 3).

19. Which graph below shows a translation of triangle *GHI* that is 2 units to   19. _____
   the left and 3 units down?

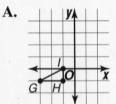 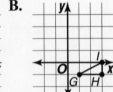 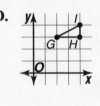 

20. Which graph below shows a reflection of triangle *GHI* about the *x*-axis?   20. _____

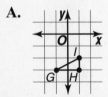 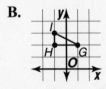 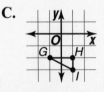 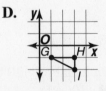

Name_____ Date _____

Chapter 11 Test, Form 1B

1. Name the integer represented by M on the number line below.

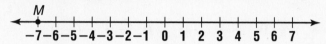

   A. -7 B. 7 C. -3 D. none of these

   1. _____

2. Which situation is represented by -6?
   A. a gain of 6 points   B. a loss of 6 points
   C. 6 stories above ground   D. a profit of $6

   2. _____

3. Which integer is the least?
   A. 0 B. -100 C. 50 D. -50

   3. _____

4. Which of the following is true?
   A. $0 < -5$ B. $50 < -60$ C. $-77 > 76$ D. none of these

   4. _____

5. Order the following from least to greatest: $8, 0, -5$.
   A. $0, -5, 8$ B. $-5, 0, 8$
   C. $8, -5, 0$ D. $-5, 8, 0$

   5. _____

6. What sum is represented by the set of counters at the right?
   A. 3 B. -4
   C. 1 D. -1

   6. _____

For Questions 7–12, use counters or a number line if necessary.

7. Find the sum: $-7 + (-8)$.
   A. -1 B. 15 C. 1 D. -15

   7. _____

8. The high temperature yesterday was $-8°F$. Today the high temperature was 6 degrees higher. What was the high temperature today?
   A. $14°F$ B. $2°F$ C. $-2°F$ D. none of these

   8. _____

9. Find the difference: $2 - (-7)$.
   A. 9 B. -9 C. 5 D. -5

   9. _____

10. Find the difference: $-6 - (-2)$.
    A. 8 B. -8 C. 4 D. -4

    10. _____

11. Find the product: $-6 \times (-4)$.
    A. 24 B. -24 C. -10 D. 10

    11. _____

12. Which product is *not* equal to 20?
    A. $-10(-2)$ B. $5(-4)$ C. $-20(-1)$ D. $-5(-4)$

    12. _____

               Mathematics: Applications and Connections, Course 1

For Questions 13–15, use counters or patterns if necessary.

13. Which quotient equals 7?
    A. $-21 \div 3$ **B.** $14 \div (-2)$ **D.** $28 \div (-4)$ **D.** $-21 \div (-3)$

13. _____

14. Which quotient is *not* equal to -4?
    A. $12 \div (-3)$ **B.** $-24 \div (-6)$ **C.** $-20 \div 5$ **D.** $-4 \div 1$

14. _____

15. Find the quotient: $32 \div (-4)$.
    A. 8   **B.** -8 **C.** 28   **D.** -36

15. _____

16. Paul has a present balance of $150 in his checking account. Since his last bank statement, he had a withdrawal of $25, a deposit of $40, and another withdrawal of $30. How much money was in his account at the time of his last statement?
    A. $135   **B.** $245   **C.** $165   **D.** none of these

16. _____

Refer to the coordinate grid.

17. Name the ordered pair for point *P*.
    A. $(3, 5)$ **B.** $(3, -5)$
    C. $(5, 3)$ **D.** $(-5, 3)$

17. _____

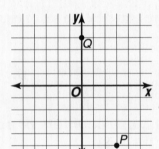

18. Name the ordered pair for point *Q*.
    A. $(0, 4)$ **B.** $(4, 0)$
    C. $(0, -4)$ **D.** $(-4, 0)$

18. _____

Triangle DEF has vertices D(1, 2), E(3, 2), and F(3, 3).

19. Which graph below shows a translation of triangle *DEF* that is 2 units to the left and 1 unit up?

19. _____

   A.    **B.** 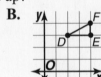   **C.**   **D.**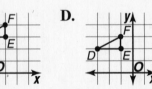

20. Which graph below shows a reflection of triangle *DEF* about the *y*-axis?

20. _____

   A.   **B.**   **C.**   **D.**

Mathematics: Applications and Connections, Course 1

11 Chapter 11 Test, Form 1C

1. Name the integer represented by Q on the number line below.

1. _____

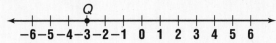

    A. 3   **B.** −3   **C.** 27   **D.** none of these

2. Which situation is represented by −10?

2. _____

    A. a loss of 10 yards   **B.** a gain of 10 yards

    C. 10 feet above sea level   **D.** a rise of 10 degrees

3. Which integer is the least?

3. _____

    A. 0   **B.** −10   **C.** −100   **D.** −500

4. Which of the following is true?

4. _____

    A. $3 < -3$ **B.** $0 < -10$ **C.** $-20 > 0$ **D.** $-3 > -50$

5. Order the following from least to greatest: 40, 0, −60.

5. _____

    A. $0, 40, -60$ **B.** $-60, 0, 40$ **C.** $-60, 40, 0$ **D.** $0, -60, 40$

6. What sum is represented by the set of counters at the right?   ⊕ ⊖ ⊖

6. _____

    A. −2   **B.** 1   **C.** −1   **D.** 0

For Questions 7–12, use counters or a number line if necessary.

7. Find the sum: $-4 + (-3)$.

7. _____

    A. −1   **B.** 1   **C.** 7   **D.** −7

8. Yesterday the low temperature was −9°F. During the day, the temperature rose 4 degrees to the high temperature. What was the high temperature?

8. _____

    A. −13°F   **B.** 5°F   **C.** −5°F   **D.** 13°F

9. Find the difference: $4 - 7$.

9. _____

    A. −3   **B.** 3   **C.** −11   **D.** 11

10. Find the difference: $6 - (-3)$.

10. _____

    A. 3   **B.** 9   **C.** −9   **D.** −3

11. Find the product: $6 \times (-4)$.

11. _____

    A. −24   **B.** 24   **C.** 2   **D.** −2

12. Which product is *not* equal to 16?

12. _____

    A. $-4(-4)$ **B.** $8(-2)$ **C.** $-16(-1)$ **D.** $-8(-2)$

For Questions 13–15, use counters or patterns if necessary.

13. Which quotient equals 4?

    A. $20 \div (-5)$ **B.** $-16 \div 4$ **C.** $-12 \div (-3)$ **D.** $-4 \div 1$

13. _____

14. Which quotient does *not* equal 5?

    A. $15 \div 3$ **B.** $-20 \div (-4)$ **C.** $-15 \div 3$ **D.** $-25 \div (-5)$

14. _____

15. Find the quotient: $-16 \div (-2)$.

    A. -8 **B.** 8   **C.** -18 **D.** 18

15. _____

16. Jenna has a present balance of $200 in her savings account. Since her last bank statement, she had a withdrawal of $30 and a deposit of $50. How much money was in her account at the time of her last statement?

    A. $220   **B.** $180   **C.** $120   **D.** $250

16. _____

Refer to the coordinate grid.

17. Name the ordered pair for point *A*.

    A. $(-1, 4)$ **B.** $(1, 4)$

    C. $(-4, 1)$ **D.** $(-1, -4)$

17. _____

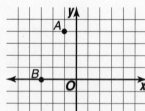

18. Name the ordered pair for point *B*.

    A. $(3, 0)$ **B.** $(0, 3)$

    C. $(-3, 0)$ **D.** $(0, -3)$

18. _____

Triangle ABC has vertices A(2, 3), B(2, 1), and C(1, 1).

19. Which graph below shows a translation of triangle *ABC* that is 2 units to the right and 1 unit down?

19. _____

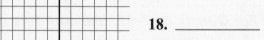

    A.   **B.**   **C.**   **D.**

  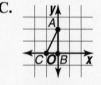

20. Which graph below shows a reflection of triangle *ABC* about the *x*-axis?

20. _____

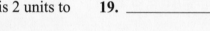

    A.   **B.**   **C.**   **D.**

1. Write an integer to describe a loss of 0 points.

1. _____

2. Write an integer to describe a gain of $15.

2. _____

3. Identify the integer that is the opposite of -38.

3. _____

4. Graph the set $\{-8, -7, -4, 0, 1, 4, 8\}$ on the number line.

4. <++++++++++++++++++++>
   -8 -4   0   4   8

Replace each ● with <, >, or = to make a true sentence.

5. -2 ● 2

5. _____

6. 0 ● -6

6. _____

7. -888 ● -8888

7. _____

8. Order $13, -7, 21, 0, -15,$ and 7 from least to greatest.

8. _____

Perform the indicated operation.

9. $-23 + 42$

9. _____

10. $-8 + (-5)$

10. _____

11. $-351 + (-48)$

11. _____

12. $51 - (-19)$

12. _____

13. $4 - 9$

13. _____

14. $76 - (-24)$

14. _____

15. $-12 - (-3)$

15. _____

16. $12(-6)$

16. _____

17. $-8(2)$

17. _____

18. $(-15)(-8)$

18. _____

19. $13(-2)$

19. _____

20. $114 \div (-19)$

20. _____

Mathematics: Applications and Connections, Course 1

Perform the indicated operation.

21. $-27 \div 3$

21. _____

22. $-312 \div (-13)$

22. _____

23. $32 \div (-4)$

23. _____

24. At midnight, the temperature was $-8°F$. By 9 A.M., the temperature had risen 10 degrees. What was the temperature at 9 A.M.?

24. _____

25. At the chili supper, Lee Ann sold 10 more tickets than Juan. Juan sold twice as many tickets as Heather. Heather sold 3 fewer tickets than Chris. Chris sold 12 tickets. How many did Lee Ann sell?

25. _____

Graph each point on the grid.

26. $Q(-5, -3)$

26–28.
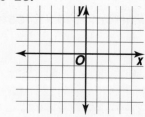

27. $R(-1, 1)$

28. $S(3, -2)$

Give the coordinates for each point on the grid.

29. M

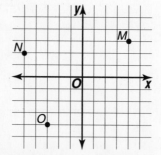

29. _____

30. N

30. _____

31. O

31. _____

The vertices of triangle PQR are P(2, 5), Q(3, 3), and R(1, 3). On the coordinate grid, draw each transformation image.

32. a translation of 6 units to the left and 2 units down

32–33.
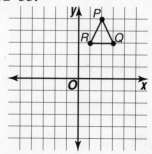

33. a reflection of triangle PQR over the horizontal axis and then the vertical axis

Name _____ **Date** _____

Chapter 11 Test, Form 2B

1. Write an integer to describe a loss of 20 points.

    1. _____

2. Write an integer to describe an increase of 5 degrees.

    2. _____

3. Identify the integer that is the opposite of 15.

    3. _____

4. Graph the set $\{-6, -3, 0, 3\}$ on the number line.

    4. ←++++++++++++++++→
        −6 −4 −2   0   2   4   6

Replace each ● with <, >, or = to make a true sentence.

5. -100 ● 90

    5. _____

6. 0 ● -10

    6. _____

7. -66 ● -666

    7. _____

8. Order $12, -9, 0, -12,$ and 7 from least to greatest.

    8. _____

Perform the indicated operation.

9. $-11 + 9$

    9. _____

10. $5 + (-4)$

    10. _____

11. $-8 + (-8)$

    11. _____

12. $7 - (-5)$

    12. _____

13. $-17 - 3$

    13. _____

14. $15 - (-2)$

    14. _____

15. $-14 - 8$

    15. _____

16. $9(-2)$

    16. _____

17. $(-8)(3)$

    17. _____

18. $(-3)(-6)$

    18. _____

19. $11(-4)$

    19. _____

20. $28 \div (-7)$

    20. _____

Mathematics: Applications and Connections, Course 1

Perform the indicated operation.

21. $-645 \div 43$ 21. _____

22. $-48 \div (-8)$ 22. _____

23. $75 \div (-25)$ 23. _____

24. At 1 A.M. the temperature was $-2°F$. By noon, the temperature   24. _____
had risen 11 degrees. What was the temperature at noon?

25. At the end of three days, a stock was selling for $18 per share.   25. _____
On the preceding three days there had been a gain of $2 per
share, a loss of $3 per share, and a gain of $1 per share. What
was the price per share at the beginning of the three days?

Graph each point on the grid.

26. $D(5, -2)$ 26–28.

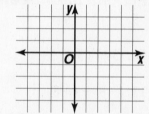

27. $E(-4, -3)$

28. $F(0, -3)$

**Give the coordinates for each point
on the grid.**

29. D 29. _____

30. E 30. _____

31. F 31. _____

**The vertices of triangle ABC are A(5, 2), B(5, 5), and C(2, 2).   32–33.
On the coordinate grid, draw each transformation image.**

32. a translation of 5 units to the left

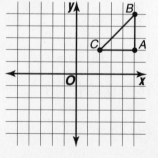

33. a reflection of triangle *ABC* over the horizontal axis

*Mathematics: Applications
and Connections, Course 1*

Chapter 11 Test, Form 2C

1. Write an integer to describe a loss of 8 yards.

2. Write an integer to describe a gain of 3 pounds.

3. Identify the integer that is the opposite of 10.

4. Graph the set $\{-5, -2, 0, 5\}$ on the number line.

Replace each ● with <, >, or = to make a true sentence.

5. -60 ● 30

6. -25 ● 25

7. -55 ● -555

8. Order $10, -13, 11, 0,$ and -50 from least to greatest.

Perform the indicated operation.

9. $-7 + 9$

10. $14 + (-9)$

11. $-3 + (-6)$

12. $5 - (-5)$

13. $-16 - 2$

14. $-8 - 2$

15. $12 - (-2)$

16. $7(-4)$

17. $-7(5)$

18. $(-6)(-5)$

19. $5(-4)$

20. $-25 \div (-5)$

1. _____

2. _____

3. _____

4. ⟵|+|+|+|+|+|+|+|+|+|+|⟶
    −5   0   5

5. _____

6. _____

7. _____

8. _____

9. _____

10. _____

11. _____

12. _____

13. _____

14. _____

15. _____

16. _____

17. _____

18. _____

19. _____

20. _____

Perform the indicated operation.

21. $32 \div (-4)$ 21. _____

22. $-18 \div 3$ 22. _____

23. $-30 \div (-10)$ 23. _____

24. At 1 A.M. the temperature was $-8°F$. By noon, the temperature   24. _____
had risen 6 degrees. What was the temperature at noon?

25. For five days, Alyson practiced for her piano recital. On each   25. _____
day after the first, she practiced 10 minutes longer than the
preceding day. On the last day, she practiced 120 minutes. How
many minutes did she practice on the first day?

Graph each point on the grid.

26. $R(-4, -4)$ 26–28.

27. $S(3, -2)$

28. $T(4, 0)$

*Give the coordinates for each point
on the grid.*

29. R 29. _____

30. S 30. _____

31. T 31. _____

*The vertices of triangle ABC are A(4, 3), B(1, 2), and C(1, 3).
On the coordinate grid, draw each transformation image.*

32. a translation 2 units down   32–33.

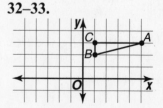

33. a reflection of triangle ABC about the vertical axis

Chapter 11 Performance Assessment

Instructions: *Demonstrate your knowledge by giving a clear, concise solution to each problem. Be sure to include all relevant drawings and justify your answers. You may show your solutions in more than one way or investigate beyond the requirements of the problems.*

1. Draw counters, ⊕ and ⊖, to represent positive and negative integers.

   a. Represent -2 in at least two ways using counters and one way on a number line.

   b. Explain how to represent $-5 + (+2)$ using counters.

   c. Show how to find $4 - (-3)$ using counters.

   d. Write an expression you would use to find the product of two negative integers. Tell what it means.

   e. Show how to use counters to find the product in part d. Explain each step.

2. a. Tell what is meant by a *translation image*.

   b. On the coordinate grid, draw a translation image of $\triangle ABC$. Give the coordinates of the translation image of A.

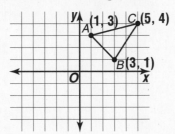

   c. Tell what is meant by a *reflection image*.

   d. Draw the reflection image of $\triangle ABC$ over the x-axis. Give the coordinates of the reflection image of B.

Name\underline{\hspace{5cm}} Date \underline{\hspace{2cm}}

Chapter 11 Mid-Chapter Test

(Lessons 11-1 through 11-4)

1. Identify the integer graphed on the number line.

1. _____

Write an integer to describe each situation.

2. The interest rate went down 1 point.

2. _____

3. LaToya moved forward 3 seats.

3. _____

Write the opposite of each integer.

4. -97 5. $+203$

4. _____

5. _____

Replace each ● with <, >, or = to make a true sentence.

6. -53 ● -51 7. -3 ● -33

8. 0 ● -12 9. -42 ● 42

10. Order -19, 17, -15, and 16 from least to greatest.

6. _____

7. _____

8. _____

9. _____

10. _____

Find each sum or difference. Use counters or a number line if necessary.

11. $5 + (-8)$

12. $-8 + (-3)$

13. $-7 + 5$

14. $-1 + (-9)$

15. $-5 + 13$

16. $-3 - (-8)$

17. $-6 - (-1)$

18. $5 - (-1)$

19. $-4 - 7$

20. $3 - 4$

11. _____

12. _____

13. _____

14. _____

15. _____

16. _____

17. _____

18. _____

19. _____

20. _____

Mathematics: Applications and Connections, Course 1

Chapter 11 Quiz A

(Lessons 11-1 and 11-2)

Write the integer represented by each letter on the number line.

1. K 2. M

3. J 4. L

Replace each ● with <, >, or = to make a true sentence.

5. -40 ● -30 6. 8 ● -8

7. 0 ● -4 8. -3 ● -6

Order the following from least to greatest.

9. $18, -12, 0, 5, -4, 1$ 10. $-73, -81, -24, -62$

1. _____

2. _____

3. _____

4. _____

5. _____

6. _____

7. _____

8. _____

9. _____

10. _____

Chapter 11 Quiz B

(Lessons 11-3 and 11-4)

Find each sum or difference. Use counters or a number line if necessary.

1. $-10 + (-8)$ 2. $12 + (-15)$

3. $-41 + (-6)$ 4. $-38 + 4$

5. $28 + (-51)$ 6. $15 - (-3)$

7. $13 - (-2)$ 8. $-6 - 8$

9. $-19 - (-4)$ 10. $-98 - (-98)$

1. _____

2. _____

3. _____

4. _____

5. _____

6. _____

7. _____

8. _____

9. _____

10. _____

Mathematics: Applications and Connections, Course 1

Chapter 11 Quiz C

1. In a game, Bill scored 12 points more than Geneva. Geneva scored twice as many points as Salif. Salif scored 3 fewer points than Becky. Becky scored 8 points. How many points did Bill score?

1. _____

2. _____

3. _____

Find each quotient. Use counters or patterns if necessary.

2. $15 \div (-3)$ 3. $-16 \div (-2)$

4. _____

5. _____

4. $-28 \div 4$ 5. $-27 \div (-9)$

6. _____

Find each product. Use counters or patterns if necessary.

6. $-5(-12)$ 7. $4(-21)$

7. _____

8. _____

8. $-3(-11)$ 9. $-9(3)$

9. _____

10. $-4(-9)$

10. _____

Chapter 11 Quiz D

Name the ordered pair for each point.

1. P 2. Q

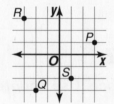

1. _____

2. _____

3. R 4. S

3. _____

4. _____

Graph and label each point.

5. $E(5, -2)$ 6. $F(-2, -1)$

5–8.

7. $G(0, -3)$ 8. $H(-3, 2)$

The vertices of triangle ABC are A(−4, 1), B(−1, 4), and C(−4, 4). On the coordinate grid, draw each transformation image.

9. a translation of 5 units to the right

9–10.

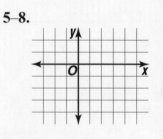

10. a reflection over the x-axis

Chapter 11 Standardized Test Practice

1. If $s = 5$ and $t = 8$, find the value of $s^3 + t^2$.
   A. 189   B. 89   C. 31   D. none of these

   1. _____

2. The ages of students in a class are 14, 13, 13, 13, 11, 11, 11, 13, 12, 14, 13, 13, 11, 11, 11, 11, and 12. If a frequency table is constructed by age, which age would have the most tallies or highest frequency?
   A. 11   B. 12   C. 13   D. 14

   2. _____

3. During a shopping trip, Tanika considered buying a sweater for $16.79, a pair of boots for $27.98, and a necklace for $5.19. To the nearest dollar, how much would Tanika need for these purchases?
   A. $50   B. $48   C. $49   D. none of these

   3. _____

4. If Saturn orbits the Sun once in 29.46 Earth years, how long will it take for Saturn to go around the Sun four times?
   A. 7.365 years   B. 33.46 years   C. 116.8 years   D. 117.84 years

   4. _____

5. Lucas has 255 CDs. He wants to give them to several friends so that they each receive the same number of CDs. What are the possible number of friends who could receive CDs?
   A. 3, 5, 15, 17   B. 10, 25, 55
   C. 3, 5, 15, 17, 51   D. 2, 3, 5, 17

   5. _____

6. Alta wants to buy a sweater that costs $24.99. The sales tax is $5\frac{3}{4}$%. Which equation would help Alta estimate the cost of the sweater?
   A. $C = 0.06 \times 25$ B. $C = 0.06 \times 25 + 25$
   C. $C = 0.575$ D. none of these

   6. _____

7. Katie made $8\frac{1}{3}$ cups of soup. How many people can she serve if each serving is $\frac{1}{3}$ cup?
   A. 12   B. 25   C. 9   D. 27

   7. _____

8. Shane was refilling his iron. The iron holds $\frac{5}{8}$ cup of water. If it took $\frac{3}{8}$ cup to fill, how much water was already in the iron?
   A. $\frac{5}{8}$ cup   B. $\frac{3}{8}$ cup   C. $\frac{1}{4}$ cup   D. 1 cup

   8. _____

9. A scientific calculator, normally priced at $60, is on sale for $\frac{4}{5}$ of the original price. How much does it cost?
   A. $50   B. $48   C. $45   D. $12

   9. _____

10. Karly purchased a 15.5 ounce bag of hard candy for $2.49. What was the cost per ounce rounded to the nearest cent?
    A. $0.15/oz   B. $0.16/oz   C. $0.12/oz   D. none of these

    10. _____

11. Ticket sales at a movie theater increased by 105% when ticket prices were cut. Express the percent as a simplified fraction.
    A. $\frac{105}{100}$ **B.** $1\frac{5}{100}$ **C.** $1\frac{1}{20}$ **D.** none of these

    11. _____

12. Josh wants to design a four-sided mirror with 2 pairs of parallel sides. The mirror will be twice as tall as it is long and have no right angles. What is the shape of the mirror?
    A. parallelogram **B.** rectangle   **C.** square   **D.** hexagon

    12. _____

13. The triangular sail on a sailboat is 12 feet tall. The area of the sail is 96 ft². How long is the base of the sail?
    A. 8 ft   **B.** 13 ft   **C.** 16 ft   **D.** 48 ft

    13. _____

14. Josie wants to give boxes of jelly beans to four of her friends. Each box measures 6 inches by 2 inches by 4 inches. What is the total volume of the boxes she will need?
    A. 48 in³   **B.** 192 in³   **C.** 164 in³   **D.** 196 in³

    14. _____

15. A piece of modern art is shaped like a triangular pyramid. Each face is painted a different color. How many colors were used?
    A. 2   **B.** 3   **C.** 4   **D.** 5

    15. _____

16. Which letter has two lines of symmetry?
    A. D   **B.** H   **C.** M   **D.** W

    16. _____

17. The table shows the average depths of five large bodies of water. Order the bodies of water from deepest to most shallow.
    A. Pacific, Indian, Atlantic, Caribbean, Arctic
    B. Arctic, Caribbean, Indian, Atlantic, Pacific
    C. Arctic, Caribbean, Atlantic, Indian, Pacific
    D. Pacific, Indian, Atlantic, Arctic, Caribbean

Body of Water	Average Depth
Arctic Ocean	−3,407 ft
Atlantic Ocean	−11,730 ft
Caribbean Sea	−8,448 ft
Indian Ocean	−12,598 ft
Pacific Ocean	−12,925 ft

    17. _____

18. At 6 A.M. the temperature was −7°F, and at noon the temperature was 12°F. What was the difference in temperature?
    A. 5°   **B.** 19°
    C. −5°   **D.** none of these

    18. _____

19. The total bill for concert tickets is $372. How much did each ticket cost if six friends are going to the concert?
    A. $53   **B.** $20   **C.** $37   **D.** $62

    19. _____

20. If the point (5, 2) is reflected around the x-axis, what is its reflection?
    A. (−5, −2)   **B.** (5, −2)   **C.** (−2, 5)   **D.** (2, 5)

    20. _____

Name_____ Date _____

Cumulative Review, Chapters 1–11

1. Find the next three numbers in the pattern: 5, 7, 9, _?_, _?_, _?_. (Lesson 1-2)

    1. _____

2. Use the graph at the right to predict Sarah's height at age 12. (Lesson 2-5)

    2. _____

Sarah's Growth Chart

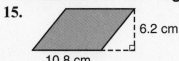

Ht. (in.)

Age

3. Round 8.729 to the tenths place. (Lesson 3-4)

    3. _____

4. Simplify $\frac{48}{88}$. (Lesson 5-4)

    4. _____

5. Round $5\frac{13}{24}$ to the nearest half. (Lesson 6-1)

    5. _____

6. Find the next number in the sequence $25, 37\frac{1}{2}, 56\frac{1}{4}, 84\frac{3}{8}, \underline{?}$. (Lesson 7-8)

    6. _____

Perform each indicated operation. (Lessons 4-7, 7-5, 11-3, and 11-5)

    7. _____

7. $4.028 \div 3.8$

8. $\frac{7}{20} \div \frac{5}{8}$

    8. _____

9. $-10 + (-30)$

10. $-5(-4)$

    9. _____

11. Express *105 miles on 15 gallons* as a rate. (Lesson 8-1)

    10. _____

12. On a map, the scale reads "1 inch = 25 miles." If the distance between two cities on the map is $2\frac{1}{2}$ inches, what is the actual distance? (Lesson 8-3)

    11. _____

    12. _____

13. How many sides does a hexagon have? (Lesson 9-4)

    13. _____

14. Tell whether the dashed line is a line of symmetry. Write *yes* or *no*. (Lesson 9-5)

    14. _____

Find the area of each figure. (Lessons 10-1 and 10-2)

15.

6.2 cm

10.8 cm

16.

28 ft

42 ft

    15. _____

    16. _____

Refer to the rectangular prism at the right.

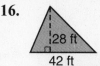

17. What is the surface area? (Lesson 10-6) 14 cm

20 cm 7 cm

    17. _____

18. What is the volume? (Lesson 10-5)

    18. _____

19. Order $-10, 0, 20, -30$, and 10 from least to greatest. (Lesson 11-2)

    19. _____

20. Write an integer to describe gaining 2 pounds. (Lesson 11-1)

    20. _____

Mathematics: Applications and Connections, Course 1

Chapter 11 Answer Key

Form 1A		Form 1B	

Form 1A

Page 281

1. C
2. A
3. B
4. C
5. D
6. A
7. B
8. C
9. D
10. B
11. A
12. C

Page 282

13. A
14. B
15. D
16. C
17. B
18. D
19. A
20. C

Form 1B

Page 283

1. A
2. B
3. B
4. D
5. B
6. D
7. D
8. C
9. A
10. D
11. A
12. B

Page 284

13. D
14. B
15. B
16. C
17. B
18. A
19. C
20. A

Mathematics: Applications and Connections, Course 1

Chapter 11 Answer Key

Form 1C

Page 285	Page 286
1. __B__	13. __C__
	14. __C__
2. __A__	15. __B__
3. __D__	16. __B__
4. __D__	
5. __B__	17. __A__
6. __C__	18. __C__
7. __D__	
8. __C__	19. __B__
9. __A__	
10. __B__	20. __D__
11. __A__	
12. __B__	

Mathematics: Applications and Connections, Course 1

Chapter 11 Answer Key

Form 2A

Page 287

1. _____ 0 _____
2. _____ +15 _____
3. _____ 38 _____
4.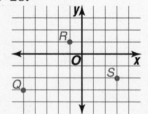
5. _____ < _____
6. _____ > _____
7. _____ > _____
8. _____ −15, −7, 0, 7, 13, 21 _____
9. _____ 19 _____
10. _____ −13 _____
11. _____ −399 _____
12. _____ 70 _____
13. _____ −5 _____
14. _____ 100 _____
15. _____ −9 _____
16. _____ −72 _____
17. _____ −16 _____
18. _____ 120 _____
19. _____ −26 _____
20. _____ −6 _____

Page 288

21. _____ −9 _____
22. _____ 24 _____
23. _____ −8 _____
24. _____ 2°F _____
25. _____ 28 _____

26–28.

29. _____ (4, 3) _____
30. _____ (−5, 2) _____
31. _____ (−3, −4) _____

32–33.

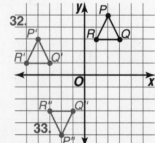

Mathematics: Applications and Connections, Course 1

Chapter 11 Answer Key

Form 2B

1. _____ −20 _____

2. _____ +5 _____

3. _____ −15 _____

4. ◄–●–┼–●–┼–●–┼–┼–┼–●–┼–┼–►
       −6 −4 −2 0 2 4 6

5. _____ < _____

6. _____ > _____

7. _____ > _____

8. _____ −12, −9, 0, 7, 12 _____

9. _____ −2 _____

10. _____ 1 _____

11. _____ −16 _____

12. _____ 12 _____

13. _____ −20 _____

14. _____ 17 _____

15. _____ −22 _____

16. _____ −18 _____

17. _____ −24 _____

18. _____ 18 _____

19. _____ −44 _____

20. _____ −4 _____

21. _____ −15 _____

22. _____ 6 _____

23. _____ −3 _____

24. _____ 9°F _____

25. _____ $18 _____

26–28.

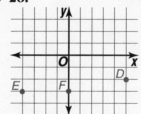

29. _____ (5, 3) _____

30. _____ (−3, 1) _____

31. _____ (−2, −3) _____

32–33.

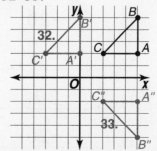

Mathematics: Applications and Connections, Course 1

Form 2C

Page 291	Page 292
1. -8	21. -8
2. $+3$	22. -6
3. -10	23. 3
4. *(number line from -5 to 5)*	24. $-2°F$
5. $<$	
6. $<$	25. **80 minutes**
7. $>$	
8. $-50, -13, 0,$ $10, 11$	
9. 2	26–28. 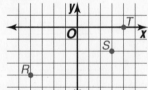
10. 5	
11. -9	
12. 10	
13. -18	29. $(2, 3)$
14. -10	30. $(-4, 2)$
15. 14	31. $(4, -4)$
16. -28	
17. -35	32–33. 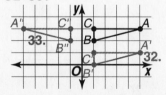
18. 30	
19. -20	
20. 5	

Chapter 11 Scoring Guide

Level	Specific Criteria
3 Superior	• Shows thorough understanding of the concepts *identifying, adding, subtracting, multiplying, and dividing integers using models* and *translation and reflection on the coordinate plane.* • Uses appropriate strategies to solve problems. • Computations are correct. • Diagrams are accurate and appropriate. • Written explanations are exemplary. • Goes beyond requirements of some or all problems.
2 Satisfactory, with Minor Flaws	• Shows understanding of the concepts *identifying, adding, subtracting, multiplying, and dividing integers using models* and *translation and reflection on the coordinate plane.* • Uses appropriate strategies to solve problems. • Computations are mostly correct. • Diagrams are accurate and appropriate. • Written explanations are effective. • Satisfies all requirements of problems.
1 Nearly Satisfactory, with Serious Flaws	• Shows understanding of most of the concepts *identifying, adding, subtracting, multiplying, and dividing integers using models* and *translation and reflection on the coordinate plane.* • May not use appropriate strategies to solve problems. • Computations are mostly correct. • Diagrams are accurate and appropriate. • Written explanations are satisfactory. • Satisfies most requirements of problems.
0 Unsatisfactory	• Shows little or no understanding of the concepts *identifying, adding, subtracting, multiplying, and dividing integers using models* and *translation and reflection on the coordinate plane.* • May not use appropriate strategies to solve problems. • Computations are incorrect. • Diagrams are not accurate or appropriate. • Written explanations are not satisfactory. • Does not satisfy requirements of problems.

Chapter 11 Answer Key

Performance Assessment Sample Answers
Page 293

1. a.

b. Place 5 negative counters and two positive counters together. Then remove the 0 pairs. $-5 + (+2) = -3$

c. Add 3 zero pairs before removing 3 negative counters.
$4 - (-3) = +7$

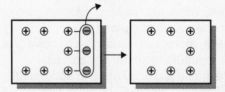

d. $-2 \times (-3)$ means to remove two sets of -3.

e. Start with a representation of zero. Then remove two sets of -3.
$-2 \times (-3) = 6$

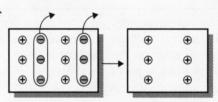

2. a. When you slide a figure from one location to another without changing its size or shape, the new figure is called a translation image.

b. 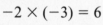 The image of A is $(-5, 3)$.

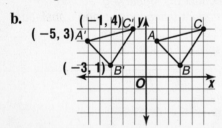

c. When you flip a figure over a line without changing its size or shape, the new figure is called a reflection image.

d. The image of B is $(3, -1)$.

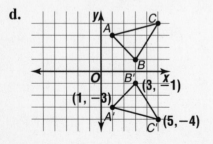

Mid-Chapter Test
Page 294

1. -4

2. -1

3. $+3$

4. $+97$

5. -203

6. $<$

7. $>$

8. $>$

9. $<$

10. $-19, -15, 16, 17$

11. -3

12. -11

13. -2

14. -10

15. 8

16. 5

17. -5

18. 6

19. -11

20. -1

Mathematics: Applications and Connections, Course 1

Chapter 11 Answer Key

Quiz A, Page 295

1. 8
2. −7
3. −4
4. 0
5. <
6. >
7. >
8. >
9. −12, −4, 0, 1, 5, 18
10. −81, −73, −62, −24

Quiz B, Page 295

1. −18
2. −3
3. −47
4. −34
5. −23
6. 18
7. 15
8. −14
9. −15
10. 0

Quiz C, Page 296

1. 22
2. −5
3. 8
4. −7
5. 3
6. 60
7. −84
8. 33
9. −27
10. 36

Quiz D, Page 296

1. (3, 1)
2. (−2, −3)
3. (−3, 3)
4. (1, −2)

5–8.

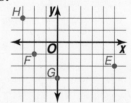

9–10.

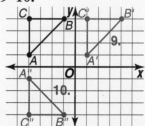

Mathematics: Applications and Connections, Course 1

Chapter 11 Answer Key

	Standardized Test Practice		

Standardized Test Practice

Page 297

1. A
2. A
3. A
4. D
5. C
6. B
7. B
8. C
9. B
10. B

Page 298

11. C
12. A
13. C
14. B
15. C
16. B
17. A
18. B
19. D
20. B

Cumulative Review

Page 299

1. 11, 13, 15
2. about 63 in.
3. 8.7
4. $\frac{6}{11}$
5. $5\frac{1}{2}$
6. $126\frac{9}{16}$
7. 1.06
8. $\frac{14}{25}$
9. -40
10. 20
11. 7 mpg
12. 62.5 miles
13. six
14. no
15. 66.96 cm²
16. 588 ft²
17. 1,036 cm²
18. 1,960 cm³
19. $-30, -10, 0,$ 10, 20
20. $+2$

Mathematics: Applications and Connections, Course 1

Chapter 12 Test, Form 1A

1. Solve $x + 7 = 10$.
   A. -3 B. 17   C. -17 D. none of these

   1. _____

2. Solve $y + (-15) = 31$.
   A. 16   B. 46   C. -46 D. none of these

   2. _____

3. Solve $-6 + w = -7$.
   A. 1   B. -1 C. -13 D. none of these

   3. _____

4. Solve $-24 = t + (-12)$.
   A. -12 B. 12   C. -36 D. none of these

   4. _____

5. Solve $z - 6 = 12$.
   A. 6   B. -6 C. 18   D. none of these

   5. _____

6. Solve $c - (-3) = 2$.
   A. -1 B. 1   C. 5   D. none of these

   6. _____

7. Solve $b - (-1) = -4$.
   A. 5   B. -5 C. -3 D. none of these

   7. _____

8. Solve $\frac{1}{3}x = 14$.
   A. 41   B. 43   C. 39   D. none of these

   8. _____

9. Solve $\frac{1}{12}x = -7$.
   A. 84   B. -84 C. 19   D. none of these

   9. _____

10. Solve $3x = -51$.
    A. -17 B. 17   C. 54   D. none of these

    10. _____

11. Solve $-6s + 3 = -27$.
    A. -5 B. 5   C. -30 D. none of these

    11. _____

12. Solve $18n - 40 = -4$.
    A. -2 B. 36   C. 3   D. none of these

    12. _____

13. Solve $-56 = 22r + 10$.
    A. -46 B. 3   C. -3 D. none of these

    13. _____

14. Wyoming's highest mountain, Gannett Peak, is two less than six times taller than Minnesota's highest mountain, Eagle Mountain. Gannett Peak is 13,804 feet tall. If x stands for Eagle Mountain's height, which equation could you solve to find Eagle Mountain's height?
    A. $(6 - 2)x = 13,804$ B. $6x - 2 = 13,804$
    C. $6x = 13,802$ D. none of these

    14. _____

     Mathematics: Applications and Connections, Course 1

15. What number should replace ▨ in the function table at the right?

    A. 7   B. 8
    C. 11   D. none of these

n	n + 9
−5	4
−3	6
2	▨

15. _____

16. Find the rule for the function table at the right.

    A. n + 8   B. 3n − 8
    C. n − 8   D. none of these

n	▨
−3	−17
1	−5
4	4

16. _____

17. Find the rule for the function table at the right.

    A. $\frac{1}{2}n - 1$ B. $\frac{1}{3}n + 1$
    C. $\frac{1}{2}n + 1$ D. none of these

n	▨
−6	−1
−4	0
6	5

17. _____

18. If a function rule is −8n − 4, what is the output for an input of −7?

    A. −52   B. 52   C. −19   D. none of these

18. _____

19. Which graph represents the function table at the right?

    A. 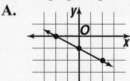   B.

x	$\frac{1}{2}x - 1$
−2	−2
0	−1
2	0

19. _____

    C.    D.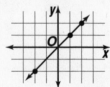

20. Which function table represents the graph at the right?

    A.

input	output
0	−8
1	−4
2	0

    B.

input	output
−8	0
−4	1
0	2

20. _____

    C.

input	output
0	8
1	4
2	0

    D.

input	output
8	0
4	1
0	2

Mathematics: Applications and Connections, Course 1

1. Solve $x + 5 = 1$.
   A. 4   B. -4 C. 14   D. none of these

   1. _____

2. Solve $y + (-4) = 11$.
   A. 7   B. 15   C. -7 D. none of these

   2. _____

3. Solve $-8 + t = 10$.
   A. 18   B. 2   C. -2 D. none of these

   3. _____

4. Solve $-7 = w + 6$.
   A. 1   B. -1 C. -13 D. none of these

   4. _____

5. Solve $z - 7 = 4$.
   A. 3   B. -3 C. -11 D. none of these

   5. _____

6. Solve $s - (-5) = -12$.
   A. 7   B. -17 C. 17   D. none of these

   6. _____

7. Solve $m - 4 = -2$.
   A. -2 B. 2   C. -6 D. none of these

   7. _____

8. Solve $\frac{1}{2}x = 10$.
   A. 20   B. 5   C. -5 D. none of these

   8. _____

9. Solve $\frac{1}{4}m = -4$.
   A. 1   B. -1 C. 16   D. none of these

   9. _____

10. Solve $4x = 20$.
    A. 5   B. -5 C. 80   D. none of these

    10. _____

11. Solve $3y - 4 = 8$.
    A. -4 B. 4   C. 1   D. none of these

    11. _____

12. Solve $-7 = 2n + 5$.
    A. -2 B. 6   C. -6 D. none of these

    12. _____

13. Solve $-6r + 11 = 13$.
    A. -2 B. 24   C. 2   D. none of these

    13. _____

14. Al's father is three times as old as Al. Al's father is 36 years old. If *x*
stands for Al's age, which equation could you solve to find Al's age?
  A. 3 + *x* = 36
  B. 36*x* = 3
  C. 3*x* = 36
  D. none of these

14. _____

15. What number should replace in the function table
at the right?
  A. 4
  B. 10
  C. 6
  D. none of these

n	n + 6
−3	3
0	6
4	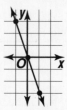

15. _____

16. Find the rule for the function table at the right.
  A. *n* + 2
  B. 2*n*
  C. *n* − 2
  D. none of these

n	
8	6
2	0
−3	−5

16. _____

17. Find the rule for the function table at the right.
  A. 3*n*
  B. $\frac{1}{3}n$
  C. *n* − 10
  D. none of these

n	
15	5
6	2
−9	−3

17. _____

18. If a function rule is 2*n* + 4, what is the output for an input of 5?
  A. 18   **B.** −18   **C.** 14   **D.** none of these

18. _____

19. Which graph represents the function table at the right?
  A.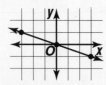
  B.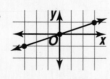

x	$\frac{x}{3}$
−3	−1
0	0
3	1

19. _____

  C.
  D.

20. Which function table represents the graph at the right?

  A.

input	output
−4	−2
−3	0
0	6

  B.

input	output
−2	−4
0	−3
6	0

  C.

input	output
4	2
3	0
0	6

  D.

input	output
2	4
0	3
6	0

20. _____

Name_____ **Date**_____

Chapter 12 Test, Form 1C

1. Solve $x + 1 = 3$.
   A. 2   B. -2 C. 4   D. none of these

   1. _____

2. Solve $y + (-3) = 7$.
   A. 4   B. 10   C. -4 D. none of these

   2. _____

3. Solve $-4 + t = 6$.
   A. 10   B. 2   C. -10 D. none of these

   3. _____

4. Solve $-5 = w + 1$.
   A. 6   B. -6 C. -4 D. none of these

   4. _____

5. Solve $x - 3 = 3$.
   A. 0   B. -6 C. 6   D. none of these

   5. _____

6. Solve $r - 1 = 0$.
   A. -1 B. 1   C. 0   D. none of these

   6. _____

7. Solve $p - 4 = 6$.
   A. 10   B. -10 C. 2   D. none of these

   7. _____

8. Solve $\frac{1}{4}x = 3$.
   A. $\frac{3}{4}$ B. 12   C. $3\frac{1}{4}$ D. none of these

   8. _____

9. Solve $\frac{1}{3}x = -5$.
   A. -15 B. 15   C. 8   D. none of these

   9. _____

10. Solve $8x = -40$.
    A. 5   B. -5 C. -320 D. none of these

    10. _____

11. Solve $-5 = 3x + 1$.
    A. 1   B. 2   C. -2 D. none of these

    11. _____

12. Solve $\frac{1}{2}y + 2 = 3$.
    A. 2   B. -2 C. 10   D. none of these

    12. _____

13. Solve $-2 - 3m = -11$.
    A. -9 B. -3 C. 3   D. none of these

    13. _____

Mathematics: Applications and Connections, Course 1

14. Cicely is saving money to buy a computer printer costing $399. She has already saved $150. If y stands for the amount she still needs to save, which equation could you solve to find the amount she still needs to save?

    A. $150 + 399 = y$ **B.** $399 + 7 = 150$

    C. $150 + y = 399$ **D.** none of these

14. _____

15. What number should replace ■ in the function table at the right?

    A. 4   **B.** 5

    C. 9   **D.** none of these

n	$n + 4$
-2	2
0	4
5	■

15. _____

16. Find the rule for the function table at the right.

    A. $n + 2$ **B.** $n - 2$

    C. $2 - n$ **D.** none of these

n	■
5	3
2	0
-3	-5

16. _____

17. Find the rule for the function table at the right.

    A. $n - 6$ **B.** $n + 4$

    C. $4n$ **D.** none of these

n	■
-2	-8
1	4
3	12

17. _____

18. If a function rule is $3n + 1$, what is the output for an input of 3?

    A. 9   **B.** 10

    C. 34   **D.** none of these

18. _____

x	$3x$
1	3
0	0
-1	-3

19. Which graph represents the function table at the right?

19. _____

    A.   **B.**   **C.**   **D.**

20. Which function table represents the graph at the right?

20. _____

A.

input	output
2	-2
0	1
2	0

B.

input	output
-2	2
0	1
2	0

C.

input	output
2	2
1	0
0	-2

D.

input	output
2	2
0	1
-2	0

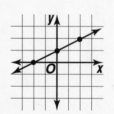

Mathematics: Applications and Connections, Course 1

Chapter 12 Test, Form 2A

Solve each equation.

1. $x + (-17) = 7$

    1. _____

2. $51 + a = 42$

    2. _____

3. $m - 32 = -9$

    3. _____

4. $h - 12 = -4$

    4. _____

5. $s + (-21) = -7$

    5. _____

6. $r - 23 = 1$

    6. _____

7. $c - 39 = -46$

    7. _____

8. $1.72b = 2.322$

    8. _____

9. $\frac{1}{9}y = 7$

    9. _____

10. $\frac{1}{5}k + 4 = 1$

    10. _____

11. $17n = 119$

    11. _____

12. $\frac{1}{7}q = -8$

    12. _____

13. $x + 67 = -22$

    13. _____

14. $26z = -182$

    14. _____

15. $12x - 71 = -11$

    15. _____

16. $-4y + 23 = 71$

    16. _____

17. $8t - 39 = -175$

    17. _____

18. Elizabeth is saving money for a school trip that will cost her
    $125. She saved $40 and has five weeks to save the rest. Find
    how much money she must save each week by writing an
    equation and solving it.

    18. _____

*Mathematics: Applications
and Connections,* Course 1

Complete each function table.

19.

n	n − 11
−4	■
2	■
13	■

19. _____

20.

n	$\frac{1}{6}n$
−24	■
−12	■
30	■

20. _____

Find the rule for each function table.

21.

n	■
−4	−13
1	−8
5	−4

21. _____

22.

n	■
−6	−1
0	0
12	2

22. _____

23. Arman does odd jobs around the neighborhood. He is saving some money for school. When he makes $50, he saves $25. When he makes $60, he saves $30. When he makes $70, he saves $35. Find the function rule that he used.

23. _____

Graph the function on the grid at the right.

24.

x	x + 3
−4	−1
−1	2
2	5

24.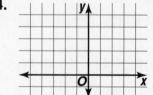

25.

x	$\frac{1}{3}x$
−6	−2
0	0
3	1

25.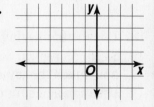

Mathematics: Applications and Connections, Course 1

Name_____ Date _____

Chapter 12 Test, Form 2B

Solve each equation.

1. $x + (-5) = 7$

2. $35 + a = 25$

3. $m - 4 = -6$

4. $h - 5 = -1$

5. $s + (-2) = -8$

6. $r - 7 = 1$

7. $c - 7 = -5$

8. $1.5b = 3.15$

9. $\frac{1}{4}y = 4$

10. $\frac{1}{5}k + 7 = 3$

11. $6n = 18$

12. $\frac{1}{5}q = -3$

13. $x + 12 = -4$

14. $8z = -24$

15. $4x - 9 = -5$

16. $3y + 2 = -1$

17. $4t - 3 = -3$

18. Kelli is saving money to buy a sweater costing $34. She already has saved $12. Find how much more money she must save by writing an equation and solving it.

1. _____

2. _____

3. _____

4. _____

5. _____

6. _____

7. _____

8. _____

9. _____

10. _____

11. _____

12. _____

13. _____

14. _____

15. _____

16. _____

17. _____

18. _____

Mathematics: Applications and Connections, Course 1

Complete each function table.

19.

n	n + 5
−3	■
0	■
4	■

19. _____

20.

n	6n
−2	■
−1	■
3	■

20. _____

Find the rule for each function table.

21.

n	■
−3	1
0	4
2	6

21. _____

22.

n	■
−4	−1
0	0
8	2

22. _____

23. Kenji works as a waiter. When he makes tips, he saves some for school. When he makes $45 in tips, he saves $35. When he makes $60, he saves $50. When he makes $40, he saves $30. Find the function rule that he used.

23. _____

Graph the function on the grid at the right.

24.

x	x − 3
5	2
3	0
−1	−4

24.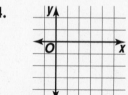

25.

x	$\frac{1}{4}x$
4	1
0	0
−4	−1

25.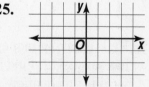

Chapter 12 Test, Form 2C

Solve each equation.

1. $x + 4 = -3$ 1. _____

2. $10 + a = 15$ 2. _____

3. $m - 6 = -9$ 3. _____

4. $h - 3 = 2$ 4. _____

5. $s + (-5) = -4$ 5. _____

6. $r - 8 = 0$ 6. _____

7. $c - 5 = -9$ 7. _____

8. $2b = 14$ 8. _____

9. $\frac{1}{6}y = 2$ 9. _____

10. $\frac{1}{2}k + 1 = 4$ 10. _____

11. $7n = 35$ 11. _____

12. $\frac{1}{2}q = -4$ 12. _____

13. $x + 10 = -6$ 13. _____

14. $5z = -30$ 14. _____

15. $2x + 1 = 3$ 15. _____

16. $3y - 4 = 2$ 16. _____

17. $5t - 3 = 12$ 17. _____

18. Jamal delivers 60 papers each day after school. Today he has   18. _____
    already delivered 22 papers. Find how many more papers he
    must deliver by writing an equation and solving it.

Complete each function table.

19.

n	n − 4
6	■
3	■
−2	■

19. _____

20.

n	5n
−2	■
0	■
3	■

20. _____

Find the rule for each function table.

21.

n	■
8	4
4	0
2	−2

21. _____

22.

n	■
−3	−6
1	2
3	6

22. _____

23. Margarita sells used books in her bookstore. For one book, she paid $2 and sold it for $5. For another book, she paid $5 and sold it for $8. For a third book, she paid $7 and sold it for $10. Find the function rule that she used.

23. _____

Graph the function on the grid at the right.

24.

x	x − 2
4	2
0	−2
−2	−4

24.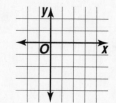

25.

x	6x
−1	−2
0	0
1	2

25.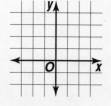

Mathematics: Applications and Connections, Course 1

Chapter 12 Performance Assessment

Instructions: *Demonstrate your knowledge by giving a clear, concise solution to each problem. Be sure to include all relevant drawings and justify your answers. You may show your solutions in more than one way or investigate beyond the requirements of the problems.*

1. Draw cups, 🥤 , positive counters, ⊕, and negative counters, ⊖, to model each of the following.

   a. Model $x - 3 = 4$. Explain your reasoning.

   b. Use modeling to solve the equation in part a. Explain each step.

   c. Model $4x + 3 = -5$. Explain your reasoning.

   d. Use modeling to solve the equation in part c. Show each step.

   e. Write a word problem concerning integers.

   f. Write an equation for the problem in part e. Solve. Explain each step.

2. **a.** Write the rule for the table. Then complete the table.

Input (n)	Output _____
−2	−4
0	0
2	4
3	
−3	

   b. Graph the function in part a.

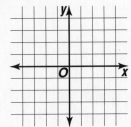

Mathematics: Applications and Connections, Course 1

Chapter 12 Mid-Chapter Test

(Lessons 12-1 through 12-3)

Solve each equation.

1. $a + 5 = -8$ 1. _____

2. $6 + c = 3$ 2. _____

3. $d - 5 = 13$ 3. _____

4. $r - 9 = -1$ 4. _____

5. $9s = -63$ 5. _____

6. $3x = -15$ 6. _____

7. $b + 22 = 17$ 7. _____

8. $m + 12 = 17$ 8. _____

9. $r - 5 = 4$ 9. _____

10. $s - 7 = -12$ 10. _____

11. $4y = 28$ 11. _____

12. $\frac{1}{3}a = 11$ 12. _____

13. $n + (-4) = 0$ 13. _____

14. $-18 + r = -22$ 14. _____

15. $t - 19 = -22$ 15. _____

16. $w - 52 = -38$ 16. _____

17. $\frac{1}{4}p = -15$ 17. _____

18. $\frac{g}{2} = -21$ 18. _____

19. Lenny rides the elevator up 12 floors and gets off at the 19th   19. _____
    floor. Write an equation to represent his movement, and solve it.

20. Jill and Amy went out to dinner. They agreed to each pay half   20. _____
    the bill. Jill paid $13.24. Write an equation for this situation,
    and find the amount of the bill.

*Mathematics: Applications
and Connections,* Course 1

Name_____ Date _____

Chapter 12 Quiz A

Solve each equation.

1. $m + 7 = 1$

2. $x - 5 = 7$

3. $x + (-6) = -5$

4. $n - 7 = -8$

5. $a + 12 = 7$

6. $b - 11 = -4$

7. $c + (-19) = -24$

8. $t - 18 = 1$

9. $p + 6 = -15$

10. $r - 53 = -38$

1._____

2._____

3._____

4._____

5._____

6._____

7._____

8._____

9._____

10._____

Name_____ Date _____

Chapter 12 Quiz B

Solve each equation.

1. $12x = -48$

2. $\frac{1}{4}a = -6$

3. $-8d = -32$

4. $51 = -17n$

5. $8s = 5.6$

6. $6m = -42$

7. $\frac{1}{3}r = 8$

8. $\frac{1}{2}x = -9$

9. $\frac{1}{3}y = -7$

10. $\frac{1}{5}c = 15$

1._____

2._____

3._____

4._____

5._____

6._____

7._____

8._____

9._____

10._____

Chapter 12 Quiz C

Solve each equation.

1. $-3t - 15 = 9$ 2. $2x + 3 = 5$

3. At one gas station, one fourth of the customers buy premium gasoline. In one hour, 12 customers bought premium gasoline. What was the total number of customers for the hour?

4. Complete the function table.

n	$n + 5$
-2	■
0	■
4	■

5. Find the rule for the function table.

n	■
-5	-1
0	4
4	8

1. _____

2. _____

3. _____

4. _____

5. _____

Chapter 12 Quiz D

Make a function table for each graph.

1. 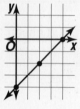   2.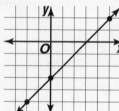

Complete each table. Then graph the function.

3.

x	$x + 3$
-2	■
0	■
2	■

4.

x	$\frac{1}{2}x$
-2	■
0	■
4	■

1. _____

2. _____

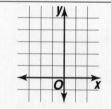

3. _____

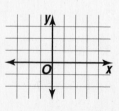

4. _____

Mathematics: Applications and Connections, Course 1

Chapter 12 Standardized Test Practice

1. Which of the following is a solution for $12d = 156$?
   A. 4 B. 12 C. 11 D. 13

   1. _____

2. The ordered pair (5, 39) represents the age and weight of a child. If the child's weight increases 5 pounds per year, which ordered pair represents weight at age 8.
   A. (5, 44) B. (8, 54) C. (13, 57) D. (8, 57)

   2. _____

3. The fastest crawling insect, a cockroach, can move at a rate of 4.64 km/hr. The maximum speed of the garden snail is 0.008 km/hr. How much faster does the cockroach travel?
   A. 3.8 km/hr B. 4.632 km/hr C. 4.56 km/hr D. 4.648 km/hr

   3. _____

4. In one year a college student earned $4,582.16 working part-time. What is the approximate average amount she earned in a month?
   A. $4,000 B. $5,000 C. $400 D. $5,500

   4. _____

5. A brick wall is $45\frac{3}{4}$ feet long. Each brick is $8\frac{1}{2}$ inches long. If there is $\frac{1}{2}$ inch of mortar between the bricks, *about* how many bricks are needed for each row?
   A. 5 B. 45 C. 62 D. 90

   5. _____

6. Kane lives $5\frac{1}{4}$ miles from school and $7\frac{1}{6}$ miles from work. How much farther is work than home?
   A. $2\frac{11}{12}$ B. $2\frac{9}{12}$ C. $1\frac{11}{12}$ D. $1\frac{1}{12}$

   6. _____

7. How many nails weighing $\frac{3}{8}$ ounce each are in a 9-ounce bag of nails?
   A. 24 B. $3\frac{3}{8}$ C. $\frac{1}{24}$ D. 8

   7. _____

8. A scale model of the Grand Canyon measures 21.7 inches. How long is the Grand Canyon if the model was built with a scale of 1 inch representing 10 miles?
   A. 21.70 miles B. 217 miles C. 2.17 miles D. none of these

   8. _____

9. The income tax rate for José's family is 9.7%. What is the rate as a decimal?
   A. 0.97 B. 0.097 C. 9.7 D. none of these

   9. _____

10. A jet plane is traveling at 1,000 kilometers per hour north from the state capitol. Due to stormy weather, the plane turns and flies directly east. What angle is formed by the flight path?
    A. 45° B. 90° C. 180° D. none of these

    10. _____

11. Triangle A has a perimeter of 24 centimeters and each side measures 8 centimeters. Triangle B has a perimeter of 48 centimeters and is similar to triangle A. Find the measure for each side of triangle B.
    A. 16 cm B. 24 cm C. 32 cm D. 48 cm

    11. _____

Mathematics: Applications and Connections, Course 1

12. An obelisk is an upright four-sided monument topped by a pyramid. How many faces, including the base, does an obelisk have?

    A. 4   **B.** 7   **C.** 8   **D.** 9

12. _____

13. An art student wants to cover a rectangular prism with mirrors. The prism measures 15 inches by 12 inches by 8 inches. What is the surface area of the prism?

    A. 1,440 in²   **B.** 492 in²   **C.** 720 in²   **D.** 792 in²

13. _____

14. The beginning balance in Kisha's checking account is $350. In one week, Kisha deposits her paycheck of $250 and withdraws $75 for food. What is Kisha's balance at the end of the week?

    A. $625   **B.** $525   **C.** $300   **D.** $25

14. _____

15. Luann's dad spends $3.50 a day on gas and tolls to drive his car to work. How much does he spend driving to work for five days?

    A. $17.50   **B.** $24.50   **C.** $14.00   **D.** $21.00

15. _____

16. The ordered pairs $(2, 0)$, $(-2, 0)$, $(2, 2)$, and $(-2, 2)$ form what shape when graphed?

    A. rectangle   **B.** square   **C.** circle   **D.** triangle

16. _____

17. Luis has 600 baseball cards. He bought C new cards bringing his total collection to 720. Luis wrote an equation to express the number of cards he owns. Which is the best equation?

    A. $600 + C = 720$ **B.** $600 + 720 = C$

    C. $720 + C = 600$ **D.** $C = 120$

17. _____

18. Trey is paid $5.75 an hour. The equation $s = 5.75 \times t$ could be used to calculate his salary. What is a reasonable estimate for Trey's weekly income if he works $t = 38$ hours in one week?

    A. $180   **B.** $200   **C.** $240   **D.** none of these

18. _____

19. The perimeter of a rectangle is 92 inches. Find the length if the width is 18 inches.

    A. 24 in.   **B.** 28 in.   **C.** 37 in.   **D.** none of these

19. _____

20. There is a difference of 3 time zones between New York City, n, and Los Angeles, ℓ. Evaluate the function rule $\ell = n - 3$ to find the time in Los Angeles when it is 1 P.M. in New York City.

    A. 4 P.M.   **B.** 11 A.M.   **C.** 2 P.M.   **D.** none of these

20. _____

Name_____ Date_____

Cumulative Review, Chapters 1–12

**Replace each ● with <, >, or = to make a true sentence.
(Lessons 3-3, 5-8, and 11-2)**

1. 0.0004 ● 0.003   2. $\frac{9}{100}$ ● $\frac{4}{25}$ 3. -100 ● -145

4. Find the elapsed time from 7:45 A.M. to 11:35 A.M. (Lesson 6-7)

5. Round 2,387 to the nearest hundred. (Lesson 1-3)

6. What is the mode for the data: 84, 80, 79, 86, 85, 86? (Lesson 2-7)

7. Solve 8 × 152 using the distributive property. (Lesson 4-2)

Estimate. (Lessons 7-1 and 8-6)

8. $\frac{1}{3}$ × 25   9. 21% of 26

10. Use a compass and straightedge to bisect the angle at the right.
(Lesson 9-3)

11. Find the area of a triangle with a base of 48 centimeters and a
height of 30 centimeters. (Lesson 10-2)

12. Find the area of a circle with a radius of 19 millimeters. Use
3.14 for π. Round to the nearest tenth. (Lesson 10-3)

13. State the number of edges in a rectangular prism. (Lesson 10-4)

**Perform the indicated operation. (Lessons 11-3, 11-4,
and 11-5)**

14. $-14 + 9$

15. $8 - (-4)$

16. $-9(-4)$

17. If a function rule is $2n + 3$, what is the output for $n = -2$?
(Lesson 12-5)

Solve each equation. (Lessons 12-1, 12-2, and 12-3)

18. $m + 5 = -9$

19. $x - 6 = -8$

20. $9n = -45$

1. _____

2. _____

3. _____

4. _____

5. _____

6. _____

7. _____

8. _____

9. _____

10.

11. _____

12. _____

13. _____

14. _____

15. _____

16. _____

17. _____

18. _____

19. _____

20. _____

*Mathematics: Applications
and Connections, Course 1*

Chapter 12 Answer Key

Form 1A

Page 309

1. D
2. B
3. B
4. A
5. C
6. A
7. B
8. D
9. B
10. A
11. B
12. D
13. C
14. B

Page 310

15. C
16. B
17. D
18. B
19. C
20. A

Form 1B

Page 311

1. B
2. B
3. A
4. C
5. D
6. B
7. B
8. A
9. D
10. A
11. B
12. C
13. D

Page 312

14. C
15. B
16. C
17. B
18. C
19. D
20. A

Mathematics: Applications and Connections, Course 1

Form 1C

Page 313		Page 314	
1. A		14. C	
2. B			
3. A		15. C	
4. B		16. B	
5. C			
6. B		17. C	
7. A		18. B	
8. B		19. C	
9. A			
10. B			
11. C		20. D	
12. A			
13. C			

Chapter 12 Answer Key

Form 2A

Page 315

1. _____ 24 _____

2. _____ −9 _____

3. _____ 23 _____

4. _____ 8 _____

5. _____ 14 _____

6. _____ 24 _____

7. _____ −7 _____

8. _____ 1.35 _____

9. _____ 63 _____

10. _____ −15 _____

11. _____ 7 _____

12. _____ −56 _____

13. _____ −89 _____

14. _____ −7 _____

15. _____ 5 _____

16. _____ −12 _____

17. _____ −17 _____

18. _____ $5x + 40 = 125; x = 17$ _____

Page 316

19. _____ −15, −9, 2 _____

20. _____ −4, −2, 5 _____

21. _____ $n − 9$ _____

22. _____ $\frac{1}{6}n$ _____

23. _____ $\frac{1}{2}n$ _____

24.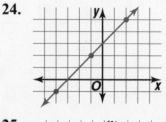

25.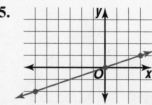

Mathematics: Applications and Connections, Course 1

Chapter 12 Answer Key

Form 2B

Page 317

1. 12
2. −10
3. −2
4. 4
5. −6
6. 8
7. 2
8. 2.1
9. 16
10. −20
11. 3
12. −15
13. −16
14. −3
15. 1
16. −1
17. 0
18. $12 + x = 34$; $x = 22$

Page 318

19. 2, 5, 9
20. −12, −6, 18
21. $n + 4$
22. $\frac{1}{4}n$
23. $n − 10$
24.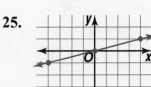
25.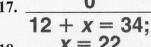

Mathematics: Applications and Connections, Course 1

Chapter 12 Answer Key

Form 2C

Page 319		Page 320	
1. -7		19. $2, -1, -6$	
2. 5			
3. -3		20. $-10, 0, 15$	
4. 5			
5. 1			
6. 8		21. $n - 4$	
7. -4			
8. 7			
9. 12		22. $2n$	
10. 6			
11. 5		23. $n + 3$	
12. -8			
13. -16			
14. -6		24.	
15. 1			
16. 2			
17. 3		25.	
18. $22 + x = 60;$ $x = 38$			

24.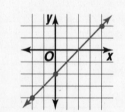

25.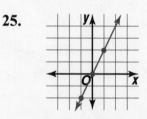

Mathematics: Applications and Connections, Course 1

Chapter 12 Scoring Guide

Level	Specific Criteria
3 Superior	• Shows thorough understanding of the concepts *solving addition, subtraction, multiplication, and division equations, completing function tables,* and *graphing functions.* • Uses appropriate strategies to solve problems. • Computations are correct. • Written explanations are exemplary. • Word problem concerning integers is appropriate and makes sense. • Graph, diagrams, and table are accurate and appropriate. • Goes beyond requirements of some or all problems.
2 Satisfactory, with Minor Flaws	• Shows understanding of the concepts *solving addition, subtraction, multiplication, and division equations, completing function tables,* and *graphing functions.* • Uses appropriate strategies to solve problems. • Computations are mostly correct. • Word problem concerning integers is appropriate and makes sense. • Graph, diagrams, and table are mostly accurate and appropriate. • Written explanations are effective. • Satisfies all requirements of problems.
1 Nearly Satisfactory, with Serious Flaws	• Shows understanding of most of the concepts *solving addition, subtraction, multiplication, and division equations, completing function tables,* and *graphing functions.* • May not use appropriate strategies to solve problems. • Computations are mostly correct. • Word problem concerning integers is somewhat appropriate and sensible. • Graph, diagrams, and table are mostly accurate and appropriate. • Written explanations are satisfactory. • Satisfies most requirements of problems.
0 Unsatisfactory	• Shows little or no understanding of the concepts *solving addition, subtraction, multiplication, and division equations, completing function tables,* and *graphing functions.* • May not use appropriate strategies to solve problems. • Computations are incorrect. • Word problem concerning integers is not appropriate or sensible. • Graph, diagrams, and table are not accurate or appropriate. • Written explanations are not satisfactory. • Does not satisfy requirements of problems.

Chapter 12 Answer Key

1. a. Let a cup represent x, 3 negative counters represent -3, and 4 positive counters represent 4.

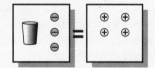

b. To remove the 3 negative counters from the left side, add 3 positive counters to each side. Then remove the 3 zero pairs.

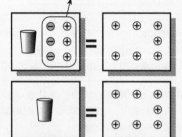

$x = 7$

c. Let 4 cups represent $4x$, 3 positive counters represent $+3$, and 5 negative counters represent -5.

d. Add 3 negative counters to each side. Remove the 3 zero pairs. Match each cup with an equal number of counters.

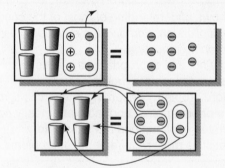

$x = -2$

e. Twice Stan's golf score plus 4 is 2. What is Stan's golf score?

f.

$$2x + 4 = 2 \qquad \text{\textit{Add} } -4 \text{ \textit{to each side.}}$$
$$2x + 4 + (-4) = 2 + (-4) \qquad \textit{Simplify.}$$
$$2x = -2 \qquad \text{\textit{Multiply each side by} } \tfrac{1}{2}.$$
$$\tfrac{1}{2}(2x) = \tfrac{1}{2}(-2) \qquad \textit{Simplify.}$$
$$x = -1$$

Stan's golf score is -1 or 1 under par.

2. a. Function rule: $2n$

b.

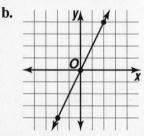

Input (n)	Output ($2n$)
-2	-4
0	0
2	4
3	6
-3	-6

1. -13

2. -3

3. 18

4. 8

5. -7

6. -5

7. -5

8. 5

9. 9

10. -5

11. 7

12. 33

13. 4

14. -4

15. -3

16. 14

17. -60

18. -42

19. $x + 12 = 19;$ $x = 7$

20. $\tfrac{1}{2}x = \$13.24;$ $x = \$26.48$

Chapter 12 Answer Key

Quiz A, Page 323

1. −6
2. 12
3. 1
4. −1
5. −5
6. 7
7. −5
8. 19
9. −21
10. 15

Quiz B, Page 323

1. −4
2. −24
3. 4
4. −3
5. 0.7
6. −7
7. 24
8. −18
9. −21
10. 75

Quiz C, Page 324

1. −8
2. 1
3. 48
4. 3, 5, 9
5. $n + 4$

Quiz D, Page 324

1.

x	$x - 4$
4	0
2	−2
0	−4

2.

x	$x - 3$
−2	−5
0	−3
5	2

3.
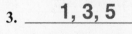
1, 3, 5

4.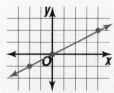
−1, 0, 2

Mathematics: Applications and Connections, Course 1

12 Chapter 12 Answer Key

Standardized Test Practice

Page 325

1. D
2. B
3. B
4. C
5. C
6. C
7. A
8. B
9. B
10. B
11. A

Page 326

12. D
13. D
14. B
15. A
16. A
17. A
18. C
19. B
20. D

Cumulative Review

Page 327

1. $<$
2. $<$
3. $>$
4. **3 h 50 min**
5. **2,400**
6. **86**
7. $(8 \times 100) +$ $(8 \times 50) +$ $(8 \times 2) = 1,216$
8. $\frac{1}{3} \times 24 = 8$
9. $\frac{1}{5} \times 25 = 5$
10.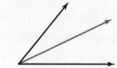
11. **720 cm²**
12. **1,133.5 mm²**
13. **12**
14. **−5**
15. **12**
16. **36**
17. **−1**
18. **−14**
19. **−2**
20. **−5**

Mathematics: Applications and Connections, Course 1

Name_____ Date _____

Chapter 13 Test, Form 1A

1. A set of 16 cards is numbered 1, 2, 3, ..., 16. Juan is equally likely to choose any one card. Find $P(5)$.
   A. 5   B. $\frac{5}{16}$ C. 16   D. none of these

   1. _____

2. A bag contains 8 black marbles and 12 white marbles. Doreen chooses a white marble from the bag and does not replace it. Then Victor chooses a marble. What is the probability that Victor's marble is black?
   A. $\frac{2}{5}$ B. $\frac{8}{19}$ C. $\frac{11}{19}$ D. none of these

   2. _____

3. A set of cards is lettered M, I, S, S, I, S, S, I, P, P, I. A person is equally likely to choose any one card. Find $P(S)$.
   A. $\frac{4}{7}$ B. 4   C. $\frac{4}{11}$ D. none of these

   3. _____

4. In a quality control test, 8 parts out of 200 were defective. If the company made 5,000 parts, predict the total number of defective parts.
   A. 25   B. 200   C. $\frac{1}{25}$ D. none of these

   4. _____

5. Of 50 people surveyed, 18 preferred rock, 12 preferred rap, 5 preferred classical, and 15 preferred music in miscellaneous categories. If a store owner orders 1,000 cassettes, how many should be rock cassettes?
   A. 900   B. 360   C. $\frac{18}{50}$ D. none of these

   5. _____

6. At a carwash, three options are available: regular, super, and deluxe. Out of 20 customers, 12 chose the deluxe option. If 3,000 people use the carwash in a month, how many would you expect to use the deluxe option?
   A. 150   B. 180   C. $\frac{3}{5}$ D. none of these

   6. _____

7. The figure at the right represents a dartboard. It is equally likely that a dart will land anywhere on the dartboard. Find the probability of a randomly thrown dart landing in the shaded region.
   A. $\frac{3}{13}$ B. $\frac{3}{8}$
   C. $\frac{3}{16}$ D. none of these

   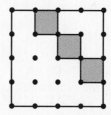

   7. _____

8. Suppose you threw a dart 100 times at the dartboard shown. How many times would you expect it to land in the shaded region?
   A. 25   B. 50
   C. 75   D. none of these

   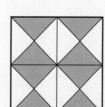

   8. _____

9. Suppose you threw a dart 160 times at the dartboard in Question 7. How   9. _____
   many times would you expect it to land in the unshaded region?
   A. 30   **B.** 130   **C.** 19   **D.** none of these

For Questions 10–11, refer to the tree diagram.

10. T-shirts are available in small, medium,   10. _____
    or large sizes. The possible colors are
    white, red, black, or yellow. How many
    different types of T-shirts can be stocked?
    A. 3   **B.** 4
    C. 7   **D.** 12

11. If a customer picks out a T-shirt at   11. _____
    random, what is the probability it will
    be a medium, white T-shirt?
    A. $\frac{1}{4}$ **B.** $\frac{1}{3}$
    C. $\frac{1}{7}$ **D.** none of these

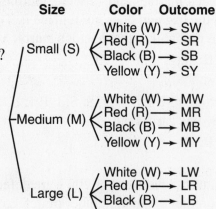

12. A coin is tossed and a number is picked at random from the set   12. _____
    {2, 4, 6, 8}. Which tree diagram is correct?
    A.   **B.**   **C.**   **D.** none of these

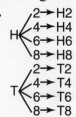 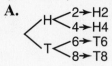

13. Suppose you toss a coin and roll a number cube. Find *P*(heads and 3 or 4).   13. _____
    A. $\frac{1}{6}$ **B.** $\frac{1}{12}$ **C.** $\frac{1}{3}$ **D.** none of these

14. Each spinner is spun once. What is *P*(white and 6)?   14. _____
    A. $\frac{1}{3}$ **B.** $\frac{1}{6}$
    C. $\frac{1}{9}$ **D.** $\frac{1}{18}$

15. Car upholstery comes in leather or vinyl, and in black, brown, tan, red, or   15. _____
    blue. If you pick a car at random, what is *P*(red, leather)?
    A. $\frac{1}{3}$ **B.** $\frac{1}{5}$ **C.** $\frac{1}{6}$ **D.** none of these

16. Which list of scores does the frequency table at   16. _____
    the right *not* represent?
    A. 92, 67, 73, 75, 96, 94, 81, 87, 71, 100
    B. 68, 94, 72, 81, 96, 87, 95, 99, 75
    C. 74, 93, 67, 73, 74, 91, 96, 87, 95, 88
    D. none of these

Score	Frequency
90–100	4
80–89	2
70–79	3
60–69	1

Chapter 13 Test, Form 1B

1. A set of 12 table tennis balls is numbered 1, 2, 3, ..., 12. Jodi is equally likely to choose any one ball. Find $P(12)$.
   A. 12   **B.** 1   **C.** $\frac{1}{12}$ **D.** none of these

1. _____

2. For the table tennis balls in Question 1, find $P(\text{odd})$.
   A. $\frac{1}{2}$ **B.** $\frac{2}{12}$ **C.** 6   **D.** none of these

2. _____

3. A set of cards is lettered C, O, N, N, E, C, T, I, C, U, T. A person is equally likely to choose any one card. Find $P(C)$.
   A. $\frac{2}{11}$ **B.** $\frac{3}{11}$ **C.** $\frac{1}{11}$ **D.** none of these

3. _____

4. Of 40 people surveyed at a bookstore, 6 like biographies, 11 like science fiction, 12 like mysteries, and 11 like general fiction. If the store owner plans to buy 800 books, how many biographies should she order?
   A. 120   **B.** 20   **C.** $\frac{11}{40}$ **D.** none of these

4. _____

5. In Question 4, how many mystery books should the store owner order?
   A. 12   **B.** $\frac{12}{40}$ **C.** 240   **D.** none of these

5. _____

6. At an ice cream shop, the sundae toppings are chocolate, strawberry, marshmallow, and pineapple. Out of 20 people, 9 chose chocolate. If 500 people buy sundaes, how many would you expect to buy chocolate?
   A. 450   **B.** $\frac{9}{20}$ **C.** 275   **D.** none of these

6. _____

7. The figure at the right represents a dartboard. It is equally likely that a dart will land anywhere on the dart board. Find the probability of a randomly thrown dart landing in the shaded region.
   A. $\frac{1}{3}$ **B.** $\frac{1}{2}$
   C. $\frac{1}{4}$ **D.** none of these

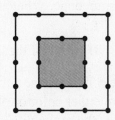

7. _____

8. Suppose you threw a dart 100 times at the dartboard shown. How many times would you expect it to land in the shaded region?
   A. 75   **B.** 25
   C. 50   **D.** none of these

8. _____

Mathematics: Applications and Connections, Course 1

9. Suppose you threw a dart 100 times at the dartboard in Question 7. How   9. _____
   many times would you expect it to land in the shaded region?

   A. $\frac{1}{4}$ **B.** 25   **C.** 75   **D.** none of these

For Questions 10–11, refer to the tree diagram.

10. Rafael and Mai-Lin are running for   10. _____
    class president while Anna, Sam,
    Tawanda, and Patrick are running
    for vice-president. How many
    different combinations of president
    and vice-president are possible?

    A. 6   **B.** 10
    C. 8   **D.** none of these

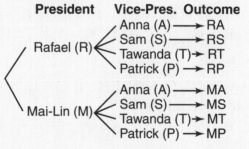

11. What is the probability that Mai-Lin will be elected president and Patrick   11. _____
    will be elected vice-president?

    A. $\frac{1}{4}$ **B.** $\frac{1}{2}$ **C.** $\frac{1}{8}$ **D.** none of these

12. A coin is tossed and a letter is picked at random from the word LOVE.   12. _____
    Which diagram shows all of the possible outcomes?

    A.   **B.**   **C.**   **D.** none of these

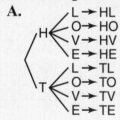

13. Suppose you toss a coin and roll a number cube. Find P(tails and 2).   13. _____

    A. $\frac{1}{2}$ **B.** $\frac{1}{8}$ **C.** $\frac{1}{12}$ **D.** none of these

14. Each spinner is spun once. What is P(red and 6)?   14. _____

    A. $\frac{1}{4}$ **B.** $\frac{1}{8}$

    C. $\frac{1}{12}$ **D.** none of these

15. For one brand of computer, monitors come in 10-inch, 12-inch, and 15-   15. _____
    inch sizes and are either color or black-and-white. If you choose a monitor
    at random, what is the probability it will be a 12-inch color monitor?

    A. $\frac{1}{3}$ **B.** $\frac{1}{5}$ **C.** $\frac{1}{6}$ **D.** none of these

16. Which list of test scores does the frequency   16. _____
    table at the right represent?

    A. 92, 73, 84, 86, 62, 65, 61, 71, 82
    B. 92, 73, 77, 84, 86, 91, 62, 65, 75, 61, 71, 82
    C. 73, 77, 86, 91, 62, 75, 71, 82
    D. none of these

Score	Frequency
90–100	2
80–89	3
70–79	4
60–69	3

Name_____ Date _____

Chapter 13 Test, Form 1C

1. A set of 7 cards is numbered 1, 2, 3, ..., 7. Martin is equally likely to choose any one card. Find $P(3)$.
   A. 3   **B.** $\frac{1}{7}$ **C.** 1   **D.** none of these

   1._____

2. A bag contains 8 blue marbles and 8 purple marbles. You reach into the bag and, without looking, pull out one marble. Find P(purple).
   A. $\frac{1}{2}$ **B.** $\frac{5}{16}$ **C.** $\frac{3}{16}$ **D.** none of these

   2._____

3. A set of cards is lettered O, H, I, O. A person is equally likely to choose any one card. Find P(I).
   A. $\frac{1}{2}$ **B.** $\frac{3}{4}$ **C.** $\frac{1}{4}$ **D.** none of these

   3._____

4. At an ice cream shop, 15 people out of 30 ordered chocolate chip ice cream. If 100 people buy ice cream, how many will likely buy chocolate chip?
   A. $\frac{15}{30}$ **B.** 50   **C.** 30   **D.** none of these

   4._____

5. Of 30 people surveyed at a baseball game, 18 preferred french fries with cheese and 12 preferred them plain. If the stadium plans to buy 120 servings of fries, how many servings of cheese should be bought?
   A. $\frac{18}{30}$ **B.** 18   **C.** 72   **D.** none of these

   5._____

6. In a survey on new school colors, 10 out of 25 people surveyed chose black as one of the colors. If 300 people are surveyed, how many would you expect to choose black?
   A. 120   **B.** 10   **C.** 25   **D.** none of these

   6._____

7. The figure at the right represents a dartboard. It is equally likely that a dart will land anywhere on the dartboard. Find the probability of a randomly thrown dart landing in the shaded region.
   A. $\frac{1}{4}$ **B.** $\frac{1}{2}$
   C. $\frac{1}{3}$ **D.** none of these

   7._____

8. Suppose you threw a dart 100 times at the dartboard in Question 7. How many times would you expect it to land in the shaded region?
   A. 25   **B.** 75   **C.** 50   **D.** none of these

   8._____

9. Suppose you threw a dart 100 times at the dartboard shown. How many times would you expect it to land in the shaded region?

   A. 25   **B.** 50

   C. about 33   **D.** none of these

9. _____

For Questions 10–11, refer to the tree diagram.

10. Drapes are available in lined or unlined panels. The possible colors are blue, green, or red. How many different type of drapes can be stocked?

   A. 3   **B.** 6

   C. 2   **D.** 9

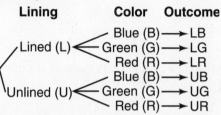

10. _____

11. If a customer picks out a drape at random, what is the probability it will be a lined, green drape?

   A. $\frac{1}{6}$ **B.** $\frac{1}{3}$ **C.** $\frac{1}{2}$ **D.** none of these

11. _____

12. A coin is tossed and a letter is picked at random from the word ONE. Which tree diagram is correct?

   A.   **B.**   **C.**   **D.** none of these

12. _____

13. Suppose you toss a coin and roll a number cube. Find P(tails and 5).

   A. $\frac{1}{2}$ **B.** $\frac{1}{8}$ **C.** $\frac{1}{12}$ **D.** none of these

13. _____

14. Each spinner is spun once. What is P(yellow and 2)?

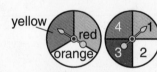

   A. $\frac{1}{7}$ **B.** $\frac{1}{12}$

   C. $\frac{1}{3}$ **D.** none of these

14. _____

15. In a pen of puppies, there are 4 males and 4 females. They are black, white, or brown. If one is picked at random, what is P(female, brown)?

   A. $\frac{1}{6}$ **B.** $\frac{1}{2}$ **C.** $\frac{1}{3}$ **D.** none of these

15. _____

16. Which list of scores does the frequency table at the right represent?

   A. 76, 87, 62, 86, 90, 94, 88, 62, 87

   B. 63, 76, 85, 93, 91

   C. 76, 81, 63, 85, 91, 93, 87, 68

   D. none of these

Score	Frequency
90–100	2
80–89	3
70–79	1
60–69	2

16. _____

Name_____ **Date** _____

Chapter 13 Test, Form 2A

A set of 50 cards has ten cards numbered 1, twenty cards numbered 2, thirteen cards numbered 3, and one card of each of the other numbers 4 through 10. Suppose you draw one card without looking. Find the probability of each event.

1. $P(2)$　　　　　　　　　　　　　　　1. _____

2. $P(3)$　　　　　　　　　　　　　　　2. _____

3. $P(4)$　　　　　　　　　　　　　　　3. _____

4. $P(1 \text{ or } 10)$　　　　　　　　　　4. _____

5. $P(\text{a multiple of } 4)$　　　　　　5. _____

In a survey of customers at a flower shop, 8 customers preferred roses, 10 customers preferred tulips, 6 customers preferred lilies, and 6 customers preferred irises. The shop owner plans to order 120 bunches of flowers for the next day. How many bunches of each type should she order?

6. roses　　　　　　　　　　　　　　　6. _____

7. tulips　　　　　　　　　　　　　　　7. _____

8. irises　　　　　　　　　　　　　　　8. _____

Suppose you threw a dart 100 times at each dartboard below. How many times would you expect it to land in the shaded region of each dartboard?

9. 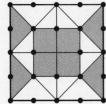　　　10. 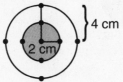　4 cm　2 cm

9. _____

10. _____

11.

11. _____

Mathematics: Applications and Connections, Course 1

12. Make a frequency table that represents the expected results of a
    number cube being rolled 120 times.

12. _____

Use the tree diagram to answer the questions.

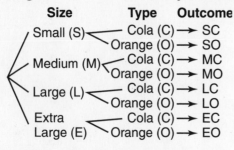

13. How many possible outcomes are there?

13. _____

14. What is the probability of an extra large cola?

14. _____

15. What is *P*(large)?

15. _____

16. What is *P*(orange)?

16. _____

Suppose you toss a coin and spin the spinner shown.
Find the probability of each of the following.

17. *P*(heads and 3)

17. _____

18. *P*(tails and 5)

18. _____

19. *P*(not heads and 1)

19. _____

20. *P*(heads and 12)

20. _____

Chapter 13 Test, Form 2B

A set of 25 cards is numbered 1, 2, 3, ..., 25. Suppose you draw one card without looking. Find the probability of each event.

1. $P(8)$

2. $P(25)$

3. $P(1 \text{ or } 9)$

4. $P(\text{an even number})$

5. $P(\text{a multiple of } 4)$

1. _____

2. _____

3. _____

4. _____

5. _____

In a survey of customers at a video store, 12 customers preferred action films, 5 customers preferred comedies, 3 customers preferred horror films, and 10 customers preferred dramas. The shop owner plans to order 90 new films. How many of each type should she order?

6. action

7. comedy

8. drama

6. _____

7. _____

8. _____

Suppose you threw a dart 100 times at each dartboard below. How many times would you expect it to land in the shaded region of each dartboard?

9.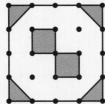

10.

11.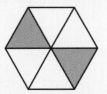

9. _____

10. _____

11. _____

Mathematics: Applications and Connections, Course 1

12. Make a frequency table that represents the expected results of a spinner numbered 1–4 being spun 100 times.

12. _____

Use the tree diagram to answer the questions.

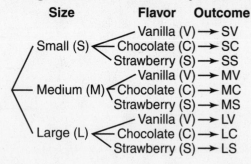

Size	Flavor	Outcome

13. How many possible outcomes are there?

13. _____

14. What is the probability of a small vanilla?

14. _____

15. What is P(medium)?

15. _____

16. What is P(chocolate)?

16. _____

Suppose you roll a 6-sided number cube and spin the spinner shown. Find the probability of each of the following.

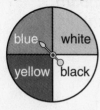

17. P(3 and white)

17. _____

18. P(even number and blue)

18. _____

19. P(not 1 and blue)

19. _____

20. P(prime and white)

20. _____

Mathematics: Applications and Connections, Course 1

Chapter 13 Test, Form 2C

A set of 10 cards is numbered 1, 2, 3, ..., 10. Suppose you draw one card without looking. Find the probability of each event.

1. *P*(6)

1. _____

2. *P*(10)

2. _____

3. *P*(1 or 3)

3. _____

4. *P*(an odd number)

4. _____

5. *P*(a multiple of 2)

5. _____

In a survey of customers at an art store, 8 customers preferred horsehair brushes, 3 customers preferred sable brushes, and 9 customers preferred acrylic brushes. The store owner plans to order 60 new brushes. How many of each type should he order?

6. horsehair

6. _____

7. sable

7. _____

8. acrylic

8. _____

Suppose you threw a dart 100 times at each dartboard below. How many times would you expect it to land in the shaded region of each dartboard?

9.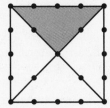

10.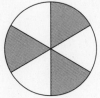

9. _____

10. _____

11.

11. _____

Mathematics: Applications and Connections, Course 1

12. Make a frequency table that represents the expected results of a coin tossed 100 times.

12. _____

Use the tree diagram to answer Questions 13–16.

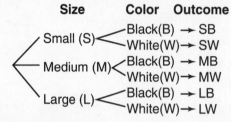

13. How many possible outcomes are there?

13. _____

14. What is the probability of a medium black?

14. _____

15. What is P(medium)?

15. _____

16. What is P(white)?

16. _____

Suppose you toss a coin and spin the spinner shown. Find the probability of each of the following.

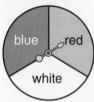

17. P(heads and blue)

17. _____

18. P(tails and red)

18. _____

19. P(not heads and white)

19. _____

20. P(heads and yellow)

20. _____

Mathematics: Applications and Connections, Course 1

Chapter 13 Performance Assessment

Instructions: Demonstrate your knowledge by giving a clear, concise solution to each problem. Be sure to include all relevant drawings and justify your answers. You may show your solutions in more than one way or investigate beyond the requirements of the problems.

1. **a.** Tell what a probability of 0 means. Give an example of an event with probability 0.

   b. Tell what a probability of 1 means. Give an example of an event with probability 1.

   c. Tell what it means for an event to have a probability of $\frac{1}{2}$. Give an example of such an event.

   d. Tell in your own words what is meant by independent events.

   e. Write a word problem that uses the probability of two independent events.

   f. Solve the problem in part e and tell in your own words what the answer means.

2. Wendy is interviewing students on her bus to see for whom they plan to vote for student body president. She found that 18 plan to vote for Kevin and 22 plan to vote for Juanita.

   a. According to Wendy's poll, what is the probability that Kevin will win? that Juanita will win?

   b. Tell why Wendy's sample may not be a random sample of students in the school.

   c. Explain how Wendy could choose a more random sample.

3. A pizza is divided into eight slices. One fourth of the pizza is mushroom, one fourth is pepperoni, one fourth is sausage, and one fourth is green pepper.

   a. If Elaine tosses an anchovy onto the pizza, what is the probability that it will land on a slice with green pepper?

   b. Reggie wants to eat a total of three different pieces of pizza. Draw a tree diagram to show his choices if he has already eaten a slice of mushroom pizza.

Chapter 13 Mid-Chapter Test

(Lessons 13-1 through 13-3)

A bag contains 8 white marbles, 5 black marbles, and 7 red marbles. Marbles are selected randomly. Find the probability of each event.

1. *P*(white)

2. *P*(red)

3. *P*(blue)

4. *P*(white or black)

5. *P*(white or black or red)

6. 100 marbles were selected randomly from the bag and replaced. Make a table showing the expected results.

In a survey at a restaurant, it was found that 12 out of 40 people order french fries with their lunch.

7. What is the sample size?

8. What is the probability that someone will order french fries with their lunch?

9. What is the probability that someone will *not* order french fries with their lunch?

10. If 120 people eat at the restaurant during lunchtime, how many will likely order french fries?

11. A survey of favorite radio stations is taken at an arena after a concert sponsored by a local station. Is this a random survey?

The figure shown represents a dartboard. It is equally likely that a dart will land anywhere on the dartboard. Find each probability for randomly thrown darts.

12. *P*(shaded)   13. *P*(unshaded)

14. Suppose you threw a dart 180 times at the dartboard. How many times would you expect it to land in the shaded region?

15. How many times would you expect it to land in the unshaded region?

16. A dart is randomly thrown at the dartboard shown at the right. It is equally likely that a dart will land anywhere on the dartboard. Find the probability of a randomly thrown dart landing in the shaded region.

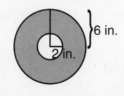

1. _____

2. _____

3. _____

4. _____

5. _____

6.

7. _____

8. _____

9. _____

10. _____

11. _____

12. _____

13. _____

14. _____

15. _____

16. _____

Mathematics: Applications and Connections, Course 1

Name _____ Date _____

Chapter 13 Quiz A

A number cube is rolled. Find the probability of each event.

1. $P(6)$ 2. P(even number)

                                              1. _____

                                              2. _____

A sack contains 10 red jelly beans, 8 black jelly beans, and 7 white jelly beans. One jelly bean is chosen at random. Find the probability of each event.

3. P(white)   4. P(red)

5. P(black or red)   6. P(green)

                                              3. _____

                                              4. _____

                                              5. _____

Maria surveyed people buying flats of plants at a garden center. The results are shown in the table.

7. What is the size of the sample?

8. What is the probability that a customer will buy petunias?

geraniums	8
petunias	12
impatiens	10
begonias	10

6. _____

7. _____

8. _____

9. What is the probability that a customer will buy impatiens or begonias?

10. If the garden center manager plans to order 400 flats of plants, how many flats of geraniums should be ordered?

9. _____

10. _____

- -

Name _____ Date _____

Chapter 13 Quiz B

Suppose you threw a dart 100 times at each dartboard shown. How many times would you expect it to land in the shaded region?

1.   2.

          4 cm

                                              1. _____

                                              2. _____

3. What is the probability that a randomly thrown dart would land in the shaded region of the dartboard in Question 1?

4. What is the probability that a randomly thrown dart would land in the shaded region of the dartboard in Question 2?

5. What is the probability that a randomly thrown dart would land in the unshaded region of the dartboard in Question 2?

                                              3. _____

                                              4. _____

                                              5. _____

Mathematics: Applications and Connections, Course 1

Chapter 13 Quiz C

(Lesson 13-4)

The tree diagram shows options for the size and finish of bookcases.

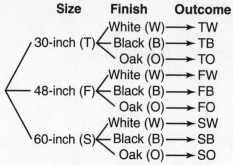

1. How many possible bookcases are there?

1. _____

2. If a bookcase is chosen at random, what is the probability of choosing a 48-inch one?

2. _____

3. If a bookcase is chosen at random, what is the probability of choosing a black one?

3. _____

4. If a bookcase is chosen at random, what is the probability of choosing a 60-inch oak one?

4. _____

5. If there were an option added for drawer pulls or no drawer pulls, how many possible bookcases would there be?

5. _____

Chapter 13 Quiz D

(Lesson 13-5)

Two number cubes are rolled. Find the probability of each event.

1. P(2 and 4)

1. _____

2. P(3 and even)

2. _____

3. P(7 and odd)

3. _____

The two spinners shown are spun. Find the probability of each event.

4. P(6 and green)

4. _____

5. P(even and yellow)

5. _____

Mathematics: Applications and Connections, Course 1

Name _____ **Date** _____

Chapter 13 Standardized Test Practice

1. Shavelle bought 12 tickets for a school raffle. If 300 tickets were sold, what is the probability that Shavelle will win?

   A. 1   **B.** 0   **C.** $\frac{1}{12}$ **D.** $\frac{1}{25}$

   1. _____

2. Marquis wanted to survey people on their favorite food. Which of the following locations would give him the most random sample?

   A. pizza shop   **B.** ice cream shop
   C. mall   **D.** bakery

   2. _____

3. The Greens want to plant 3 trees in their yard. The nursery has 5 different types that will work in their yard. How many different combinations can the Greens choose?

   A. 10   **B.** 5   **C.** 3   **D.** 8

   3. _____

4. A coin is tossed and a number cube is rolled. Find the probability of getting a head and a 5.

   A. $\frac{1}{6}$ **B.** $\frac{1}{2}$ **C.** $\frac{1}{12}$ **D.** $\frac{1}{4}$

   4. _____

5. Solve $15 + 3x = 0$.

   A. 5   **B.** -5 **C.** -15 **D.** 0

   5. _____

6. Add: $-23 + 31$.

   A. 8   **B.** -8 **C.** 54   **D.** none of these

   6. _____

7. An eraser measures 5 centimeters by 3.5 centimeters by 1.7 centimeters. What is the volume of the eraser?

   A. 10.2 cm^3 **B.** 20.4 cm^3 **C.** 17.5 cm^3 **D.** 29.75 cm^3

   7. _____

8. An angle measures 152°. If bisected, what will the resulting angles measure?

   A. 152°   **B.** 76°   **C.** 38°   **D.** 114°

   8. _____

9. Hummingbird nectar is to be mixed 1 part concentrate to 4 parts water. What proportion would be used to determine how much water must be added to 3 oz of concentrate?

   A. $\frac{1}{4} = \frac{x}{3}$ **B.** $\frac{4}{1} = \frac{3}{x}$ **C.** $\frac{1}{4} = \frac{3}{x}$ **D.** none of these

   9. _____

10. Estimate $\frac{1}{4} \times 11$.

    A. $\frac{1}{4} \times 10 = 2$ **B.** $\frac{1}{4} \times 12 = 3$
    C. $\frac{1}{4} \times 11 = 2.75$ **D.** none of these

    10. _____

11. A recipe calls for $\frac{1}{2}$ cup blueberries and $\frac{1}{3}$ cup cranberries. What is the total amount of berries in the recipe?

   A. $\frac{5}{6}$ cup   **B.** $\frac{4}{5}$ cup   **C.** $\frac{2}{5}$ cup   **D.** 1 cup

11. _____

12. Rewrite $7\frac{1}{4}$ as an improper fraction.

   A. $\frac{1}{74}$ **B.** $\frac{29}{7}$ **C.** $\frac{71}{4}$ **D.** $\frac{29}{4}$

12. _____

13. The capacity of a teaspoon is 4.93. What metric unit would be used for this measurement?

   A. mg   **B.** g   **C.** mL   **D.** L

13. _____

14. The winning times for the men's 200-meter run in the Summer Olympics since 1980 are 20.19 s, 19.80 s, 19.75 s, 20.01 s, and 19.32 s. Put these times in order from greatest to least.

   A. 20.01, 20.19, 19.32, 19.75, 19.80
   B. 20.19, 20.01, 19.80, 19.75, 19.32
   C. 19.32, 19.75, 19.80, 20.01, 20.19
   D. 19.80, 19.75, 19.32, 20.01, 20.19

14. _____

15. What is the mean time for the data listed in Question 14?

   A. 19.80 s   **B.** 0.87 s   **C.** 19.814 s   **D.** none of these

15. _____

16. Evaluate $5^2 + 2 \cdot 6 - 4^3 \div 2$.

   A. 5   **B.** 49   **C.** 130   **D.** 14

16. _____

17. A modern art painting is in a frame shaped like a parallelogram. The frame measures 2.5 feet wide by 1.75 feet tall. How large is the painting?

   A. 8.75 ft²   **B.** 4.375 ft²   **C.** 2.1875 ft²   **D.** 4.25 ft²

17. _____

18. The rule for a function table is $x + 4$. The input is -4, -2, and 0. Which graph shows the function?

   A.   **B.** 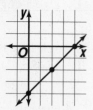   **C.**   **D.**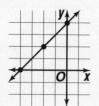

18. _____

19. The differences below all produce the same number except for one. Which is different?

   A. $3 - (-1)$ **B.** $6 - (+2)$ **C.** $-6 - (-2)$ **D.** $5 + (-1)$

19. _____

20. Trey read 32 pages in his novel for English class. He has 59 pages left to read. He wrote the equation $p - 32 = 59$ to find out the total number of pages in the book. What is the value for p?

   A. 91   **B.** 87   **C.** 32   **D.** 27

20. _____

Name_____ Date _____

Cumulative Review, Chapters 1–13

1. Evaluate x^5 if $x = 2$. (Lesson 1-6)

2. Find the median of the following scores: 90, 98, 80, 82, 80. (Lesson 2-7)

3. Add: 8.06 + 13.6. (Lesson 3-6)

Complete. (Lessons 4-8, 6-7, and 7-7)
4. 3 h 21 min = 2 h _?_ min

5. 9 qt = _?_ pt   6. 7.5 g = _?_ mg

7. Express 0.84 as a fraction in simplest form. (Lesson 5-9)

8. Find 75% of 225. (Lesson 8-7)

9. Classify a 40° angle as *acute, right,* or *obtuse.* (Lesson 9-2)

Refer to the rectangular prism. (Lessons 10-6 and 10-5)
10. Find the surface area.

11. Find the volume.

28 mm
8 mm
42 mm

Perform the indicated operation. Use counters if necessary. (Lessons 11-4 and 11-6)
12. $-8 - (-1)$ 13. $-12 \div (-2)$

Solve each equation. Use cups and counters if necessary. (Lessons 12-1 and 12-3)
14. $x + (-3) = -10$ 15. $5x = -20$

16. Make a function table for the rule $x + 3$ using -3, 0, and 2 as the input. (Lesson 12-6)

17. A set of 25 cards is numbered 1, 2, 3, ..., 25. A card is chosen at random. Find P(even). (Lesson 13-1)

18. In a survey of 50 people at a popcorn stand, 16 people preferred caramel popcorn. If 1,000 people buy popcorn, how many are likely to order caramel popcorn? (Lesson 13-2)

19. Suppose you threw a dart 100 times at the dartboard shown. How many times would you expect it to land in the shaded region? (Lesson 13-3)

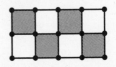

20. Suppose you toss a coin and roll a number cube. What is P(heads and 4)? (Lesson 13-5)

1. _____
2. _____
3. _____
4. _____
5. _____
6. _____
7. _____
8. _____
9. _____
10. _____
11. _____
12. _____
13. _____
14. _____
15. _____
16.
17. _____
18. _____
19. _____
20. _____

Mathematics: Applications and Connections, Course 1

13 Chapter 13 Answer Key

Form 1A

Page 337

1. D

2. B

3. C

4. B

5. B

6. D

7. C

8. B

Page 338

9. B

10. D

11. D

12. B

13. A

14. D

15. D

16. B

Form 1B

Page 339

1. C

2. A

3. B

4. A

5. C

6. D

7. C

8. C

Page 340

9. B

10. C

11. C

12. A

13. C

14. D

15. C

16. B

Mathematics: Applications and Connections, Course 1

Chapter 13 Answer Key

Form 1C

Page 341

1. ___B___
2. ___A___
3. ___C___
4. ___B___
5. ___C___
6. ___A___
7. ___B___
8. ___C___

Page 342

9. ___C___
10. ___B___
11. ___A___
12. ___B___
13. ___C___
14. ___B___
15. ___A___
16. ___C___

Mathematics: Applications and Connections, Course 1

Chapter 13 Answer Key

Page 343

1. $\dfrac{2}{5}$

2. $\dfrac{13}{50}$

3. $\dfrac{1}{50}$

4. $\dfrac{11}{50}$

5. $\dfrac{1}{25}$

6. 32

7. 40

8. 24

9. 50

10. 25

11. 40

Page 344

12.

Number	Frequency
1	20
2	20
3	20
4	20
5	20
6	20

13. 8

14. $\dfrac{1}{8}$

15. $\dfrac{1}{4}$

16. $\dfrac{1}{2}$

17. $\dfrac{1}{16}$

18. $\dfrac{1}{16}$

19. $\dfrac{1}{16}$

20. 0

Chapter 13 Answer Key

Form 2B

Page 345

1. $\dfrac{1}{25}$

2. $\dfrac{1}{25}$

3. $\dfrac{2}{25}$

4. $\dfrac{12}{25}$

5. $\dfrac{6}{25}$

6. 36

7. 15

8. 30

9. 25

10. 25

11. about 33

Page 346

12.

Number	Frequency
1	25
2	25
3	25
4	25

13. 9

14. $\dfrac{1}{9}$

15. $\dfrac{1}{3}$

16. $\dfrac{1}{3}$

17. $\dfrac{1}{24}$

18. $\dfrac{1}{8}$

19. $\dfrac{5}{24}$

20. $\dfrac{1}{8}$

Mathematics: Applications and Connections, Course 1

Chapter 13 Answer Key

Form 2C

Page 347

1. $\dfrac{1}{10}$

2. $\dfrac{1}{10}$

3. $\dfrac{1}{5}$

4. $\dfrac{1}{2}$

5. $\dfrac{1}{2}$

6. 24

7. 9

8. 27

9. 25

10. 50

11. 20

Page 348

12.

Number	Frequency
H	50
T	50

13. 6

14. $\dfrac{1}{6}$

15. $\dfrac{1}{3}$

16. $\dfrac{1}{2}$

17. $\dfrac{1}{6}$

18. $\dfrac{1}{6}$

19. $\dfrac{1}{6}$

20. 0

Mathematics: Applications and Connections, Course 1

Chapter 13 Scoring Guide

Level	Specific Criteria
3 Superior	• Shows thorough understanding of the concepts *probability, making predictions using samples, probability and area, finding outcomes,* and *independent events.* • Uses appropriate strategies to solve problems. • Computations are correct. • Written explanations are exemplary. • Word problem concerning probability of two independent events is appropriate and makes sense. • Diagram is accurate and appropriate. • Goes beyond requirements of some or all problems.
2 Satisfactory, with Minor Flaws	• Shows understanding of the concepts *probability, making predictions using samples, probability and area, finding outcomes,* and *independent events.* • Uses appropriate strategies to solve problems. • Computations are mostly correct. • Word problem concerning probability of two independent events is mostly appropriate and makes sense. • Diagram is mostly accurate and appropriate. • Written explanations are effective. • Satisfies all requirements of problems.
1 Nearly Satisfactory, with Serious Flaws	• Shows understanding of most of the concepts *probability, making predictions using samples, probability and area, finding outcomes,* and *independent events.* • May not use appropriate strategies to solve problems. • Computations are mostly correct. • Word problem concerning probability of two independent events is somewhat appropriate and makes sense. • Diagram is somewhat accurate and appropriate. • Written explanations are satisfactory. • Satisfies most requirements of problems.
0 Unsatisfactory	• Shows little or no understanding of the *probability, making predictions using samples, probability and area, finding outcomes,* and *independent events.* • May not use appropriate strategies to solve problems. • Computations are incorrect. • Word problem concerning probability of two independent events is not appropriate or does not make sense. • Diagram is not accurate or appropriate. • Written explanations are not satisfactory. • Does not satisfy requirements of problems.

Chapter 13 Answer Key

Performance Assessment Sample Answers
Page 349

1. a. A probability of 0 means that the event is impossible. Example: The probability of rolling a 7 on a number cube is 0.

b. A probability of one means an event is certain to happen. Example: The probability of rolling a number less than 7 on a number cube is 1.

c. A probability of $\frac{1}{2}$ means that an event has an equally likely chance of occurring or not occurring. Example: The probability of getting a head when tossing a coin is $\frac{1}{2}$.

d. Two events are independent when neither event affects the outcome of the other.

e. What is the probability of tossing a head on a coin and rolling a 6 on a number cube?

f. $P(\text{head and } 6) = P(\text{head}) \times P(6) = \frac{1}{2} \times \frac{1}{6} = \frac{1}{12}$.
A probability of $\frac{1}{12}$ means that $P(\text{head and } 6)$ has a chance of occurring 1 out of 12 tries.

2. a. $P(\text{Kevin}) = \frac{18}{40}$ or $\frac{9}{20}$, $P(\text{Juanita}) = \frac{22}{40}$ or $\frac{11}{20}$

b. Wendy's sample may not be random because students on the same bus may be similar in ways that do not represent the whole school. Juanita or Kevin may ride Wendy's bus or students on that bus may live in the same section of the school district.

c. She could get a list of all the students in the school and interview every tenth student on the list.

3. a. $\frac{1}{4}$ of the area of the pizza is green pepper, so the probability would be $\frac{1}{4}$.

b.

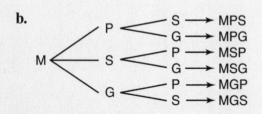

Mid-Chapter Test
Page 350

1.	$\frac{2}{5}$
2.	$\frac{7}{20}$
3.	0
4.	$\frac{13}{20}$
5.	1
6.	(table below)

Color	Frequency
white	40
black	25
red	35

7.	40
8.	$\frac{3}{10}$
9.	$\frac{7}{10}$
10.	36
11.	no
12.	$\frac{5}{9}$
13.	$\frac{4}{9}$
14.	100
15.	80
16.	$\frac{8}{9}$

© Glencoe/McGraw-Hill

Mathematics: Applications and Connections, Course 1

Chapter 13 Answer Key

1. $\frac{1}{6}$
2. $\frac{1}{2}$
3. $\frac{7}{25}$
4. $\frac{2}{5}$
5. $\frac{18}{25}$
6. 0
7. 40
8. $\frac{3}{10}$
9. $\frac{1}{2}$
10. 80

1. 9
2. $\frac{1}{3}$
3. $\frac{1}{3}$
4. $\frac{1}{9}$
5. 18

1. 50
2. about 21
3. $\frac{1}{2}$
4. about $\frac{1}{4}$
5. about $\frac{3}{4}$

1. $\frac{1}{36}$
2. $\frac{1}{12}$
3. 0
4. $\frac{1}{18}$
5. $\frac{1}{6}$

Mathematics: Applications and Connections, Course 1

13 Chapter 13 Answer Key

Standardized Test Practice

Page 353

1. D
2. C
3. A
4. C
5. B
6. A
7. D
8. B
9. C
10. B

Page 354

11. A
12. D
13. C
14. B
15. C
16. A
17. B
18. D
19. C
20. A

Cumulative Review

Page 355

1. 32
2. 82
3. 21.66
4. 81
5. 18
6. 7,500
7. $\dfrac{21}{25}$
8. 168.75
9. acute
10. 3,472 mm^2
11. 9,408 mm^3
12. −7
13. 6
14. −7
15. −4
16.

x	x + 3
−3	0
0	3
2	5

17. $\dfrac{12}{25}$
18. 320
19. 50
20. $\dfrac{1}{12}$

How to Use the Placement Tests

These tests are designed to help teachers determine whether students beginning Course 1 of *Mathematics: Applications and Connections* should use the *Transition Booklet* or whether they can begin with Chapter 1 in an average course or an honors course.

The placement tests are just one tool in assessing a student's readiness for a particular course. You may also want to consider such factors as classroom performance, chapter test scores, and cumulative test scores.

Two types of placement tests are offered in this booklet: multiple choice and free response. There is one form (Form A or Form B) of each type of test. You may choose whichever type and form of test you prefer. Each test is designed to be completed in a 40-45 minute class period. The multiple-choice test has 30 questions, and the free-response test has 25 questions. The multiple-choice test has more questions because multiple-choice questions can usually be answered more quickly. Both tests, however, cover the same basic skills necessary for success in *Mathematics: Applications and Connections,* Course 1.

It is not recommended that students use calculators to take these tests. Space is provided on each page for calculations, drawings, and any scratchwork necessary to answer the questions.

The table below gives recommendations for evaluating each test and determining which course a student may be ready for.

Recommended Placement
Minimum Numbers of Correct Answers on the Placement Tests

Placement	Multiple-Choice Test	Free-Response Test
Transition Booklet	18–22 questions (60%–73%)	14–17 questions (56%–68%)
Average Course	23–26 questions (77%–87%)	18–21 questions (72%–84%)
Honors Course	27–30 questions (90%–100%)	22–25 questions (88%–100%)

Since free-response questions are typically more difficult than multiple-choice questions, the recommended percentages are slightly lower for the free-response test.

If a student does not score high enough to begin with the *Transition Booklet,* you will want to check these test results against the student's classroom performance and grades before making a recommendation for his or her placement.

Name_____ Date _____

Placement Test, Form A

There are 30 multiple-choice questions on this test. Answer each question, using any available space on the page for scratchwork. Then write your answer in the blank provided.

1. Write $\frac{26}{39}$ in simplest form.   1. _____

   A. $\frac{2}{13}$ B. $\frac{2}{3}$

   C. $\frac{6}{9}$ D. $\frac{1}{3}$

2. Complete: $3\frac{3}{4}$ yd = __?__ in.   2. _____

   A. $\frac{15}{4}$ B. $9\frac{3}{4}$

   C. 135   D. 39

3. Replace the ● with $<$, $>$, or $=$ to make -1.9 ● -1.6 a true sentence.   3. _____

   A. $<$ B. $>$

   C. $=$

4. Add $4.43 to $2.09.   4. _____

   A. $5.52   B. $6.52

   C. $6.43   D. $2.34

5. Round 6.1$\underline{4}$9 to the underlined place value position.   5. _____

   A. 6.1   B. 6.15

   C. 61.4   D. 6.2

6. Multiply 18 by $4\frac{1}{2}$.   6. _____

   A. 81   B. 32

   C. 37   D. 72

7. Find $\frac{3}{8} + \frac{1}{8}$. Write the answer in simplest form.   7. _____

   A. $\frac{3}{5}$ B. $\frac{1}{4}$

   C. $\frac{1}{2}$ D. $\frac{3}{16}$

8. Find $\frac{3}{4} - \frac{3}{8}$. Write the answer in simplest form.   8. _____

   A. $\frac{5}{8}$ B. $\frac{3}{4}$

   C. 0   D. $\frac{3}{8}$

Mathematics: Applications and Connections, Course 1

Placement Test, Form A (Continued)

9. Which integer is greatest?
   A. -5 B. 9
   C. 0   D. 3

9. _____

10. What is the best estimate for the weight of a space shuttle?
    A. 20 pounds   B. 20 tons
    C. 200 pounds   D. 20 ounces

10. _____

The circle graph indicates the popularity of 5 small kitchen appliances in Eierville. Use this information for Questions 11 and 12.

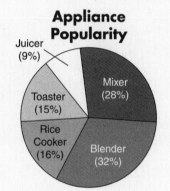

Appliance Popularity

Juicer (9%)
Mixer (28%)
Toaster (15%)
Rice Cooker (16%)
Blender (32%)

11. What fraction of the small kitchen appliances preferred are toasters?
    A. $\frac{1}{5}$ B. $\frac{5}{10}$
    C. $\frac{3}{20}$ D. $\frac{1}{3}$

11. _____

12. What fraction of the small kitchen appliances preferred are both mixers and blenders?
    A. $\frac{3}{5}$ B. $\frac{6}{11}$
    C. $\frac{5}{6}$ D. $\frac{2}{3}$

12. _____

13. Find $a - b$ if $a = 7$ and $b = 2$.
    A. 5   B. 7
    C. 2   D. 3

13. _____

14. Find $\frac{3}{11} + \frac{5}{22}$. Write the answer in simplest form.
    A. $\frac{8}{33}$ B. $\frac{1}{2}$
    C. $\frac{3}{4}$ D. $\frac{4}{11}$

14. _____

15. Divide 14 by $6\frac{2}{3}$. Write the answer in simplest form.
    A. $1\frac{9}{10}$ B. $\frac{10}{21}$
    C. $2\frac{1}{10}$ D. $\frac{2}{9}$

15. _____

Mathematics: Applications and Connections, Course 1

Placement Test, Form A (Continued)

16. Estimate $4\frac{1}{9} + \frac{9}{10}$.

   A. $4 + 1 = 5$ **B.** $5 + 1 = 6$

   C. $4 + 0 = 4$ **D.** $4 + 2 = 6$

16. _____

17. Evaluate $16 - 4 \times 3 \div 2$.

   A. 0   **B.** 4

   C. 10   **D.** 18

17. _____

18. Choose the next term in the sequence 16, 14, 12, 10, 8, ...

   A. 6   **B.** 5

   C. 7   **D.** 4

18. _____

19. Find $6.5 + 4.5$.

   A. 10   **B.** 9

   C. 12   **D.** 11

19. _____

20. Find $45 \div 15$.

   A. 4   **B.** 3

   C. 5   **D.** 6

20. _____

21. Find $26 - 9$.

   A. 34   **B.** 17

   C. 35   **D.** 18

21. _____

22. Complete: 6 quarts = _?_ cups. Use 4 cups = 1 quart.

   A. 20   **B.** 10

   C. 24   **D.** 12

22. _____

23. Which temperature is the better estimate for ice cream?

   A. 30°F   **B.** 45°F

   C. 0°F   **D.** 60°C

23. _____

Mathematics: Applications and Connections, Course 1

Placement Test, Form A (Continued)

24. Choose the best estimate for the length of a bicycle.

    A. 3 feet   **B.** 3 inches

    C. 3 yards   **D.** 30 feet

24. _____

25. Round 41.9<u>0</u>6 to the underlined place-value position.

    A. 41.10   **B.** 41.96

    C. 41.90   **D.** 41.91

25. _____

26. Choose the trapezoid.

    A.   **B.**

    C.   **D.**

26. _____

27. Which integer is least?

    A. -1 **B.** 4

    C. 2   **D.** -2

27. _____

28. Sixteen cats were in a barn. Four went out, two came back inside, then six more went out. How many cats are still in the barn?

    A. 12   **B.** 10

    C. 8   **D.** 6

28. _____

29. Choose the letter on the number line that represents 3.

    A. A **B.** B

    C. C **D.** D

29. _____

30. Replace the ● in 512,000 ● 5,120,000 with $<$, $>$, or $=$ to make a true sentence.

    A. $<$ **B.** $>$

    C. $=$

30. _____

Mathematics: Applications and Connections, Course 1

Placement Test, Form B

There are 25 free-response questions on this test.
Answer each question, using any available space on the
page for scratchwork. Then write your answer in the
blank provided.

1. Write *six-hundred forty-seven* as a number.

1. _____

2. Order 129, 72, 560, and 203 from least to greatest.

2. _____

3. Find $2a + b$ if $a = 2$ and $b = 5$.

3. _____

4. Find the next term in the sequence 9, 15, 21, 27, ...

4. _____

5. Multiply 8 by 6.

5. _____

6. Solve $2 + 6 \div 3$.

6. _____

Placement Test, Form B (Continued)

7. A bus arrives at 4th and Main Streets at 8:09 A.M. If it reaches the end of its run in 36 minutes later, what time will it be?

7. _____

8. Draw a rectangle.

8. _____

9. Write $\frac{16}{24}$ in simplest form.

9. _____

10. Find $11 - 9$.

10. _____

11. Find $10 + 13$.

11. _____

12. Divide 36 by 4.

12. _____

13. Complete: __?__ feet = 2 yards.

13. _____

Placement Test, Form B (Continued)

14. Is the pound, ounce, or ton the best unit for measuring a box of 5 soft taco shells?

14. _____

15. If a bricklayer has 19 bricks and he started with 50 bricks, how many bricks did he use?

15. _____

16. Round 5,265 to the nearest thousand.

16. _____

17. If 176 kids want to play soccer and there should be 22 kids on each team, how many teams can be formed?

17. _____

18. Replace the  in 14,000  4,000 with $<$, $>$, or $=$ to make a true sentence.

18. _____

19. Find $n - 2m$ if $n = 6$ and $m = 3$.

19. _____

Mathematics: Applications and Connections, Course 1

Placement Test, Form B (Continued)

20. Write $\frac{14}{10}$ in simplest form.

20. _____

21. Estimate $41 - 12$.

21. _____

22. One day in December it was 15°C in Tallahassee. That same day it was 1°C in Seattle. What is the difference in temperature?

22. _____

23. Is ten degrees Fahrenheit (10°F) *greater than, less than,* or *equal to* zero degrees Celsius (0°C)? Use $F = 1.8C + 32$.

23. _____

24. The Griffiths go to a baseball game that is 1 hour and 15 minutes away from their home. If they arrive at 4:35 P.M., when did they leave?

24. _____

25. Find $2x \div y$ if $x = 4$ and $y = 8$.

25. _____

Mathematics: Applications and Connections, Course 1

Semester Test, Form A
(Chapters 1–7)

1. Use the bar graph at the right to determine how much greater the sales were for Friday than for Thursday.

   A. $400   **B.** $500
   C. $900   **D.** $800

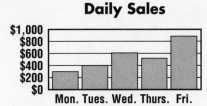

Daily Sales

1. _____

2. Choose the best interval to form a scale for this set of data: 18, 32, 58, 63, 58, 28, 98, 75.

   A. 1   **B.** 98   **C.** 100   **D.** 10

2. _____

3. What is the length of the segment to the nearest centimeter?

   A. 5 cm   **B.** 6 cm   **C.** 52 cm   **D.** 53 cm

3. _____

4. Which decimals are in order from least to greatest?

   A. 0.1, 0.02, 0.003, 0.0004   **B.** 0.0004, 0.003, 0.02, 0.1
   C. 0.5, 0.06, 0.7, 0.09   **D.** 0.1, 0.05, 0.07, 0.8

4. _____

5. Estimate 7,219 ÷ 8 using rounding.

   A. 7   **B.** 70   **C.** 700   **D.** 77

5. _____

6. Find the value of $8 \times 10 + 6 \times 2$.

   A. 7   **B.** 92   **C.** 256   **D.** 176

6. _____

7. Evaluate $6 + 2m$ if $m = 3$.

   A. 12   **B.** 24   **C.** 29   **D.** 11

7. _____

8. Which of the following would be most useful to show the most frequently sold shirt size in a clothing store?

   A. mean   **B.** median   **C.** mode   **D.** range

8. _____

9. What is the decimal for *two and nine hundredths*?

   A. 2.9   **B.** 209   **C.** 2.09   **D.** 2,900

9. _____

10. What is the decimal for $\frac{29}{10,000}$?

    A. 0.29   **B.** 0.029   **C.** 0.2900   **D.** 0.0029

10. _____

11. Which unit would you use to measure the mass of a horse?

    A. gram   **B.** milligram   **C.** kilogram   **D.** liter

11. _____

Mathematics: Applications and Connections, Course 1

Semester Test, Form A (Continued)
(Chapters 1–7)

12. How many milligrams are in 87 grams?

    A. 870 mg   **B.** 0.087 mg   **C.** 8,700 mg   **D.** 87,000 mg

12. _____

13. Solve $x = 12.8 \div 3.2$.

    A. 4   **B.** 40   **C.** 0.4   **D.** 40.96

13. _____

14. Each lap around a running track is 0.25 kilometer. If Alonso runs 50 laps around the track, how far has he run?

    A. 200 km   **B.** 125 km   **C.** 1.25 km   **D.** 12.5 km

14. _____

15. 186 is divisible by which of these numbers?

    A. 2, 3, and 5   **B.** 2, 3, and 6   **C.** 3, 5, and 9   **D.** 5 and 10

15. _____

16. Express $\frac{1}{12}$ as a decimal. Use bar notation to show a repeating decimal.

    A. $0.08\overline{3}$ **B.** $0.0\overline{83}$ **C.** $0.\overline{083}$ **D.** $0.\overline{83}$

16. _____

17. Round $\frac{24}{25}$ to the nearest half.

    A. 0   **B.** $\frac{1}{2}$

    C. 1   **D.** none of these

17. _____

18. Estimate $5\frac{1}{6} + 7\frac{11}{12}$.

    A. 12   **B.** 13   **C.** 14   **D.** 15

18. _____

19. Add $\frac{7}{20} + \frac{3}{20}$. Write the solution in simplest form.

    A. $\frac{1}{2}$ **B.** $\frac{1}{4}$ **C.** $\frac{10}{40}$ **D.** $\frac{5}{20}$

19. _____

20. Find the circumference of a circle with a diameter of 6.6 meters. Use 3.14 for π. Round to the nearest tenth.

    A. 20.7 m   **B.** 10.4 m   **C.** 3.5 m   **D.** 21.7 m

20. _____

21. Find the value of $6 \times 10 + 6 \times 4$.

21. _____

22. Evaluate $5 + 6x$ if $x = 7$.

22. _____

Mathematics: Applications and Connections, Course 1

Semester Test, Form A (Continued)

(Chapters 1–7)

23. Complete the line graph to show the daily temperatures for five days.
Monday, 40°F
Wednesday, 50°F
Friday, 45°F
Tuesday, 45°F
Thursday, 40°F

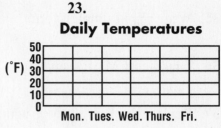

23.

Daily Temperatures

24. What is the mean of the following test scores?
78, 92, 89, 78, 96, 92, 84

24. _____

25. What is the median of the test scores?

25. _____

26. What is the mode of 2, 2, 78, 80, and 83?

26. _____

27. Write the decimal for *seven and eight hundredths*.

27. _____

28. Round 6.7338 to the nearest thousandth.

28. _____

29. Subtract.   89.4
                    − 46.68

29. _____

30. Find the perimeter of the rectangle.

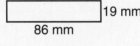
19 mm
86 mm

30. _____

31. Find the area of the square.

7.4 cm

31. _____

32. Find the circumference of a circle with a radius of 16 inches. Use 3.14 for π. Round to the nearest tenth.

32. _____

33. Find $52.5 \div 15$.

33. _____

34. What is the GCF of 36 and 81?

34. _____

Mathematics: Applications and Connections, Course 1

35. Write $\frac{125}{150}$ in simplest form.

35. _____

36. Find the LCM of 30 and 40.

36. _____

37. Replace the ● in $\frac{5}{18}$ ● $\frac{7}{12}$ with $<$, $>$, or $=$ to make a true sentence.

37. _____

38. Express $\frac{11}{18}$ as a decimal. Use bar notation to show a repeating decimal.

38. _____

39. Round $\frac{1}{32}$ to the nearest half.

39. _____

40. Estimate $7\frac{1}{16} + 8\frac{13}{16}$.

40. _____

41. Find $\frac{7}{25} + \frac{3}{25}$. Write the answer in simplest form.

41. _____

42. Solve $y + \frac{5}{32} = \frac{17}{32}$. Write the answer in simplest form.

42. _____

43. Find $\frac{11}{12} - \frac{2}{3}$. Write the answer in simplest form.

43. _____

44. At the start of the year, a tree was $7\frac{3}{4}$ feet tall. At the end of the year, it had grown to a height of $10\frac{1}{2}$ feet. How much did the tree grow during the year?

44. _____

45. A ballgame started at 1:20 P.M. and was over at 4:05 P.M. How long did the ballgame last?

45. _____

46. Solve $x = 4\frac{2}{3} \div 1\frac{2}{5}$.

46. _____

47. What is the value of gk if $g = 10$ and $k = 3\frac{1}{5}$?

47. _____

48. Estimate $\frac{1}{6} \times \frac{11}{12}$.

48. _____

49. Complete: 7 qt = __?__ c.

49. _____

50. Find the next two numbers in the sequence 243, 81, 27, 9, ...

50. _____

Semester Test, Form B
(Chapters 8-13)

1. Solve $\frac{6}{j} = \frac{3}{5}$.
   A. 20   **B.** 30   **C.** 10   **D.** 90

   1. _____

2. Express 142% as a fraction in simplest form.
   A. $1\frac{4}{10}$ **B.** $1\frac{2}{5}$ **C.** $1\frac{15}{16}$ **D.** $1\frac{21}{50}$

   2. _____

3. Estimate 47% of 291.
   A. 150   **B.** 170   **C.** 29   **D.** 50

   3. _____

4. Use a protractor to find the measure of the angle. Then classify the angle as *acute, right,* or *obtuse.*
   A. acute   **B.** right   **C.** obtuse

   4. _____

5. Name the polygon.
   A. square   **B.** parallelogram
   C. rectangle   **D.** triangle

   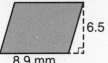

   5. _____

6. How many lines of symmetry does a square have?
   A. 2   **B.** 4   **C.** 6   **D.** 1

   6. _____

For Questions 7–9, find the area of each figure to the nearest tenth. Use 3.14 for π.

7.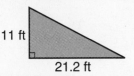
   6.5
   8.9 mm
   A. 15.4 mm²   **B.** 28.9 mm²   **C.** 30.8 mm²   **D.** 57.9 mm²

   7. _____

8.
   11 ft
   21.2 ft
   A. 32.2 ft²   **B.** 233.2 ft²   **C.** 66.6 ft²   **D.** 116.6 ft²

   8. _____

9. 31 in.
   A. 97.4 in²   **B.** 48.7 in²   **C.** 754.4 in²   **D.** 153.0 in²

   9. _____

10. Find (-6)11.
    A. −11   **B.** −6   **C.** −66   **D.** 66

    10. _____

11. Find −60 ÷ 5.
    A. −12   **B.** 12   **C.** −300   **D.** 30

    11. _____

Mathematics: Applications and Connections, Course 1

Semester Test, Form B (Continued)

(Chapters 8–13)

Name the ordered pair for each point in Questions 12 and 13.

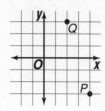

12. Q

    A. $(4, -4)$ **B.** $(2, 3)$

    C. $(4, -3)$ **D.** $(3, 3)$

12. _____

13. P

    A. $(3, -3)$ **B.** $(2, 4)$

    C. $(4, -3)$ **D.** $(2, 3)$

13. _____

14. Solve $x + 14 = 11$.

    A. 3   **B.** 25   **C.** -25 **D.** -3

14. _____

15. Solve $16 = 3 - y$.

    A. 13   **B.** 19   **C.** -13 **D.** -19

15. _____

16. Solve $-2z = 35$.

    A. 70   **B.** -70 **C.** $-17\frac{1}{2}$ **D.** $17\frac{1}{2}$

16. _____

17. Solve $4 - 7a = 25$.

    A. 3   **B.** -3 **C.** 7   **D.** $-4\frac{1}{7}$

17. _____

18. A running dog comes to a large tree branch lying across a stream. He can go around it, go over it, or go under it. What is the probability that he will go under it?

    A. $\frac{1}{4}$ **B.** $\frac{1}{3}$ **C.** $\frac{1}{5}$ **D.** $\frac{1}{6}$

18. _____

19. Alison is bouncing a ball against a wall that has a target on it. It is equally likely that the ball will hit any point on the wall. Find the probability that Alison will hit the target with the ball.

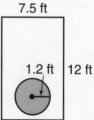

    A. about $\frac{1}{18}$ **B.** about $\frac{1}{10}$

    C. about $\frac{1}{15}$ **D.** about $\frac{2}{5}$

19. _____

20. Jaime rolls a number cube and tosses a nickel. Find P(6 or 1 and tails).

    A. $\frac{3}{8}$ **B.** $\frac{1}{3}$ **C.** $\frac{1}{6}$ **D.** $\frac{1}{12}$

20. _____

Semester Test, Form B (Continued)

(Chapters 8–13)

For Questions 21–23, the two spinners shown are spun. Find the probability of each event.

21. P(vowel and prime)

21. _____

22. P(S and 16)

22. _____

23. _____

23. P(M or N and even)

24. Name the figure.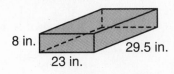

24. _____

25. Find the volume of the rectangular prism.

25. _____

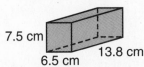

8 in. 29.5 in. 23 in.

26. Find the surface area of the rectangular prism.

26. _____

7.5 cm 13.8 cm 6.5 cm

27. Find the area of a circle with radius 9.8 feet to the nearest tenth.

27. _____

28. Find the area of the triangle to the nearest tenth.

4.3 m   21 m

28. _____

29. Find the area of the parallelogram.

29. _____

2.5 yd 5.6 yd

30. Sally throws a dart at the dartboard shown. Find the probability that her dart will land in the shaded area given that it is equally likely that the dart will land anywhere on the dartboard.

30. _____

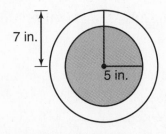

7 in.   5 in.

31. If a function rule is $2n - 8$, what is the output for an input of 7?

31. _____

32. Graph the function represented by the function table.

32.

Input	Output
−1	−2
0	0
1	2

Mathematics: Applications and Connections, Course 1

Semester Test, Form B (Continued)
(Chapters 8–13)

33. Solve $x = 44 \div \frac{1}{4}$.

34. Graph -4 on a number line.

35. Write an integer to describe a $30 deposit made to a bank account.

Replace each ● with <, >, or = in Questions 36 and 37 to make each sentence true.

36. -16 ● -17

37. -3 ● 3

38. Find the sum of -9, 8, and 1.

39. Find the value of $g + h$ if $g = -4$ and $h = 11$.

40. Find the value of $j - k$ if $j = 5$ and $k = 15$.

41. Write the ratio *8 out of 22 pens are green* in three different ways.

42. On a drawing of a house, the height is $4\frac{2}{3}$ inches. What is the actual height of the house if the drawing has a scale of $\frac{1}{3}$ inch $= 22$ inches?

43. Express $\frac{16}{25}$ as a percent.

44. Express 0.004 as a percent.

45. Express 13.6% as a decimal.

46. Find 65% of 80.

47. Is the angle shown greater than, less than, or about equal to 60°?

48. In the figure shown, name the side that appears to bisect $\angle QRS$.

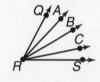

49. Is $\angle QRS$ in Question 48 *acute, right,* or *obtuse?*

50. Are the polygons shown *congruent, similar,* or *neither?*

33. _____

<---+++++++++++++--->
34. -4 -2 0 2 4

35. _____

36. _____

37. _____

38. _____

39. _____

40. _____

41. _____

42. _____

43. _____

44. _____

45. _____

46. _____

47. _____

48. _____

49. _____

50. _____

Name _____ Date _____

Final Test, Form A

1. Estimate $6,321 \div 9$ using rounding.
   A. 70 **B.** 700 **C.** 800 **D.** 900

   1. _____

2. Find the value of $16 + 8 \div 2 \times 4$.
   A. 48 **B.** 17 **C.** 24 **D.** 32

   2. _____

3. Find the median of 71, 65, 68, 68, 80, 89, and 91.
   A. 76 **B.** 68 **C.** 26 **D.** 71

   3. _____

4. What is the decimal for $\frac{7}{10,000}$?
   A. 0.007 **B.** 0.0007 **C.** 70,000 **D.** 0.7000

   4. _____

5. What is the length of the segment to the nearest millimeter?

   A. 78 mm **B.** 8 mm **C.** 7 mm **D.** 7.8 mm

   5. _____

6. Change 74 grams to milligrams.
   A. 740 mg **B.** 7.4 mg **C.** 7,400 mg **D.** 74,000 mg

   6. _____

7. Solve $4.1y = 20.5$.
   A. 5 **B.** 0.5 **C.** 50 **D.** 84.05

   7. _____

8. Express $\frac{7}{12}$ as a decimal. Use bar notation to show a repeating decimal.
   A. $0.\overline{583}$ **B.** $0.58\overline{3}$ **C.** $0.5\overline{83}$ **D.** $0.5\overline{8}$

   8. _____

9. Add $\frac{7}{50} + \frac{3}{50}$. Write the answer in simplest form.
   A. $\frac{1}{5}$ **B.** $\frac{1}{10}$ **C.** $\frac{5}{50}$ **D.** $\frac{21}{50}$

   9. _____

10. Subtract $\frac{14}{15} - \frac{3}{5}$. Write the answer in simplest form.
    A. $\frac{11}{10}$ **B.** $\frac{1}{3}$
    C. $\frac{11}{30}$ **D.** none of these

    10. _____

11. Complete: 12 gal = _?_ pt.
    A. 24 pt **B.** 6 pt **C.** 48 pt **D.** 96 pt

    11. _____

12. Classify an angle that measures 130°.
    A. acute **B.** obtuse
    C. right **D.** none of these

    12. _____

13. Estimate which angle has a measure closest to 92°.
    A. **B.** **C.** **D.**

    13. _____

Mathematics: Applications and Connections, Course 1

Final Test, Form A (Continued)

14. Find 8% of 48.

   A. 6

   C. 384

   B. 60

   D. none of these

14. _____

15. Find the area of the parallelogram at the right.

   A. 840 mm²   **B.** 672 mm²

   C. 336 mm²   **D.** none of these

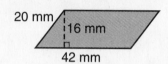

15. _____

16. Find the volume of the rectangular prism at the right.

   A. 882 mm³   **B.** 441 mm³

   C. 1,620 mm³   **D.** none of these

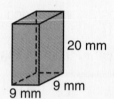

16. _____

17. Which integer is least?

   A. 0   **B.** -175 **C.** 20   **D.** -50

17. _____

18. Which graph represents the function at the right?

x	$x - 1$
2	1
0	-1
-2	-3

18. _____

A.

B.

C.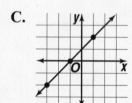

D.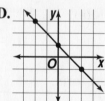

19. Which graph shows the solution of $x + 3 \geq -1$?

19. _____

A.

B.

C.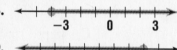

D.

20. A set of cards is lettered A, L, A, B, A, M, A. Joe is equally likely to choose any one card. Find $P(A)$.

   A. $\dfrac{4}{7}$

   C. $\dfrac{4}{3}$

   B. $\dfrac{3}{4}$

   D. none of these

20. _____

Final Test, Form A (Continued)

21. Use the pictograph at the right to determine the number of sandwiches served on Wednesday.

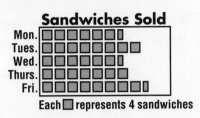

Sandwiches Sold

Each ▢ represents 4 sandwiches

21. _____

22. Find the mean of 45, 40, 46, 49, and 40.

22. _____

23. What is the length of the segment to the nearest millimeter?

23. _____

24. Order 2.003, 2.3, 2.01, 2.0004 from least to greatest.

24. _____

25. Find 7.8×3.78.

25. _____

26. Find the perimeter of the rectangle.

8.5 in.

28.5 in.

26. _____

27. Find the circumference of a circle with a diameter of 40 feet. Use 3.14 for π.

27. _____

28. State whether 279 is divisible by 2, 3, 5, 6, 9, or 10.

28. _____

29. What is the GCF of 55 and 77?

29. _____

30. The length of a piece of wood is $58\frac{1}{2}$ inches. A carpenter needs a piece that is $55\frac{11}{16}$ inches long. How much length must be trimmed from the piece of wood?

30. _____

31. A concert starts at 2:25 P.M. and is over at 4:07 P.M. How long is the concert?

31. _____

32. Find $\frac{5}{16} \times \frac{14}{15}$. Write the answer in simplest form.

32. _____

33. Solve $6\frac{1}{4} \times 1\frac{1}{10} = m$. Write the answer in simplest form.

33. _____

34. Find $\frac{5}{24} \div \frac{5}{6}$. Write the answer in simplest form.

34. _____

35. Divide $8\frac{3}{4}$ by $1\frac{7}{8}$. Write the answer in simplest form.

35. _____

36. Complete: 16 qt = _?_ c.

36. _____

37. Solve $\frac{x}{15} = \frac{60}{90}$.

37. _____

Mathematics: Applications and Connections, Course 1

Final Test, Form A (Continued)

38. What is the actual length of the patio shown in the scale drawing? Refer to the side labeled *s*.

$\frac{1}{4}$ in. = 2 ft

38. _____

39. Express $\frac{13}{25}$ as a percent.

39. _____

40. Find 12% of 72.

40. _____

41. Tell whether the dashed line is a line of symmetry. Write *yes* or *no*.

41. _____

42. Describe the polygons at the right as *congruent, similar,* or *neither*.

42. _____

43. Find the area of the triangle shown at the right.

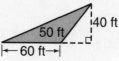

50 ft 40 ft 60 ft

43. _____

44. Find the area of a circle with a radius of 4.9 inches to the nearest tenth. Use 3.14 for π.

44. _____

45. Name the ordered pair for point *A*. Refer to the grid at the right.

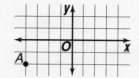

45. _____

46. Solve $x + (-3) = 7$.

46. _____

47. Find the rule for the function table below.

n	
−6	0
0	6
10	16

47. _____

48. The figure at the right represents a dartboard. If a dart is thrown randomly, what is the probability it will land in the shaded region?

48. _____

49. Sweaters are available in small, medium, or large. They are available in black, white, or red. Draw a tree diagram to show all of the possible outcomes.

49. _____

50. Suppose you toss a coin and roll a number cube. What is *P*(heads and 4)?

50. _____

Mathematics: Applications and Connections, Course 1

Final Test, Form B

1. Use the pictograph at the right to determine the number of pizzas sold on Monday.
   A. 80   B. 95
   C. 85   D. 100

   Pizzas Sold

   Mon. ◯◯◯◯◯◯◯◯◯◖
   Tues. ◯◯◯◯◯◯◯◯
   Wed. ◯◯◯◯◯◯◯◯
   Thurs. ◯◯◯◯◯◯◯
   Fri. ◯◯◯◯◯◯◯◯◯◯

   Each ◯ represents 10 pizzas

   1. _____

2. Find the median of 36, 18, 91, 4, 11, 63, and 9.
   A. 63   B. 18   C. 4   D. 11

   2. _____

3. Which decimals are ordered from least to greatest?
   A. 3.004, 3.2, 3.05, 3.008   B. 3.2, 3.004, 3.05, 3.0008
   C. 3.0008, 3.004, 3.05, 3.2   D. 3.2, 3.05, 3.004, 3.0008

   3. _____

4. Evaluate 11^2.
   A. 121   B. 22   C. 112   D. 1,331

   4. _____

5. Find 8.6×1.34.
   A. 11.524   B. 115.24   C. 1,152.4   D. 1.1524

   5. _____

6. Find the perimeter of the rectangle.
   A. 19 cm   B. 38 cm
   C. 81.25 cm   D. 8.125 cm

   6.5 cm
   12.5 cm

   6. _____

7. What is the GCF of 24 and 60?
   A. 2   B. 6   C. 12   D. 30

   7. _____

8. Which fraction is greatest?
   A. $\frac{2}{5}$ B. $\frac{1}{3}$ C. $\frac{1}{6}$ D. $\frac{4}{15}$

   8. _____

9. A train leaves Orlando at 8:46 A.M. and arrives in Jacksonville at 11:02 A.M. How long does the trip take?
   A. 3 h 16 min   B. 2 h 16 min
   C. 3 h 44 min   D. none of these

   9. _____

10. Find $\frac{3}{10} \times \frac{5}{9}$. Write the answer in simplest form.
    A. $\frac{1}{6}$ B. $\frac{1}{5}$
    C. $\frac{2}{5}$ D. none of these

    10. _____

11. Find the circumference of a circle with a diameter of 7.2 feet. Use 3.14 for π.
    A. 226.08 ft   B. 22.608 ft   C. 11.304 ft   D. 113.04 ft

    11. _____

Final Test, Form B (Continued)

12. Express 0.07 as a percent.
- **A.** 70%
- **B.** 7%
- **C.** 0.07%
- **D.** none of these

12. _____

13. Which dashed line is a line of symmetry?
- **A.**
- **B.**
- **C.**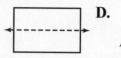
- **D.**

13. _____

14. Describe the polygons at the right.
- **A.** congruent
- **B.** similar
- **C.** neither
- **D.** regular

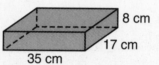

14. _____

15. Find the surface area of the rectangular prism at the right.
- **A.** 2,022 cm²
- **B.** 1,011 cm²
- **C.** 4,760 cm²
- **D.** none of these

8 cm
17 cm
35 cm

15. _____

16. A sixth-grade class has 29 students. Of these, 11 students are on the tennis team, 9 students are on the track team, and 4 students are on both the tennis and the track team. How many students are on neither team?
- **A.** 4
- **B.** 5
- **C.** 13
- **D.** none of these

16. _____

17. Solve $\frac{1}{4}x = -4$.
- **A.** −1
- **B.** 1
- **C.** 16
- **D.** −16

17. _____

18. Find the rule for the function table at the right.
- **A.** $n - 2$
- **B.** $2n$
- **C.** $n + 2$
- **D.** none of these

n	
2	4
0	2
−3	−1

18. _____

19. Out of 50 parts tested, 3 parts were found to be defective. If 10,000 parts were made, how many would likely be defective?
- **A.** 60
- **B.** 600
- **C.** 6
- **D.** none of these

19. _____

20. If a dart is thrown randomly at the dartboard at the right, what is the probability it will land in the shaded region?
- **A.** $\frac{1}{5}$
- **B.** $\frac{1}{2}$
- **C.** $\frac{1}{3}$
- **D.** $\frac{1}{8}$

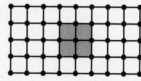

20. _____

Mathematics: Applications and Connections, Course 1

Final Test, Form B (Continued)

21. Estimate $4{,}812 \div 8$ using rounding.

21. _____

22. Find the value of $24 + 16 \div 4 \times 3$.

22. _____

23. Evaluate $4np + s$ if $n = 2$, $p = 4$, and $s = 6$.

23. _____

24. Choose an appropriate scale for a frequency table for the data $14, 7, 9, -1, 5, 11, 2,$ and 6.

24. _____

A group of 6th graders at Jones High School were surveyed about their favorite cookie flavors. The circle graph shows the results of the survey. Use this information for Questions 25–27.

Favorite Cookie Flavors

25. What two types of cookies together are almost as popular as chocolate chip?

25. _____

26. Which two types of cookies are 25% of the favorite cookies?

26. _____

27. What is the difference between the most popular and least popular cookies?

27. _____

28. Round $4.0\underline{9}6$ to the underlined place-value position.

28. _____

29. Estimate $0.95 + 0.47$ using rounding.

29. _____

30. What is the value of $x - y + z$ if $x = 3.6$, $y = 7$, and $z = 1.06$?

30. _____

31. Divide 19.467 by 6.3.

31. _____

32. Change 42 grams to milligrams.

32. _____

33. Solve $6.1y = 42.7$.

33. _____

34. Find $6.2 \div 3.16$ to the nearest tenth.

34. _____

35. Find the prime factorization of 63.

35. _____

36. Find the LCM of 18 and 22.

36. _____

37. Find the LCD of $\dfrac{9}{10}$ and $\dfrac{3}{16}$.

37. _____

Mathematics: Applications and Connections, Course 1

Final Test, Form B (Continued)

38. Round $16\frac{4}{11}$ to the nearest half.

38. _____

39. Estimate $\frac{6}{13} + 4\frac{1}{8}$.

39. _____

40. Estimate $\frac{7}{8} \times 10\frac{1}{5}$.

40. _____

41. Express 3.4% as a decimal.

41. _____

42. Name the polygon. Then tell if the polygon is a regular polygon.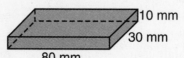

42. _____

43. Find the surface area of the rectangular prism at the right.

43. _____

44. Name the figure.

44. _____

45. Find $-6(-2)$.

45. _____

46. Find $-25 \div (-5)$.

46. _____

47. Solve $j - (-3) = -14$.

47. _____

48. Complete the function table. Then graph the function on the grid.

x	$\frac{x}{3}$
3	■
0	■
-3	■

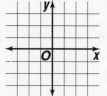

48. _____

49. A set of 20 cards is numbered 1, 2, 3, . . . , 20. Sara is equally likely to choose any one card. Find $P(16)$.

49. _____

50. Out of 25 people surveyed, 8 chose red as their favorite color. If 2,000 people were surveyed, how many would be likely to choose red?

50. _____

Placement Test Answer Key

Form A

Page 367

1. __B__
2. __C__
3. __A__
4. __B__
5. __B__
6. __A__
7. __C__
8. __D__

Page 368

9. __B__
10. __B__
11. __C__
12. __A__
13. __A__
14. __B__
15. __C__

Mathematics: Applications and Connections, Course 1

Placement Test Answer Key

Form A

16. _____ A _____   24. _____ A _____

17. _____ C _____   25. _____ D _____

18. _____ A _____   26. _____ C _____

19. _____ D _____

                            27. _____ D _____

20. _____ B _____

                            28. _____ C _____

21. _____ B _____

                            29. _____ A _____

22. _____ C _____

                            30. _____ A _____

                   Mathematics: Applications and Connections, Course 1

Placement Test Answer Key

Form B

Page 371

1. _____647_____

2. _72, 129, 203, 560_

3. _____9_____

4. _____33_____

5. _____48_____

6. _____4_____

Page 372

7. __8:45 A.M.__

8. □ _____

9. _____$\frac{2}{3}$_____

10. _____2_____

11. _____23_____

12. _____9_____

13. _____6_____

Mathematics: Applications and Connections, Course 1

Placement Test Answer Key

Form B

14. ___ounce___

15. ___31___

16. ___5,000___

17. ___8___

18. ___>___

19. ___0___

20. ___$1\frac{2}{5}$___

21. ___$40 - 10 = 30$___

22. ___14°C___

23. ___less than___

24. ___3:20 P.M.___

25. ___1___

Semester Test Answer Key

Form A

Page 375	Page 376
1. A	12. D
	13. A
2. D	14. D
3. A	15. B
4. B	16. A
5. C	17. C
6. B	
7. A	18. B
8. C	19. A
9. C	20. A
10. D	21. 84
11. C	22. 47

Mathematics: Applications and Connections, Course 1

Semester Test Answer Key

Form A

Page 377

Page 378

23.

Daily Temperatures

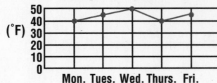

35. $\dfrac{5}{6}$

36. 120

37. <

24. 87

38. 0.61

25. 89

39. 0

26. 2

40. 16

27. 7.08

41. $\dfrac{2}{5}$

28. 6.734

42. $\dfrac{3}{8}$

29. 42.72

43. $\dfrac{1}{4}$

30. 210 mm

44. $2\dfrac{3}{4}$ ft

45. 2 hr 45 min

31. 54.76 cm²

46. $3\dfrac{1}{3}$

47. 32

32. 100.5 in.

48. $\dfrac{1}{6}$

33. 3.5

49. 28

34. 9

50. 3, 1

Mathematics: Applications and Connections, Course 1

Semester Test Answer Key

Form B

Page 379	Page 380
1. C	12. B
2. D	13. C
3. A	14. D
4. A	15. C
5. B	16. C
6. B	17. B
7. D	18. B
8. D	19. A
9. C	20. C
10. C	
11. A	

Mathematics: Applications and Connections, Course 1

Semester Test Answer Key

Page 381

21. $\dfrac{2}{27}$

22. $\dfrac{1}{54}$

23. $\dfrac{5}{27}$

24. pentagonal prism

25. 5,428 in³

26. 483.9 cm²

27. 301.7 ft²

28. 45.2 m²

29. 14 yd²

30. $\dfrac{25}{49}$

31. 6

32.

Page 382

33. 176

34.

35. +30

36. >

37. <

38. 0

39. 7

40. −10

41. 8 to 22, 8:22, $\dfrac{8}{22}$

42. 308 in.

43. 64%

44. 0.4%

45. 0.136

46. 52

47. less than

48. side *RB*

49. acute

50. congruent

Final Test Answer Key

Form A

Page 383

1. B
2. D
3. D
4. B
5. A
6. D
7. A
8. B
9. A
10. B
11. D
12. B
13. D

Page 384

14. D
15. B
16. C
17. B
18. B
19. B
20. A

Final Test Answer Key

Form A

21. _____ 26 _____

22. _____ 44 _____

23. _____ 76 mm _____

24. 2.003, _____ 2.0004 _____ 2.01, 2.3 _____

25. _____ 29.484 _____

26. _____ 74 in. _____

27. _____ 125.6 ft _____

28. _____ 3, 9 _____

29. _____ 11 _____

30. _____ $2\frac{13}{16}$ in. _____

31. _____ 1 h 42 min _____

32. _____ $\frac{7}{24}$ _____

33. _____ $6\frac{7}{8}$ _____

34. _____ $\frac{1}{4}$ _____

35. _____ $4\frac{2}{3}$ _____

36. _____ 64 _____

38. _____ 11 ft _____

39. _____ 52% _____

40. _____ 8.64 _____

41. _____ yes _____

42. _____ similar _____

43. _____ 1,200 ft^2 _____

44. _____ 75.3914 in^2 _____

45. _____ $(-4, -2)$ _____

46. _____ 10 _____

47. _____ $n + 6$ _____

48. _____ $\frac{3}{8}$ _____

49. _____ 9 outcomes; see students' work. _____

50. _____ $\frac{1}{12}$ _____

Final Test Answer Key

Form B

Page 387	Page 388
1. **C**	12. **B**
2. **B**	13. **C**
3. **C**	14. **A**
4. **A**	15. **A**
5. **A**	16. **B**
6. **B**	17. **D**
7. **C**	18. **C**
8. **A**	19. **B**
9. **B**	20. **D**
10. **A**	
11. **B**	

Final Test Answer Key

Form B

21. $5{,}000 \div 10 = 500$

22. 36

23. 38

24. −1 to 14

25. vanilla wafers and gingerbread

26. oatmeal raisin and shortbread

27. 35%

28. 4.10

29. $1 + 0.5 = 1.5$

30. −2.34

31. 3.09

32. 42,000 mg

33. 7

34. 2.0

35. $3^2 \times 7$

36. 198

37. 80

38. $16\frac{1}{2}$

39. $\frac{1}{2} + 4 = 4\frac{1}{2}$

40. $1 \times 10 = 10$

41. 0.034

42. rhombus, not regular

43. 7,000 mm²

44. cone

45. 12

46. 5

47. −17

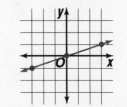

48. 1, 0, −1

49. $\frac{1}{20}$

50. 640